LABOUR
OF LOVE

LABOUR OF LOVE

LABOUR OF LOVE

THE STORY OF ROBERT SMILLIE

TORQUIL COWAN

FOREWORD BY DENNIS SKINNER, MP

PREFACE BY BLAIR SMILLIE

Neil Wilson Publishing • Glasgow

First published by:

Neil Wilson Publishing

www.nwp.co.uk

© Torquil Cowan, 2011

Foreword © Dennis Skinner, 2011

A catalogue record for this book is available from the British Library.

The author has asserted his moral right under the Copyright,
Designs and Patents Act, 1988, to be identified as Author of this Work

Print edition ISBN: 978-1-906476-61-8

Ebook ISBN: 978-1-906476-62-5

Printed and bound in Poland.

CONTENTS

PREFACE

OVER THE years, from a very early age, I had heard a few stories of the achievements of my great-grandfather Robert Smillie MP. In some ways I used to have a fascination with him and this constantly niggled away at the back of my mind. At a very early age, I was presented with a copy of his brief autobiography *My Life for Labour*, published in 1924 by Mills & Boon. I found the aged pages very difficult to read as the story was very factual and not what I was used to reading. Time and time again I tried to read it to the end but never achieved my goal. Factually, it was a wonderful resumé of his life mentioning many famous characters such as Winston Churchill, Stanley Baldwin and David Lloyd George but to me as a young lad it was not an inspiring read.

Later in life I looked it out again and was at last fascinated with the life changes my forebear had helped make to the working practices in the UK. I felt it only right that I should find a way to retell his story in order for it to have universal interest, not just to those solely interested in the 20th-century history of the working classes.

Being a stronger 'persuader' than a writer I used my abilities to engage my now friend and fellow Scot, writer Torquil Cowan, to take on this mammoth task, and I must say he has excelled in revealing the character of Robert Smillie. He has cleverly created a 'story within a story' and set the main narrative within its time as a long-lost manuscript that comes to light some 70 years after the death of its 'writer', who is his fictitious grandfather, Robert James MacGregor. The combination of Smillie's personal life and his political struggles brings together a story of almost unimaginable dedication to the cause of helping others.

This remarkable tale, about an equally remarkable man, will entertain, educate, shock and amuse the reader who enters a bygone world far removed from that of today. His struggle, together with other great working-class men, helped to improve the lives of millions throughout this historic period and should never be forgotten.

Labour of Love is my way of bringing back the memory of a man who had been one of the leading lights in the Labour Movement and trade union history; a man who had been a main mover in the setting up of the Scottish Miners' Federation, the Scottish Trades Union Congress, The Miners' Federation of Great Britain, the Labour Party and the Triple Alliance. Honoured in America and across

Europe, founder of the National Council for Civil Liberties, a member of the Committee of Honour of Save the Children and a Member of Parliament.

My resolve to reveal this remarkable man drove me on and I went as far as undertaking considerable research through documentation and conversations with older members of my extended family. I was confident that I had all the information I needed to rewrite my great-grandfather's story and portray him as a man, not just a tireless worker on behalf of others. And that is where Torquil Cowan came in. Having cornered him at the creative writing group that he ran, I knew that I had found the ideal person to take on the monumental task of bringing Bob Smillie back to life.

Torquil's achievement is now here for all to enjoy. When I first read it, I realised that I finally knew my great-grandfather at long last, a man who selflessly dedicated his life to the betterment of others. His life was full of struggle yet I know that he was uncomplaining about that. He gave so much of himself to everybody else, yet still lived a full, private life as this new book will reveal. Now when I hear the word 'hero', I think of only one man, my great-grandfather.

This book is dedicated to that very special man, 'Bob' Smillie.

Blair Smillie

FOREWORD

ROBERT SMILLIE is one of the great names of the Labour Movement. At one time I'd felt a debt of gratitude to him. Thanks to a scholarship endowed in his name, I was awarded a place at Ruskin College in 1959. For a variety of reasons, I didn't take up that place until 1967 when I spent my time writing essays on politics and industrial relations. Oh aye, and spending some time playing the All England Club's favourite sport. Which is why, when I'm asked about my student days, I always tell people that I went to Oxford to read tennis!

As one of ten children brought up in a Derbyshire mining community, you might imagine that I know exactly what life must have been like for Robert Smillie, his wife Ann and their nine children. You'll be thinking that their circumstances were like mine: big families living in similar environments, facing the same difficulties, that sort of thing. But let me tell you that the more I've found out about Robert Smillie's life and times, the more convinced I've become that what he and his contemporaries faced was a lot tougher than my early life.

Yes, money was in relatively short supply when I was growing up and we had to work hard, learning from a very early age the value of it. But when Smillie was a young man, each day was a struggle for survival in a way in which those of us born later would find difficult to understand. And if life for people like me down the mines was tough enough, it was a damned sight easier than the mining life Smillie experienced. Reading about his time as a miner made me think and wonder – it really did. Seventeen years old, employed as a hand pumper, trapped underground for twelve hours at a time, was bad enough; I can hardly imagine what the regular twenty-four-hour shifts – no other humans in sight, only rats for company – must have been like. I shudder to think about it.

However, it's not Robert Smillie the miner who is the real focus of interest; it's the Smillie who co-founded the Scottish Miners' Federation, the Scottish Trades Union Congress and, alongside his great friend Keir Hardie, the Labour Party. The Smillie who became President of the Miners' Federation of Great Britain and led it for nine taxing years which took in the first National Miners' Strike and the formation of the Triple Alliance. Then there was Smillie the MP who crossed swords with Asquith, Churchill and Lloyd George among others. Finally, the man who founded what became known as the National Council for Civil Liberties and was a member of the Committee of Honour for Save the Children.

When I consider the roles he held and the achievements of his life, I can only conclude that many people have become renowned for much less. In part that's down to the way history is written. Also it's due to the nature of the man. He worked tirelessly for what he saw as the righteous cause of the Labour Movement. Closely though I've looked, I have found no trace of him doing anything for the sake of personal ambition. He even turned down government posts from Lloyd George and Ramsay MacDonald so that he could concentrate his efforts on behalf of the miners and working people everywhere. In my opinion, that is the key to the man. He did everything for the sake of other people, never for himself.

Time hasn't changed me much. Ask my political opponents. They'll concede that, I'm glad to say. I am as much a Socialist now as I have ever been. The same could be said of Robert Smillie. From the humblest of backgrounds in which deprivation was a daily condition, his political creed was forged by experience. Brought up by his grandmother in Belfast, he moved to Glasgow at the age of fifteen and worked in the boiler shops in very draining conditions. By the age of seventeen he was a Lanarkshire miner and his eyes were opened to a world in which the lives of the majority were virtually owned by a privileged few. He rebelled against the abuses visited on miners and decided to make it his life's work to help to improve their lot. By the time I became a miner, many of the improvements in our working and living conditions were due to early pioneers like Robert Smillie.

I wonder how he would view the 21st century? I have no doubt that he would continue to rail against injustice wherever he found it because that was his nature. Of course, the political and industrial landscapes have changed since his day. The life conditions which he and his contemporaries faced are no more, thank God. But there are still evils, iniquities and injustice all around us. And that is all that the true Socialist needs to spur him on. I'm getting on in years now but there are still plenty of issues which stir my Socialist soul. If he were among us today, I'm sure Robert Smillie would feel the same way. Some of his targets may have changed, but the crusade goes on!

Some people are renowned for their great deeds, others almost in spite of themselves. Robert Smillie deserves renown for his unstinting work on behalf of others, his selfless humanitarianism and the unique contribution he made to industrial politics. I commend *Labour of Love* to anyone with an interest in humanity.

Dennis Skinner, MP
& member of the NUM

PROLOGUE

WE EXPERIENCE MANY different emotions during our lives. Among the rarest, and all the more special for that, is a feeling of being privileged. You may experience that on the day of your engagement, or your wedding, or perhaps at the birth of a child. It is an emotion unsurpassed by any other and it remains fresh in the memory.

Little did I realise in the summer of 1939 that the task given to me by the editor of our local newspaper would cause me to end up feeling very privileged indeed. I was asked to go to the Crichton Royal Hospital in Dumfries and obtain permission from the manager to interview one of his patients, a man who, according to my editor, warranted a human-interest story. The man in question was named Robert Smillie.

My editor back then was a man with a strong interest in politics which, as a young, newly married man myself, I hardly shared. He told me that Robert Smillie, who he referred to as 'Bob', had been a major figure in what he called the Labour Movement, that he was ailing, and he wanted a piece in celebration of the man's achievements. It hardly excited me. My preference was being sent to Palmerston Park to report on Queen of the South's footballing exploits. However, an editor's word is law, so I obtained the necessary permission and set off to interview Mr Smillie.

What should have been at most two hours of conversation ended up as six months of lengthy interviews! From the start, I was much taken by Robert Smillie. By then he was 82 years old and his health was failing badly. For some years he had suffered from a degenerative brain disorder and, by 1939, he was also physically weak. Even so, the qualities in the man absolutely commanded my interest.

The first time I met him, he was sitting in a wheelchair on a terrace outside his ward, enjoying the summer sunshine. He was reading a book which turned out to be a large-print collection of Robert Burns' poetry. That endeared me to him straight away for I was a lover of Burns' verse myself. Aware of my visit and the purpose behind it Mr Smillie, or Bob as he insisted I should call him, answered all my questions with great patience. Indeed, he often went beyond the facts of his life experiences, which was essentially what I was trying to discover, and offered opinions about the great events he had lived through and the many great men he had known. He was so forthright and clear in his comments that, almost in spite of myself, I began to become engrossed in what he was saying. I noticed that he said little about his own achievements, which he only hinted at, as and when necessary, and concentrated instead on other people. It quickly became clear to me that here was a very modest man whose greatest interests were his family, of whom he talked a little, and ordinary working people, particularly the miners, of whom he talked a lot.

I became so immersed in listening to him that I took fewer notes than I had intended to, and I asked if he would mind if I called again. He didn't mind at all, saying that he enjoyed a 'good blether' and that, apart from visits by his wife Ann, he rarely got the chance to talk much.

As I was leaving, almost shyly he handed me a book. It was entitled *My Life for Labour*, written by him and published by Mills & Boon in 1924. He suggested that, if I read it, I might get the answers to my questions, adding that even if I did find the answers, he would be pleased to see me again.

That night, I read the book in one sitting, much to my wife Jean's displeasure. She had thought of going to the pictures! When I finished, I think that I had already made my mind up that I wanted to know more about my new friend Bob. The book was very readable, even if it was written in the rather dry style of its day, and I found myself wondering why I had never heard of the man before. In his day he had been a giant in his field, that of industrial politics and the Labour Party, yet he was totally unknown to me. I had little doubt that he was equally unknown to most other people of my generation as well. This seemed totally ludicrous to me and an idea began to flower in my mind.

From the book and what I could remember of what Bob had told me, I cobbled together an article which my editor then savaged with his red pen before having it re-typed and sent to the print room. My next reporting task was to go to Palmerston to report on the Queen's game against Ayr United, and that suited me just fine. But I was even more interested in keeping my next appointment with Bob.

This time he wasn't feeling so well and was complaining a little about headaches. But he perked up when I told him I had read and enjoyed his book and he was absolutely taken aback when I told him about the idea I had been nurturing since reading it. Put simply, I believed that there was a wonderful story to tell, a story of an earlier world told through his eyes. At first he protested against the idea, saying that surely the 1924 book had already done that. I pointed out to him that the book did not cover his whole life, nor all the events he had witnessed and the people he had known. I refrained from pointing out to him that the book also suffered from a lack of chronology which would be confusing to readers.

He still did not seem very keen on the idea, wondering who on earth would be interested in a story with him at the centre. That was typical of his modesty so I put it another way and told him that, while the story would obviously be about him, it would actually be a story about the world he had known as seen through his eyes. I could see that he was wavering so I threw in my big weapon. I reminded him that histories and commentaries were always told from the point of view of the people with power and influence. Did he not think that it was high time the story was told from the viewpoint of those whom he liked to call 'his own folk'? That idea seemed to please him and he gave his consent.

I visited Bob so often at the Crichton that I should have had my own bed there! On several occasions I met his wife, Ann, who travelled down regularly from their home in Larkhall to see him. I got the impression of a very strong woman who seemed suspicious of me at first. Her attitude thawed over time but, on the few occasions when I managed to talk to her on her own, she had little to say about her part in Bob's life, apart from the fact that she loved him dearly and respected him hugely. I got the feeling that she was trying to protect him as much as possible.

From numerous visits and by asking prepared questions, I was able to build up a much fuller picture of Bob's life and his views on events and people than had been provided in *My Life for Labour*. I also got glimpses into his private life which he had not recorded there. Some days, if he wasn't feeling too well, we would just blether, as he always put it, and I became very aware of the uniqueness of the man. I had never met before, and have not since, a person who was so entirely driven by his concerns for other people and with such little thought for himself.

Now and again, my visits were wholly unproductive. Bob would be at a low ebb, hardly seeming alive, his eyes full of tears, incapable of speech, or perhaps unwilling to speak. I could never be exactly sure which it was. On two occasions, a great rage seemed to overtake him and male nurses had to rush in to control him. The sad thing was that, after such episodes of moroseness or near violence, he was fully aware of them, unable to account for them, and thoroughly embarrassed by them. More than once he confided in me that he would rather be dead than live like that.

Eventually, dear old Bob got his wish. He passed away on February 16th, 1940. It was sudden, if not unexpected, and he died alone. The funeral was held in a Glasgow crematorium with hundreds of people attending. My editor would not give me the time off to attend and I have regretted my absence ever since.

For two years now I have wrestled to produce a manuscript worthy of the man and his contribution to our world. Finished in second-draft form, it tells the story of a man from the most disadvantaged of backgrounds who witnessed at first hand the miserable plight of so many industrial workers, particularly the miners, and quite simply and undramatically, decided to try to do something about it. For over fifty years, he fought injustice wherever he saw it and did everything he could to bond men together in common cause to improve the lot of workers everywhere. His achievements were remarkable, even more remarkable than the incredible modesty he displayed in respect of those achievements.

Someday, I will seek a publisher. However, that will have to wait. I enlisted a while back and shortly, along with the rest of the regiment, I will be leaving on my first posting. Rumour has it that we are bound for North Africa to deal with a gentleman called Rommel. We shall see.

I am leaving this manuscript in the care of my beloved wife, Jean, and I have asked her to look after it with the same care as she will in looking after our wee girl, Kirsty. I dedicate the manuscript to the memory of my late friend, Bob Smillie. Meeting with him was one of the great privileges of my life.

Robert James MacGregor.
Dumfries
May 1942

I
Belfast Years

I WAS BORN in the city of Belfast on March 17th 1857. That much I can be sure of, though there is a great deal about my first few years on this earth that is less certain.

At that time, Belfast was growing. For years it had been the largest northern habitation on the great island that is Ireland, but by the time I arrived on the scene it was swelling at a rate that placed a huge strain on the old areas of the city. The Great Famine which had destroyed so much of Ireland's rural life had led to thousands of agricultural folk, people like my grandmother, heading for the cities to look for work. It was at this time that Dublin in the south and Belfast in the north more than doubled in size.

I cannot vouch for Dublin, but the expansion of Belfast was no great blessing for the ordinary folk who flocked there. Many of them did find employment in the new industries which developed in Belfast in much the same way as they did in other British cities. Large textile and engineering factories, huge ugly places, had grown up and the once beautiful shoreline of Belfast Lough was being despoiled by boat yards. But if employment was growing, so were other problems.

The Belfast of my childhood spawned generations who would never know the meaning of a good living. Wages were low and living conditions were oppressive. To accommodate the new army of industrial workers, large housing blocks were thrown up quickly, too quickly for real safety or comfort. These tenements, as they were called, provided only the most basic of accommodation. Large families were often housed in one big room or two smaller rooms. A whole floor of rooms shared but one primitive toilet, and bathing facilities were non-existent. All the families I knew had a large metal tub which would be placed in front of the fire and filled with hot water. Then each member of the family would take it in turns to wash in that tub. Privacy was impossible.

These tenements were busy, noisy places. Feet clattered on the stone steps and in the alleyways, or closes, at all times of the day. We were as far away from the sights and smells of nature as it was possible to be. That must have been a particular hardship for those who had come to Belfast from the countryside. Birth, life and death jostled together in those dark grey houses, old from the time they were built. And in those confined spaces, disease was an ever-present companion. By the time I was born, Ireland had been ravaged by typhus, which in 1847 alone had killed 350,000 people, and tuberculosis, resulting from the Great Famine, which was still killing victims many years later. In those tenements, such diseases were endemic. Perhaps they accounted for my parents.

I have no memory of my father, William Smillie. A mill worker, he died in late 1858 when I was hardly more than a year old. I do remember a very little of my mother, Jane Smillie, though how much of that is memory and how much is mere fancy, I am not sure. Whatever the truth of it, I treasure the recollection of a bonny, smiling face and warm, brown, curly hair. She passed away in 1860 when I was three years old. I do not know what claimed my parents – worn out by hard work, taken by some industrial accident, or snuffed out by disease; it might have been any one of these. All I can be certain of is that they went early, far too early.

Neither do I have anything to remember them by. Poor as they were, I doubt if they ever had more than enough money to feed and clothe myself and James, my brother and elder by two years, and themselves. Certainly, there would have been no money left over for the fripperies of life such as jewellery. So, I never had a watch of my father's, or a brooch of my mother's, for there were no such things. Nor were there such things as photographs and if there were, I never saw them. I think it unlikely that any ever existed. After all, photographs cost money. Over the years, and even now, I have thought of my parents and wondered what kind of people they were. How I have wished that I had more to remember them by.

My paternal grandmother took us in. I do not have the words to express how much I owe her. Everybody called her Nan Smillie. I am sure that Nan was not her given name, though I never knew in those days what that might have been. The Great Famine, and the death of her agricultural labourer husband, had driv-en her into the cold arms of the city where, at least, she was close to her son and daughter-in-law. What it cost her when they passed away I will never know. In spite of the anguish she must have felt, she took to her new role as our surrogate mother with a Christian zeal and great helpings of love. Had she not done so, it would have been the cheerlessness of the orphanage for James and me. No child deserves a fate such as that.

We lived in a tall terrace not far from the Crumlin Road. These houses had but two storeys and so had fewer people living in them than the newer tenement blocks. Even so, life was far from gracious. We lived in a single room with a small scullery off. There was one window which provided a view of the terraces opposite. Behind them rose the tall chimneys of the local spinning mill. In all, it was hardly a scene to inspire the imagination. In our one room, there was a fireplace with hobs on which a kettle could be boiled at the same time as food was being heated. In front of the fire hearth lay a rug. That rug remained for all the twelve years I lived with Nan Smillie. She cleaned it every day but nothing could remove the marks made by the occasional sparks from the fire. The remaining space of the room was bare floorboards.

As I remember it, there was one bed in a corner near to the window. I'm sure my memory is correct because, at an early age, the only way I could see out of that window was by climbing onto the bed and looking out. Before we were old enough to be let out on our own, James and I experienced the world from that window, and we were fascinated by our view of it. The men dressed in the roughest of clothes making their way to and from their work, mainly at the mill. They worked twelve-hour shifts, of which there were two a day, so the mill never closed. The smoke from the chimneys was constant; all the houses were permanently covered in ash and soot. Many women worked in the area too and they were no better clothed than the men. Old before their time, all of them.

In all weathers, we saw women cleaning the stairs and steps leading to their doors. On their knees, scrubbing brushes going ninety to the dozen, their faces red with the effort. Given the amount of ash and soot from the chimneys, theirs was a thankless task, but they went at it with a will. One of the biggest insults which could be offered to a woman in those days would be to say that she kept dirty stairs. Most women were determined that no such accusation could be levelled at them.

Almost all day the street would be busy. As well as the workers leaving and coming home, and the women cleaning their steps, there would be a succession of pedlars selling all kinds of goods. The women carried baskets in which they kept their clothes-pegs, boxes of matches, flowers, home-made floral sprays and many other kinds of light wares. The men would push barrows, some of them so cumbersome that they were obviously rough, home-made affairs. The occasional longer-established pedlar might have a pony and cart. From these barrows and carts they sold heavier goods, ranging from potatoes and turnips to timber and coal. We rarely made much use of any of them. There wasn't enough money around for that.

At times, the most interesting sights were seen late at night. If Nan went off to sleep early, and the lamplighter had done his work properly, James and I would creep out of bed to the window to look out. At the corner with the next street there was a public house. I think it was called the Green something-or-other but I can't quite remember. Late at night its customers would begin to make their way home, some of them, I regret to say, rather the worse for wear. For us, as they staggered along tripping and falling, it was free entertainment. We were far too young to understand the sadness of their condition. We had to be careful not to laugh too loudly at their antics because, if we did, there was a risk of waking up Nan.

'In the name of heavens!' she would exclaim, rising from bed and drawing her blanket around her. 'I thought I told you wee boys before!' Many years later in Scotland, I found that her accent was very similar to that heard in rural Ayrshire, but when she was telling us off, her gentle, rustic accent did not soften the message. 'Let me see what you're gawping at.' She'd push us aside, look out the window, and gasp in horror as she saw Maxwell or Docherty or old Finnigan measuring his length in the road. 'Disgusting! Absolutely disgusting! They'd make better men if they spent their time reading the good book.' Then she would turn to us. 'And if you two are not back in bed in two seconds, the bogeyman will get you!'

'Yes Nan' we would whimper, then dive back under the blankets. If Nan was fond of telling us stories from the Bible, she was even fonder of telling us tales of folklore, in which the bogeyman was a frequent visitor.

For a period of perhaps two or three years, we actually slept with our grandmother. After all, there was only one bed in the room. Then she had a word with a neighbour from across the close. MacNaughton I think his name was. A widower for several years, two bairns to look after, he was a jack of all trades, a handyman as you might say. In return for Nan looking in on his children while he was out, washing his steps and providing him with an occasional meal, he made a bed for James and myself. Really, it was just a big wooden box on short legs but, once Nan had found from somewhere an old mattress and a few blankets, it seemed like a wee four-poster to us. Far too big for us to start with, we grew into it. By the time James left home when I was thirteen years old, our feet were dangling over the end.

I don't remember ever actually starving, even if there was never a lot of food around and what there was rarely provided a delightful meal. I have no doubt that Nan did her best and she knew a thousand different ways of using potatoes and turnips. Our usual main meal was a broth of some kind. Most women of that generation had soup heating up most days. It was the most economical way of feeding families in hard-pressed times. Now and again Mr MacNaughton would present her with a scrag of beef or ham. We never asked where it came from. Straight into the soup pan it would go and we'd have a richer broth that day.

Now and again, if his daughters were with relatives or friends, Mr MacNaughton would eat with us. James and I looked forward to his visits for he was a great story-teller. He was particularly fond of telling war stories. He had been in the British Army, serving with the artillery which was where he had learnt his carpentry. He had never risen above the rank of private, except for one brief spell as a lance-corporal. One night he'd got drunk, insulted an officer and got demoted again, with a dozen lashes across his back into the bargain. The highlight of his career in the army had been during the Crimean War. According to his version, he'd won the Battle of Alma all on his own and, if he'd had his way, the siege of Sebastapol would have been a speedier success. He even claimed to have seen Lord Cardigan leading his Light Brigade into the North Valley under the Sapoune Heights before the famous Charge of the Light Brigade.

'Why did you leave the army, Mr MacNaughton?' I once dared to ask him.

'Because of this, wee man,' he told me. He raised his right leg, pulled up his trousers and, wonder of wonders, his leg was made of wood from the knee down.

'Lost it in a skirmish with some Russkies near Odessa,' he explained.

'I think you will cover your leg now, Mr MacNaughton,' Nan tut-tutted. But I could tell she was as excited by his tale as we were.

As we got a little older, James and I became less and less convinced of the truth of our neighbour's stories, even though we still enjoyed listening to them. We couldn't quite see that short, one-legged old man as a military hero. By then, of course, he was probably nearer sixty than fifty years old and worn out by a hard life. Perhaps he guessed at our increasing incredulity because, one evening, he brought something to show us.

'What do you think of that then?' he demanded, placing a large, rather creased photograph on the table.

'What is it?' I asked. The images were faded and everything looked rather brown. I could see the outlines of a lot of men standing beside a large cannon.

'My platoon,' he replied with some pride. He pointed at the figure nearest the end of the long barrel. In spite of fading, I could make out a solidly built man in uniform. He had a thick moustache and a heavy beard. 'That's me.'

'You, Mr MacNaughton?' I said excitedly. I had never before met anyone who had been photographed.

'That's right, wee fellow. That was me some years ago.' For a moment, I thought he was going to cry. Then he pointed to some words scribbled across the bottom of the photograph. 'And what does that signature say?'

'I'm sorry, but I can't read,' I said, flushing red with embarrassment.

'I can,' James piped up. He squinted his eyes. 'It says ... William Russell.'

'That's right,' Mr MacNaughton beamed. 'Man, but that fellow loved his drink.'

Years later I found that Russell had been the eminent war correspondent whose regular reports from the Crimea had so angered Cardigan and others, and alarmed readers back home. If Mr MacNaughton had known him, then he had kept illustrious company indeed. In which case, perhaps his war stories hadn't been tall tales after all. However, I never got the chance to apologise to him because he died within months of displaying his photograph.

While I was not much more than a toddler and James but two years older, our grandmother would take us for walks. If the weather was fine, we would walk as far as Linfield Park. There we saw another world. This was the other end of town. No narrow streets, no ill-dressed workmen, no smell from factory chimneys. Instead, there were well laid large areas of grass parkland, gravel driveways, riding paths, fountains, a beautiful bandstand and a well maintained cricket pitch. Most of all, there were people of a type I'd never seen before.

Horse-drawn carriages with golden fretwork would pull up and disgorge their passengers. Beautiful women and handsome men would get out, sometimes accompanied by well dressed children. The coachman would bow, the carriage would disappear and the family would begin a sedate walk across the parkland. Along riding paths, magnificent horses, so different to the ones pulling carts along our street, would canter carrying their sparkling riders to ... I didn't know where. Families in their finery would picnic on the grass while others reclined in chairs listening to a regimental band performing in the band stand. Everything was so clean and perfect, I could hardly believe it was part of the same world in which I lived. When I asked Nan who the brilliant people were, she used words like 'gents,' 'ladies' and 'toffs'. I had no idea what she meant.

For reasons I could never understand, far less explain, I was strongly drawn by the games of cricket being played on the long fields on the edge of the park. There was something very attractive about the maintained grass, the startling white dress of the players, the polite applause for good play, and the satisfying noise of wood on leather. I took it all in keenly from a young age and, as I will discuss later, played that fine game when the opportunity arose when I grew older.

You will no doubt be wondering why I have said so little about my schooling. Well, the truth is, I am ashamed to admit, that there was so little of it that there is hardly anything to mention. Before I was eight or nine years old, I did attend an infants' school on an occasional basis. Like many other children, there were reasons why I was not a regular attender. The school was some distance away and Nan was worried for my safety in the teeming streets. Then there was the problem of clothes, particularly shoes. I always had clothes to wear though they were never of good quality and I think that embarrassed my grandmother. Shoes were even more of a problem. I remember a time when James and I had but one rain-proof pair between us, really too large for me and too tight for him, and Nan would not have dreamed of sending either one of us out without shoes on our feet. Also at that time among labouring folk there was still a great fear about the infectious diseases which had claimed so many lives and many children were kept away from small, busy schools which were regarded as breeding grounds for disease. Finally, and possibly most important of all, there was so little money coming into the house that I was forced to find small jobs to supplement our meagre income.

The upshot of all those unfortunate truths was that my attendance at infants' school was sporadic at best and certainly not very long-lived. To the best of my recollection, I achieved little more than a mastery of the alphabet and only the most basic rudiments of reading and writing. My only other experience of formal education would come a little later at the age of eleven, when I was a half-timer at work and went to school for the occasional morning or afternoon. However, that did not amount to much.

But my education was not wholly ignored, I have to say. For that, as for so many other things, I have to thank my wonderful grandmother. She spent hours every day quilting, the only way she knew how to make any money, and I used to sit beside her and learn. Not how to quilt, I hasten to add, but about words and language. She encouraged me to spell out words to her from an old children's book. I remember the book as well as if it was only yesterday I had read it, as opposed to the more than seventy years ago it really was, but I have no recollection where it came from. Did I steal it on one of my occasional visits to infants' school? I sincerely hope not.

She would listen to my halting efforts, smile and say, 'Try again, wee Robert.' When I got a spelling right reading from the book, she would close it. 'Now from memory,' she would tell me. This would go on for hours at a time and eventually I began to spell words more easily. What patience she had, because I do not believe that I was the quickest of pupils.

Not only did she encourage me in basic matters of language, she also fired my imagination. Her lovely, soft accent had been bred in the countryside where she had learned more folk tales than any city woman would know. And she regaled me with these tales. She spoke of banshees, goblins and fairies so vividly that is seemed to me that she had actually seen and heard them. She entranced me with such stories, particularly through the long, cold, winter evenings.

She must have had a powerful memory because she was also able to recite poetry at great length. She was particularly fond of ballads. I enjoyed them hugely but she made sure that it went further than that. She would get me to repeat verses until I was word perfect. By this method, I committed to heart no small number of ballads. The one I remember best was 'Sir James the Rose'. What made it not only rewarding but particularly agreeable for me was the fact that I loved her speaking voice. She recited verses in what is often called 'pure Doric' and, though she had never crossed the water to Scotland, she sounded as if she might have been brought up in South Lanarkshire or Ayrshire.

Years later, I would delight my own children by repeating the folktales and ballads I first heard at my grandmother's knee; not only because they were wonderful to listen to but also because I believed they had real educational value. Certainly, when my grandmother recited to me, not only was my fancy stirred and great delight gained, but I also learned many new words and found out a great deal about other people and other places. Perhaps the greatest benefit of what my grandmother did for me in this respect was that she implanted in me a love of the written word and a great desire to read more fluently which, by and by, I was able to do.

As I pointed out earlier, between the ages of eleven and twelve I did receive a little more formal schooling but the greatest boon to the progress I made came courtesy of my brother. James proved to be a fair scholar, certainly better than I ever was, and he was a very keen reader. Not only that but he possessed a wonderful memory, much like our grandmother and after two or three readings could quote long extracts from anything that interested him. We often read together with him helping me over more difficult passages. In this way, I became better and began to read more and more. In fact, I read anything I could lay my hands on, however difficult it was.

It is unfortunately true that, from time to time, neither of us made the best use of the gift of reading. Like young boys of all over the world, I suppose, we tended to find interesting that reading matter which Nan Smillie would describe as 'dangerous and degrading'. In our excitement, such warnings meant little to us. On the occasions when we had a copper or two, thanks to the small jobs we both did to earn more household income, we would buy periodicals like *Dick Turpin*, *Tom King* or *Three-Fingered Jack* and devour their exciting tales. Never in the sight of our grandmother, of course. She would have regarded such publications as an affront.

We did read material of which she approved. Periodicals like *The Boys of England* and *The Young Men of Great Britain* were, in Nan's opinion, quite respectable. Like many young boys of our class at that time, we looked after these with great care, always stored them carefully and regarded them as treasured possessions. That kind of early reading was to lead onto rather better things. Over time, we managed to borrow or buy from second-hand bookstalls rather more elevated reading matter. I clearly remember that we acquired two of Scott's *Waverley* novels and two of Dickens' novels. I found these rather heavy going. You must remember that I was still a rather unskilled reader. However, there was always that deep glow of satisfaction when I felt that I had mastered the text. We even ventured to obtain some battered copies of several of Shakespeare's plays and a collection of his sonnets. Now they really were hard work, but even at a young age I felt the power of the man's words. Perhaps my favourite possession was a hard-used copy of Burn's poetry. I loved many of his poems and found many a wise word in those pages.

It may seem an odd thing to say but I think that the rare visits I made to the theatre improved my education. Of course, I did not have the money to be a regular patron, but I was the lucky beneficiary of some friendly assistance. You see, some of the bigger lads who were in full-time work and were therefore drawing regular, if not large wages, used to take pity on James and myself. They would let us accompany them into the theatre, so it cost us nothing. On other occasions, we would hang around outside and prevail on people leaving the theatre early to give up their pass-out checks so we, instead of them, could go back inside and enjoy the rest of the performance. Some of the theatre productions we saw were little more than a series of acts, everything from sopranos to magicians. On the other hand, we also saw some excellent performances of serious drama from some of the finest performers of the day. I vividly remember, for example J. L. Toole playing The Artful Dodger and I will never forget Barry Sullivan in *Richard III*. I discovered that reading drama is all very well, but nothing compares to actually watching it unfold in front of you.

From everything I have written you might be beginning to imagine that I was the quiet, studious type who hid behind his books and his grannie's skirts. Well I have to tell you, with some small sense of embarrassment, that nothing could have been further from the truth. Yes, I did come to love books and I certainly enjoyed Nan Smillie's company and protection. But I was no little angel. For reasons which I will describe in just a moment, I was no stranger to the streets of Belfast, and from a very young age. I wasn't short of friends either. Now, I remember their faces clearly even though many of their names have slipped by me, except for those with the most memorable nicknames. There was 'Bull', for example, not because he looked bovine but because his face resembled that of a bull terrier. Without doubt, he was the ugliest boy in our street. Then there was 'Squint' with the odd eyes which always seemed to be looking two ways at once. Not forgetting 'Wet', a poor wee boy with bladder-control problems. Youngsters can be cruel with their nicknames can they not? Not that Bull, Squint or Wet ever seemed to mind. You will notice that I have not mentioned any girls. There is a simple reason for that. Girls would not have been seen dead in our company!

You see, we were a pretty rough and untameable bunch of young ragamuffins, always up to nonsense. Most of which was innocent enough, silly boys' games in the main. We would wrestle and fight, chase one another, and make plenty of noise in the process. Now and again we might indulge in the kind of activities which incurred the wrath of the adults. Watching through the window until pretty Miss McWinter had filled the tin bath in front of her fire and got undressed, then chapping like mad at her front door and running as far as the corner. Then we'd laugh like mad when she came to the door with only a towel to cover her, discover there was nobody there and start hurling vile insults at the world in general. Or the times when we used to drive old Fergus Boyle into a temper. He ran a small food shop three streets away. We would send Liam into the shop because he was the biggest and could talk well when he was of a mind to. While he kept Boyle busy, we would sneak some apples from the front of the shop and run away, Liam catching up with us back on our own street. Once or twice old Boyle got the peelers after us, but they never caught us. Just as well, as Nan Smillie would have exploded at me. But it's no surprise the girls didn't want to play with us, is it?

Earlier, I mentioned that I had to work to bring some much-needed money into the house. In fact, by the age of eleven I'd already had three jobs. The money which Nan made quilting wasn't enough to keep us, so we had to do our share. James used to chop firewood from timbers he found at the boatyards then sell it door to door. He had a way with words, James did, and kept working at that for several years, using his charm to sell the firewood in the streets around our home. I started off at the age of eight as what we called a 'runner'. I knew where all the older folk lived and, for a farthing, I would go to the shop and buy their messages for them. Then, for a while, I helped James with his firewood round. I wasn't nearly as good a salesman as he was, so I tended to do a lot of the foraging for timber and the chopping. But grannie put a stop to that, saying that at the tender age of nine I was too young to be wandering around the boatyards. And what she said was law. Well, it was when she knew what we were up to.

For about two years I had steady work as a simple errand boy, which was but one step up the ladder from my earlier work as a runner. I even got work from old Fergus Boyle who obviously never recognised me as one of the gang who helped themselves to apples from the front of his shop. I also worked for Slattery the butcher and Munro the baker. The work was simple enough though it could be heavy at times for a boy of my age. The shopkeepers made up the orders which they then put in a large wicker basket with carrying handles. It was my job to deliver the orders around the streets of our part of Belfast. Using shank's pony of course. No horse and cart or barrow for the likes of me. It was often tiring work. The baskets could be very heavy and the streets were long. I would often put in six or seven hours a day so, by the time I got home, I only had the energy to eat, perhaps read a wee while, then get off to bed. And people might wonder why I didn't see much of the inside of a schoolroom!

In such ways, James and I were able to bring some money into the house and 'keep the wolf from the door' as Nan used to say. We weren't the only children in the same position either, not by a long shot. There were plenty of widow women with children, and families who were simply on the cusp of poverty, and their children had to bring in money too from an early age. When I was coming up to my twelfth birthday, I got my first real job. James had got work at the local spinning mill a year earlier and I joined him there. To start with I was what they called a half-timer. This meant that one week I would attend school in the morning and work at the mill in the afternoon, and the next week that order would be reversed. That arrangement lasted for six months. Then, once I was past my twelfth birthday, I became a full-timer, my brief reacquaintance with formal education ceased, and I spent my days at the mill.

To be perfectly frank, I never took to that mill, whereas James did. He proved adept at operating several of the main machines and got heavily involved in the dye department. One the other hand, I never enjoyed the noise of the machines or the smells of the fabrics and dyes. There again, I was making regular money, so I was hardly liable to complain. In fact, I put up with the work there for almost three years. Sadly, only one of these was with James as a fellow worker.

'There's no great future here,' he told me one day as we walked home.

'How do you mean?' I asked.

'They're not taking on men any more,' he told me. 'And Archie in the office told me the order book is not as full as it should be.'

'So what's going to happen?' Remember that I was only thirteen years old, and pretty green. And if James was only two years older, he had a wise head on his shoulders for a youth of his age. 'Tell me, James.'

'I'll tell you and Nan when we get home,' he said grimly.

Nan and I were both rather shocked by what he had to say. It seemed that, because of the size and strength of the ever-growing textile industry in the north of England, the Belfast mills, so much further away from the exchanges, were finding it hard to compete. It seemed likely that the Belfast mill owners would try to maintain production levels with fewer workers and therefore lower costs. James mentioned the names of three older men who had been laid off that week. It seemed as if only the youngest and fittest would be kept on and they would be expected to work even harder. Even at that tender age, I felt an ill-defined sense of injustice at that news.

'So I'm off to Glasgow,' James concluded.

'Glasgow!' Grannie and I gasped together,

'I've read that they're crying out for men over there in the new foundries,' James explained. 'And they pay higher wages too.'

A few weeks later he was gone, promising to write regularly, which he did. I wished that I could go with him, but I was only thirteen years old and I also worried what would happen to our grandmother if she was left on her own. So I soldiered on at the mill, even though I was less than fond of the work. When James' letters arrived, Nan and I would pore over them in excitement. He appeared to be doing well enough. His work was hard but more interesting than mine. He had found lodgings with good people and several of his Belfast friends had gone over to join him. Not only that but he was being paid much better wages than he had been at our local mill. I'm sure Nan realised that I was desperate to go and join him but neither of us spoke of that. She carried on with her quilting while I continued to undress bales at the mill.

Then two events occurred which changed everything. At the mill, many more men were laid off. The workforce was now only half the size it had been when I had first started work there. For those of us who remained, the shift hours grew longer and the work more back-breaking. All for the princely reward of 4/- a week! I was desperate to be away and find better employment elsewhere, but what would happen to Nan? Then fate took a hand.

'Poor little Lizzie Cochrane,' she said one night. We had eaten, then re-read James' most recent letter. 'It's an awful shame.'

'What is Nan?' I asked. I knew Lizzie who lived across the road with the sternest parents in the world.

'She's with child,' Nan told me.

'But she's only ... ' I hardly dared say it.

'That's right, boy. Sixteen years old, no man, and a child on the way.' She shook her head sadly. 'And those parents of hers want her out of the house. Such an awful shame.'

You may well guess what happened next. I do not recall if it was Nan or myself who suggested it. Anyway, within a fortnight Lizzie Cochrane became Nan's lodger, I'd left the mill and I was heading for Belfast Lough and the boat to Glasgow. I left with mixed emotions.

I was distraught at leaving Nan. She was equally upset to see me leave, but we both knew that the time had come. Like James, I promised to write regularly and I kept to that vow for the remaining years of her life. As often as I could, I enclosed a little money to help her, not for the sake of charity but as an admittedly poor repayment for all she had done for me. Sadly, I never saw her again, my work keeping me so busy. Somewhere, I still have those letters which she wrote to me in the last years of her life. And I have always known that I owed her a debt as great as any son ever owed his real parents. The leaving of her was the end of a chapter in my young life.

But as I stood on the pier, impatiently awaiting the packet to Glasgow, I was also excited, buoyant even, anticipating a great adventure. Not only was I about to be reunited with my dear brother but, at the tender age of fifteen, I was about to travel to a new country and meet new people. I was determined to make my mark on life. But even with the raw naïveté of youth, I could never have imagined the twists and turns my new life would take.

II

A Lesson in Glasgow

ALL TOO SOON I discovered I was not destined to be a man of the sea. Later in life I would undertake several significant sea voyages, which I will tell you of in due course, but they were at least experienced in relative comfort. For most of my years I was, as they say, a landlubber which was more beneficial to my constitution than that first voyage in the early summer of 1872. Shortly after leaving Belfast Lough and finding ourselves in the North Channel, we were assailed by relatively rough seas and my body reacted accordingly. In no time at all, I was leaning over the railings by the taffrail, vomiting horribly. All of Nan Smillie's last meal made for me, a rich ham broth, came up. From the pain in my abdomen, so did everything else.

I was horribly ill for several hours and remember no details of that part of the journey. It was not until we were nearing the Rhinns of Galloway that my stomach stopped retching. I felt weak but at least my brain seemed clear. I searched in my canvas luggage sack and pulled out the orange which my grandmother had given to me as her last present. I felt that digesting some fruit would be good for me, and so it proved, at least to the extent that I enjoyed the orange's tang and it stayed inside me. At that point, I took notice of my surroundings for the first time.

It had been virtually dark when we'd left Belfast in the early hours and, in my excitement to get aboard, I'd paid little attention to our vessel. Now, on a brass plate on the helmsman's cabin, I saw the name *Rathlin*. Clearly, it had been named after the island off Ireland's north coast so I deduced that it was an Irish-registered vessel, which it turned out to be. The *Rathlin* was no sleek, modern craft. My limited knowledge of nautical matters told me that it was a brig, or brigantine to give it its proper title, a two-masted, square-rigged vessel. Judging by her condition, which was clean enough but worn in every respect, she had seen a deal of service and, in my opinion, had been built in the days before steam power became commonplace.

In truth, it did have a steam engine. Even as I glanced round the vessel, I could feel it vibrating as the screw turned and, looking upwards, I saw smoke pouring from the single funnel situated more or less midships. Around the funnel area there was a wooden shed-like construction which I correctly took to be the engineers' area and behind that, covers removed, were coal bunkers. But everything about the funnel, the shed and the bunkers was clearly of a newer origin than the ship itself. Obviously the engine and all its accompaniments had been added to an already ageing vessel. The old pair of masts still stood tall, their canvas sails wrapped just above head level atop the main deck. In the course of our voyage to Glasgow, I was grateful for their existence for the engine broke down twice and the sails had to be unfurled.

In theory, our journey was only one of about one hundred and thirty miles from start to finish, with calls at Stranraer, Brodick and Ardrossan. Unfortunately, theory is not always the master of a situation and what should have been a voyage of some twenty hours ended up taking more than twice that time. Not that there were signs of problems to start with, apart from my stomach, which, by the time we were past the North Channel and turning by Milleur Point at the head of Loch Ryan, had settled down very well. I felt sufficiently recovered to strike up conversations with a few fellow passengers. I remember one of those in particular. A large, well built fellow in middle age, dressed in well cut tweed; he was a farmer from Ballymoney in Antrim. He was only going as far as Stranraer to attend the cattle sales. He talked at length about how he was stocking his large farm with what he called Belted Galloway cattle which, he claimed, were superior to anything back in Antrim. When he found out that I was heading for Glasgow, he wished me the best of good luck, as I did to him. I have often wondered if his farming life turned out to be as adventurous as mine proved to be.

Heading past Lady Bay towards true Loch Ryan and Stranraer, I took more note of the other passengers, of which there was a considerable number. I did not know anybody but, to judge by their youth and clothing, I guessed that a number of men were as determined on reaching Glasgow as I was, and for much the same reason. There were people of all classes on board. In addition to young men like myself and my farmer friend, there were some whose well cut clothes suggested that they were merchants of some kind. They tended to gather together in an enclosed lounge area where they involved themselves in lengthy conversations, no doubt about markets and money, and regularly produced hip flasks from which they drank something which I took to be rather stronger than water. On the foredeck, which was shielded from the rest of us by large sheets of canvas, I occasionally glimpsed a couple so well dressed as to make the merchants look like paupers. A crewman I briefly engaged in conversation told me that they were Lord and Lady somebody – I do not recall their names – that they owned thousands of acres in Wigtonshire and County Down, that they had the only proper cabin on the vessel, and that they were putting off at Stranraer. It seemed to me as if the world and his wife were travelling that day.

The ship's first problem occurred as we were steaming gently toward the head of Loch Ryan and Stranraer itself. I was just admiring the scenic delights of the Rhinns on one side and the gentle, brooding hills beyond Cairnryan on the other, when the steady vibrations of the vessel gave way to a series of bangs and lurches. Looking round, I saw a man stagger out of what I thought of as the engineers' shed. His face was blackened, his eyes were streaming, and he was shouting for help. A minute later, as several of his colleagues joined him and disappeared into the bowels of ship, there was a loud coughing noise which had the gulls shrieking their displeasure, following which there was a heavy silence punctuated only by the sounds of lapping water.

A grinning seaman told me that the engine had seized up, which it did at least once each voyage, but not to worry because we were still making way on the current and would soon be berthing in Stranraer harbour. That is exactly what happened. Slowly and silently, like a ghost ship, we made the security of the quayside, and then there was a frenzy of activity. Gangplanks slammed down, dock workers disappeared into the ship's hold and began off-loading cargo, and a number of port engineers came aboard to investigate the problems with our engine. My farmer friend shook hands and left, as did a number of other passengers including the Lord and Lady who were immediately whisked away in a splendid carriage. We should have stopped in Stranraer for only an hour, but it was nearer five before we cast off.

The engine was running again, but not with the steady smoothness which it had earlier. So the ship's master, a tall heavily-bearded fellow with a powerful Belfast voice, ordered the sails to be broken out. So we headed north out of Loch Ryan under steam and sail. Two hours or so later, as we were hugging the coast near Ballantrae, the engine seemed to pick up and the sails came down. By this time it was late evening, the sun was dying, and the light was fading. Suddenly, I felt exhausted, no doubt because of the excitement I felt at my great adventure, my sea sickness and the hours in a strange environment. I placed my canvas sack on the deck and lay down, using it as a pillow. Before falling asleep, I realised that I would not reach Glasgow on schedule and worried what James, awaiting my arrival, would make of it. But sleep overcame me before I could give too much thought to the situation.

Daylight on the second day of my voyage found me not very much closer to my destination. Sometime during the night, the engine had failed again and, rather than raise the sails in the hours of darkness, the master had anchored close to the shore near the village of Woodland, just south of Girvan. When I awoke and stretched away the stiffness caused by sleeping on the deck, I could hear the crew's shouts down in the engine room. Their language was of the rich variety, shall I say, no doubt caused by their frustration at yet another stoppage and the hard labour they were carrying out in their attempts to put things right. I saw that many other of the younger male passengers were still sleeping wherever they could find relative comfort and the small lounge was full of merchants, all of whom seemed to be deeply asleep, not a few shuddering as they snored. I had little doubt that the contents of their hip flasks were at least partly responsible for the depth of their slumber.

As it was a gentle, pleasant morning with not even the slightest offshore breeze, there would have been no point in raising the sails. So there was nothing for it but to rein in impatience and wait. As I did so, I studied the coastline which I found to be very pleasant. Golden, sandy beaches gave way to rich farmland and, in the distance, low-lying hills basking in the morning sunshine. Looking to the north, I saw the church spires of Girvan from where the occasional fishing boat was venturing out to sea. All in all, it was an idyllic scene or, should I say, it would have been if I hadn't been so impatient to be on the move and get to Glasgow and my waiting brother. By this time, the vessel was coming to life, passengers rising, stretching then, like me, taking in their surroundings. I do believe that the level of patience might have grown to something unpleasant if the delay had lasted much longer but, at last, there were the welcome mechanical sounds of an engine returned to health and the screw began turning again. We were on our way once more, albeit many hours behind schedule.

I will not bore you with the details of the middle passage of the voyage. In truth, it was slow and rather tedious and I was anxious to set foot on land again. We passed to the east of Ailsa Craig, a huge forbidding rock which boasted more seabirds than I'd seen in the whole of my life. Then we called into Brodick, where we set down and picked up some cargo and passengers. It was around that point that I finished the last of the bread and cheese that Nan had packed for me. As I ate the last piece, I thought of her and briefly felt the pricking of tears. But I steeled myself with thoughts of James and my new life, and the sadness passed.

It was dark when we had crossed the Firth of Clyde and berthed at Ardrossan, which was a busy little port in those days. I watched as deckhands and stevedores struggled to offload a large piece of machinery partly covered in canvas. When I asked what it was, I was told that it was some kind of pumping device for one of the pits in the Ayrshire coalfield. If I had known which direction my life was about to take, I might have paid greater attention to it.

Leaving Ardrossan not long after midnight, it was lights on and no mistake. Because, as we navigated our way between Great Cumbrae Island and the Isle of Bute, the waterways were suddenly alive with seagoing traffic. I will be honest with you; to begin with, I found this sudden business rather frightening. I wondered how on earth the masters of the vessels knew which sea lane to follow in order to avoid colliding with other vessels. Soon, though, my panic subsided as it became obvious that, with the aid of night-riding lights and their own experience, the vessels' masters knew exactly what they were doing. Soon we escaped that narrow channel, the Firth of Clyde broadened again and we were on the home stretch.

I found out that in early summer, the hours of darkness are very brief in Scotland, no doubt because of the northerly latitudes. As we bore east I was able to see both banks of the firth, and at first the views were very pleasant. To the northern shore were the attractive burghs of Helensburgh, Craigendoran and Cardross while on the southern shore were the busier towns of Gourock and Greenock. Those were quite pretty places back then though it wouldn't be long before the industrial age caught up with them and they would grow darker. By the time we passed Dumbarton's great rock and were thrusting towards Erskine, the river traffic grew heavier and heavier. Vessels of all shapes and sizes, some being large ocean-going affairs mixing, rather hazardously it seemed to me, with smaller vessels powered by steam or sail.

We were well upriver by now and I was no longer the tourist taking in the scenery. Instead, with a crowd of other young men, I was by the rails, straining for a first glimpse of the city of Glasgow itself. Shortly, it was on both sides of us and I almost gasped in disbelief. I had always believed that Belfast was a large place, which indeed it was, but nothing had prepared me for the size and frenzied business of Glasgow. Whichever direction my eyes took, there was row upon row of buildings. Tenement blocks like Belfast, but bigger and more numerous. Huge factories crowded the banks of the river, with thousands of men in and out of them. In the distance were graceful spires and the roofs of beautiful, tall buildings, and no end to it, none at all. In every direction, the city seemed to run on forever.

At last, the *Rathlin* was berthing at the Broomielaw quayside which was busier than anything I had ever seen. I could not count the number of ships. Neither could I identify the flags of all the countries which they flew. Briefly, I gasped at the frenzy of it all and wondered how on earth I would ever make my way in such a place. Then I remembered that it was my decision to come here, squared my shoulders and made my way down the gangplank, saying goodbye forever to the ship. Immediately, I was swallowed up by a seething, swirling mass of humanity and felt the onset of panic. It was a much-loved voice which saved me.

'Robert, is that yourself?' It was James, smiling broadly, pumping my hands. 'My, but you've grown up.'

'And so have you,' I told him. He was not much taller than he had been two years earlier, but considerably broader, every inch the man. And his upper lip bore a heavy moustache. 'Still not learnt to shave?' I said.

'As cheeky as ever was,' he grinned.

'How did you know when to meet me?' I asked. 'We are more than a day late.'

'Because we don't live in the dark ages here,' he laughed. 'The harbour masters keep in touch by telegraph.' He gripped my elbows and held them at arm's length, looking me up and down. 'Man, but it does my heart good to see you.' He then embraced me.

'And me you,' I added. With some difficulty, let me say, for he was squeezing the breath out of me.

Arms round one another's shoulders, he led me away from the quayside and the whole dock area, then through a warren of factories until we reached a more residential area which he called Govan. With its tall tenements, it reminded me of our part of Belfast but on a much larger scale. Even at that early hour - it could scarcely have been six o'clock - the streets were busy with traffic and the endless comings and goings of people, mainly men on their way back to work on the early shift. Eventually, we reached a long narrow road called Gilmour Street. Half-way along, James dived into a close and I followed him up three flights of steps, past dozens of doors, until we reached the very top where he unlocked a heavy, brown door which he pushed open.

'Welcome to your new home, your lordship,' he said, laughing.

'Thank you, my man,' I replied grandly and walked in.

My new home, as James put it, reminded me of my old one in Belfast, except for the fact that it was bigger. There was the same kind of fire with hobs, the same sort of view of other tenements from the main window, and the floors were planking with a scorched rug in front of the fire, much like Nan Smillie's. But there were two rooms as well as a scullery. The sitting-room was of a fair size with a table and two chairs in the middle and James' bed against a wall. The second room was not much larger than a cupboard, but it did have a small window and a narrow bed which I was told would be mine. The small scullery had a sink, a plate rack and, as I had expected, a metal tub for bathing which was hanging from a hook on the wall. The ceilings were higher than the ones in Belfast and the main window was larger. Altogether, it was rather grander than I was used to even if it would have seemed small by many people's standards. I noticed on the table some books and a few pamphlets on which the word 'Socialism' frequently appeared. I asked James about those.

'No time to explain now, Robert. My shift starts in twenty minutes.' He passed over a sheet of paper with a map drawn on it. 'That shows you how to get to Brown's Foundry where I work. You're to report to the Factor in the office at noon.' He grinned widely. 'He'll explain your duties.'

'My duties,' I gasped. 'You mean ... '

'Yes, you've got work to go to at the same place as me,' he said. 'When I got your letter I went straight to the office and told them about you. You'll be working with castings.'

'Castings?'

'They'll explain it to you. But remember this, Robert, I told them you were a good honest lad, keen to work and quick to learn. So you will have to pretend to be somebody else, won't you?' With a laugh he was gone, shouting over his shoulder that there was soup in the pan if I wanted some.

Well, my mind was in a whirl and no mistake. So much had happened so quickly. But if my mind was asking a lot of questions, that was as nothing compared to the demands my stomach was making. How long had it been since I had eaten the last of Nan's bread and cheese? I couldn't remember. All I knew was that I was famished. I swung the hob plate over the banked-up fire then went to the scullery and found a bowl and a spoon. A few minutes later, the soup was bubbling nicely so I turned the hob back and poured a good quantity into my bowl. Man, I tell you that drop of soup was as good as any I'd ever tasted. Not only had James obviously progressed as a cook, but he'd also added more meat of some kind that I'd never tasted before. At which point, I wasn't sure if that meant he was making good money or whether he had made a special effort because of me. That thought made me feel rather guilty and I peered anxiously into the pan. I was relieved to note that there was plenty left, more than enough for a meal later for both of us, if that's what James had in mind.

After rinsing my bowl, I unpacked my few belongings in the smaller room, then had a quick look at the pamphlets on the sitting room table. I glanced at a number and read only one. It was rather heavy going. It seemed to be an attack on something called the Criminal Law Amendment Act of 1871 which made something called 'picketing' illegal. None of which meant anything to me, though I gathered that whoever had written the pamphlet felt that the Act was a dreadful thing and was calling on people to stand up against it. It might as well have been written in German for all I understood of it but I remember wondering why James had such pamphlets in his possession.

In those days, I did not own a watch. Indeed, it would be several years before I could afford to buy one. By the time I'd eaten and done a little reading, I was very unsure what time it was. I guessed it might have been about nine o'clock but, with an appointment to keep, a guess was not good enough. So I decided that the best thing to do was to go out, take a good look round the area, find a clock on some public building, then make my way to Brown's Foundry in good time for my noon appointment. I locked the door, put the key in my deepest pocket, and went out to explore.

If I'd thought Glasgow was huge from the Broomielaw, my excursions that morning proved to me that I did not really understand the meaning of the word 'huge.' In all sorts of ways, what I saw reminded me of Belfast but the scale was so much greater. The same sort of streets but so many more of them. The same sort of people but much more numerous. More shops gathered together too, as if the area was a large village with its own centre. In one of them, I stopped and bought an apple. Yes, I bought it. I had no intention of getting involved with the local peelers. I dawdled a little in that shop, which was quite busy, and listened to how people were speaking and what they were talking about. I heard a variety of accents there, varying from the soft lilting kind which reminded me of my grandmother's to a faster, harsher one which I took to be local. The snippets of conversation were much the same as those in Belfast, the price of food, health and sickness and hard work. I felt reassured by all that I heard. The voices may have been a little different but the people were very much what I was used to.

The marked rows of terraced streets gave way to a harsher landscape as I got closer to the River Clyde. James' map was clear and, from it, I worked out that eventually all roads led to the river. I was able to keep a check on the time from the clocks of several fine churches that I passed so, by the time I reached the river area, I had half-an-hour to spare before my noon appointment. That was not nearly enough time to take in the sights and activities which greeted me. I would have though it impossible that so many different industries and thousands of men could be found anywhere in the world. The length of the river, as far as I could see, was crowded with workplaces. A great river port of course has factories and other large sites dedicated to the shipping trade. On Clydeside they built whole ships to all manner of designs. They also refurbished them, repaired them, fitted them out, made parts for them and, when their useful days were over, broke them up. Then, of course, there were quayside areas packed with ships from all over the world, bringing goods in and sending goods out. Late morning now, it was even busier than when the *Rathlin* had berthed in the early hours. How the men who worked there made sense of the bedlam was beyond me.

Not that ships and ships' parts were the only things being produced there: far from it. There were factories producing all manner of goods from smaller items like cutlery and kettles to huge ones like bridge girders and huge metal sheets for all manner of uses. I was astonished by the variety and energy of the area and scarcely had the time to take it all in before it was time for me to report to the office by the main gate of Brown's Foundry, a large concern dealing in brasswork. The shift foreman, Willie Armstrong, was expecting me and quickly put me at my ease. He didn't think to remark on my youth and inexperience and was of the opinion that, if I was half as good a worker as my brother, then I would get on fine, as he put it. I was to work at dressing castings. I had to tell him that I had no idea what that meant. He laughed and told me that if I could learn to use a hammer, chisel and file properly, then I would manage well enough. Then he took my breath away.

'Mind you, laddie, as you're only starting you will not be on a man's full wages,' he said rather dolefully, as if imparting bad news.

'And what will the wage be, Mr Armstrong?' I asked, rather fearfully.

'Never mind the "Mr Armstrong", it's Willie,' he told me rather gruffly but with a smile on his battered, old face. 'And the wage is fourteen shillings a week and not a penny more.'

'Fourteen shillings?' I gasped. I'd never earned more than five shillings in Belfast.

'Aye, only fourteen shillings' he repeated. 'And not a penny more.'

He took down all my details, copying them into a large ledger. I could tell that he was no great hand at writing by the way the pen scratched slowly on the paper and his tongue hung out of the end of his mouth as he concentrated. There was a problem when I had to confess that I did not know my new address but he solved that by looking up James' address and copying it down. Then he took me in to see my new place of work. He told me the names of several of my new workmates who nodded at me agreeably enough before returning to their efforts. Willie left me there with them and I watched with interest what they were doing which mainly consisted of shaping the brass into whatever design was called for. One of the more experienced workers, a local man called Geordie, took a little time to show me what was required and briefly let me use his tools on a piece of scrap. I had become fairly well used to the use of a hammer, chisel and file back in the mill in Belfast. Geordie watched me, smiled and remarked that I would 'get on fine,' which seemed to be a favourite phrase in Glasgow.

Promising Willie Armstrong that I would report on time for work the next morning, I left Brown's and spent a few more hours looking at the riverside where I found the hustle and bustle of the docks absolutely fascinating. Then I realised that it was nearing the end of the day shift at Brown's and hurried back to the main gate where I was due to meet James. I was totally unprepared for the rush as hundreds of men poured out and hundreds more made their way in for the night shift. I was pressed back against a wall and was afraid I would miss my brother. Luckily, he was more used to the mêlée and he found me. Laughing, he dragged me out of the crowd and marched me home, peppering me with questions about how my day had gone.

I had guessed right that morning. The remains of the soup were for our evening meal, which we thoroughly enjoyed. No doubt, part of that enjoyment was due to the fact that we were together again after two years apart. I don't think I've ever felt closer to my brother than I did that night. Our meal over, I cleaned our bowls while James prepared vegetables and diced a little meat, all of which went into the pan over the fire in preparation for the next day's meal. You may think it strange that there was a fire burning all day in June. Perhaps you will think it was because of the cold Scottish weather, about which I have heard too many jokes over the years. But that was not the reason. Rather, in addition to being used for cooking food, it was also used to heat a thing called a back boiler, a device I had never heard of before. At the back of the fire lay a metal tank, constantly full of water which was heated by the fire. This meant that, as long as the fire was lit, there was a plentiful supply of hot water to the taps in the scullery. What a wonderful idea! I have no idea whether it was a Scottish development or not, but it was in Glasgow that I first came across it.

My, how we talked that night! At first, of course, it was about personal matters. We both professed our admiration and love for Nan Smillie and vowed to write a letter each to her as soon as possible. Then James enquired about our friends back in Belfast and I enquired about his in Glasgow. It turned out that he had not a few, mainly fellow workers from Brown's Foundry. I asked him about girls and he blushed furiously, admitted that he knew a few, but would say nothing more. From which I deduced that he was making some progress with one or perhaps more, because James was a handsome young fellow. And that is how much of the evening passed with recollections and jokes against one another. We said little of what we thought the future might hold. We were too full of the present for that. Then, as we were enjoying a late night cup of tea, I asked him about the pamphlets lying on his table.

'Well now Robert. I've been taking some interest in political matters,' he said, lighting up a clay pipe, looking quite the man of affairs.

'Politics? What kind of politics?' Not that, at that age, I would have known one kind from the other.

'Serious politics, Robert. Serious politics indeed.'

'Well then, are you a Liberal or a Conservative?' I asked, more or less exhausting my knowledge of the subject.

'Hah! One of those two?' With a note of such contempt as I'd never have believed possible from such a well mannered fellow.

'Why? What's wrong with them?' Not that I really cared very much, to tell the truth, but I wanted to carry on listening to my brother talking.

'What's wrong with them?' he snorted. 'You might more properly ask what's right with them! Let me tell you the truth of things, young Robert.'

I sat enthralled. I'd never heard anyone talk at such length before. And my, but he was keen on his subject. There was too much of it for my young brain to take in, and no doubt I didn't clearly understand what I did take in. Neither do I have the historian's ability to cut through the chaff and get to the important facts. But to the best of my recollection and limited understanding, I will set down the details of what he talked to me about that night.

According to him, there were really only two kinds of people. There were those who owned things, by which he meant titles, land, money and great business. Then there were the other kind of people, like himself and me, who worked for the first kind of people. Perhaps it was more complicated than that, but that was what I understood him to say. The biggest problem, indeed I think he called it an iniquity, was that people like us, the vast majority, could do nothing to influence the small number who owned everything. He asked me if I thought that was fair.

Well, I did not know what to say. After all, I was but fifteen years old and I'd never given any thought to the matter. Then he prompted my memory by reminding me of the older men who had been laid off back at the mill in Belfast. Did I think that was fair? I supposed it wasn't. He reminded me of the fact that we had missed out on our schooling because we had to earn money from the age of eight. Was that fair? I could heartily agree with him that that was certainly unfair. Then he asked me to consider the dire living conditions in which Nan Smillie had been forced to live. And told me his opinion that the fine folk we used to see riding in the park probably spent more money feeding their horses than Nan had ever been able to spend feeding us. And was there any way on God's earth that that was fair? By then of course I was seeing things entirely from his point of view and offered the opinion that nothing could be less fair.

'But what can be done about it all?' I asked.

'Change the world,' he replied. Then he laughed. 'One step at a time, of course.'

He went on to explain that he had become a Socialist, that he dreamed of a day when all men had equal rights and dignity, then asked me if I had ever heard of Karl Marx. In my ignorance, I suggested that he may be a German king, at which James laughed uproariously then told me that Marx was a great philosopher who had written a manifesto advocating control of production and exchange by the State rather than wealthy individuals. The significance of which totally escaped me, of course, though I loved the sound of the fine words.

James went on to provide a brief history of what he called the Labour Movement. This was far less philosophical so I understood more of it, but there was so much of it that it was difficult to keep track. He talked admiringly about a Welshman called Robert Owen who was a partner in the New Lanark cotton mills and created wonderful conditions for the workmen there. He also set up cooperative communities of working men, a barter exchange in London and the London Cooperative Society. He even went to the United States to set up an experimental cooperative society there but that had little success. But as far as the Labour Movement was concerned, James was of the view that his setting up of the Grand National Consolidated Trades Union was his greatest achievement, bringing together trades and federations of workers from around the country. However, the Liberal Government supported local measures to limit the influence of the GNCTU and, following the dreadful fate of the Tolpuddle Martyrs, the GNCTU collapsed.

James then told me about groups like the Rochdale Pioneers who began the system of cooperative stores of which by 1872 there were over two hundred. He also talked about the sad story of the Chartists, organised workers who had three times presented charters to the Government advocating changes to the electoral roll system to allow for participation by ordinary working men, but on all three occasions these charters were rejected. James said that the Chartists were the first working-class political organisation, that their experience was proof of his view that there were only two classes of people, and in his opinion it was high time that the working class was better organised.

And oh, he talked about so much more that night. For reasons I didn't quite understand, he didn't seem supportive of recently formed trade unions like the Amalgamated Society of Engineers and the Amalgamated Society of Carpenters because in his opinion they were not political enough. They did not want to change society, merely improve the position of their members within the system. James was derisory about that. He was convinced that the only way to improve the lot of the majority was to change the system, indeed all society.

He finished with a brief lecture on the laws governing the treatment of workers. He was full of praise for a certain Lord Eghley who, earlier in the century, had been instrumental in obtaining legislation which offered protection to children, particularly those working in factories and mines. He was less enthusiastic about Gladstone's attitudes towards the growing trade unions. It was difficult for me to understand then but, on reflection, I know that he was talking about the Trade Union Act of 1871 and the Criminal Law Amendment Act later that same year. The first of those recognised trade unions as legal bodies with the right to strike and to protect their funds in law. This had been long overdue and, even if James felt that the unions of the day were not political enough, he believed that the Act represented real progress in the history of working people. However, the second Act made picketing illegal. This meant that it was almost impossible to demonstrate and encourage solidarity, thus making strikes almost haphazard without any means of enforcing them. He believed that these Acts, taken together, illustrated the power of the owning class exercised through obedient politicians.

He had a lot to say about mining legislation too, and, as I remember, talked about five different Acts of Parliament which affected miners. Then, as bed beckoned, he astonished me.

'I intend to be a miner one day,' he told me.

'You, a miner? Why James?'

'I believe that, among the miners, there is a greater opportunity than anywhere else for the fellowship of workers with political as well as industrial aims.'

'I see,' I replied though, in all honesty, I didn't.

'Besides,' he grinned, 'the pay's not bad and it will get me out of the city. You don't see many mines in cities, do you Robert?'

'So you don't like Glasgow then?'

'Oh, I like it fine, little brother,' he told me. 'But it's a bit big and a wee bit busy. I'd like to be nearer the countryside and pits usually have plenty of that close by.'

'So where will you go?'

'I don't know yet,' he replied. 'Either Ayrshire or Lanarkshire.'

'And what will I do?' I'd only just found my brother, and it sounded like I was about to lose him again.

'Follow me when you've a mind to, if you want.' He must have seen the concern on my face, and he slapped me on the shoulders. 'Don't worry about it, little brother, I won't be leaving for some time yet.'

My mind in a whirl from everything he had said, I was more than ready for bed. But I was reckoning without James. He produced some paper and a quill. 'Don't forget Nan Smillie,' he said. 'Write and let her know you got here safely.'

'Yes, I'd better do that,' I agreed, though I hardly felt up to the task. So I scratched away, telling her my news as best I could though keeping it to the barest details or I would have been writing all night. Now and again, I had to stop and ask James how to spell a word. He helped me with his usual unflagging patience. Briefly, I was reminded of the old days back in Belfast when he helped me with my reading. At last, the letter was complete and I ended it with some loving words. After the quickest of washes, I went through to my small room and gratefully slipped into bed. From outside there were the sounds of continuing life for, as you will no doubt know, a big city is never truly asleep. Snug in my bed as I was, it was not difficult for me to ignore those sounds for my mind was racing with other matters.

What an amazing day it had been, certainly the most turbulent of my life so far. I relayed the events in my thoughts. Sailing up the Clyde, berthing at the quayside, then the joyous reacquaintance with James. Discovering a new place, a new roof over my head, a new job to go to. Everything was new in fact, and very exciting. And then there was the new side to James. He had always been better with words and more learned than me, but his talk that night had revealed something else about him. That he was a deep thinker, convinced of the righteousness of his views. Like smaller brothers everywhere, I suppose, I looked up to him and tended to believe in what he said. But where would that lead me?

Over the years, many experiences would shape my view of the world and, for good or ill, make me the man I became. But, although I was too young at the time to understand everything that James had said to me, I do believe that the shaping of Robert Smillie began with my brother's words on that first night in Glasgow.

III
The Heat of the City

MY TIME IN Glasgow absolutely flew by. In part that was no doubt due to the bloom of youth but there were other reasons. First, I was never out of work during my time there even if, for reasons which I will explain shortly, I was rarely in the same job for very long. But, second, and more important, my closeness to James meant that I greatly enjoyed the time I spent with him and, as we all know, time enjoyed always passes quickly. We spent our time together in many different ways, as I will describe, but perhaps the most important as far as my growing up was concerned, was the time we spent in lengthy conversations. Perhaps we were making up for lost time, or maybe we were just naturally talkative. Whatever, we talked a lot. Often enough, we chatted about ordinary enough things such as our childhoods, Nan Smillie, our scrapes on the streets of Belfast and so on. Sometimes we would just laugh and joke and, as young men are apt to do, talk about girls. But I have to confess that the conversations I most treasure were about more serious matters, in which James would reveal himself to be even more knowledgeable and thoughtful than I had imagined.

'Do you know that a million British soldiers keep a hundred million Indian people under check?' he would ask. He usually started conversations with a serious question.

'I know that we are in India but I don't know much about it,' I would be forced to admit.

'Did you know of the mutiny less than twenty years ago?' he asked.

'Well, I have heard of it.' That was about the sum of my knowledge.

'And tell me, little brother,' he said smiling, 'why are British troops in India? Why is Britain there at all?'

'I don't know,' I replied.

'You don't know!' he said, pretending to be horrified. 'Why shame on you, Robert.'

'So why are we in India?' I fell into his trap. You see, James always had the skill to order a conversation in such a way as if to make me believe that I had absolutely demanded to hear his opinion.

'For possessions, Robert. That's why we are there.'

'What kind of possessions?'

'Oh the usual ones,' he replied. 'Land, titles, money, goods, those sorts of

26

things.' Then he leaned forward and stared at me earnestly. 'Tell me Robert, do you own land in India? Do you have a title to any part of that land? Do you perhaps have any boxes full of precious stones and rupees hidden away somewhere?'

'No of course not.'

'Of course not,' he nodded. 'But some people do. Not the likes of us of course. Not the likes of most people who toil all day to earn a bare living. And certainly not the ordinary soldiers who spill their blood on foreign shores. But some people do,' he repeated. 'And that is why we are in India.'

At which point, he would put the kettle on the fire and make a pot of tea, which we would drink with perhaps a slice of bread and dripping for bulk. While eating and drinking, we would return to lighter subjects like his enormous moustache and, of course, young women. But that was just his tactic, you see. He was letting my poor brain turn over the earlier conversation, to let the serious bits sink in. Then, when he thought I'd had enough time to think, he would start again.

'Ever heard of Africa, Robert?'

'Of course I have!' with a little heat, indignant at the thought that he believed me totally ignorant.

'So you know about places like Cape Colony and Natal then?'

'Well ... no ... not really.'

So he would proceed to tell me all about them, or as much as he knew and believed, which was considerable. In all such conversations, he was always making the point that he detested exploitation, whether it was on the basis of class, colour or nationality. So much of what he had to say resonated with me.

As I have already told you, I started my working life in Glasgow at Brown's Foundry, employed as a castings dresser for the princely wage of fourteen shillings a week, almost three times as much as I had earned in the mill in Belfast. Although I was only fifteen years old, I found no difficulty in keeping pace with my older workmates. My task involved giving proper shape to pieces made out of brass. These pieces were often to be sent on to the dockyards to be used as ornate embellishments in ships' cabins and offices. In Belfast, I had grown pretty well used to handling chisels and files so I took to the work easily enough. However, the shop I was working in made pieces to very limited designs and it was not long before I found the work rather tedious. Back in Belfast, as I told you, I did not greatly enjoy the work in the mill, but at least there had been some variety in what I did. So, in spite of the fact that I was being paid more than I'd dreamed possible, I soon began to wonder if there might not be some more interesting work available for me.

The other feature of work at Brown's that disappointed me was that I saw far less of James than I had expected to. With the naïveté of youth, I had assumed that, as we were both working in the same foundry, our paths would cross regularly. It turned out that nothing could have been further from the truth. We worked in different shops and, as the foundry was a very large concern, this meant that we rarely saw one another during the day. Not only that but we were quite often not on the same shift so we would not walk to work or return from work together. Altogether, my boredom at work and my frustration at not seeing more of James caused me to look around for something better after only five months or so at Brown's.

Naturally, I told James of my intentions. I would never have dreamed of concealing anything from him. He simply warned me to be careful about which way I jumped, because a boring job was better than no job at all. I agreed with him about that, of course, but he could tell that I was fairly set in my opinion and he promised to keep his ears open on my behalf. Which was no less that I would have expected from the kindest of brothers.

Every Sunday morning a man called Crombie would come round to collect our rent which was 10/- in total. James insisted on paying the greater part of 5/6d, leaving me but 4/6d to pay. I protested that I should he paying an equal half but he would not have that. He pointed out that he had been paying all 10/- before my arrival and that he was earning more than I was, so I could forget about paying my full share. Again, that was so typical of him in his dealings with me.

Even if varying shifts meant that we sometimes saw little of one another during the week, we spent most Sundays together. With me being new to the city, that was when James took me under his wing as you might say. Although we were both earning good money for young fellows, we were hardly wealthy so any outings we made rarely involved the spending of much money. Often enough, we would just walk for miles at a time, with James pointing out places of interest as we did so. I remember the day we reached as far as Hamilton Crescent, home of the West of Scotland Cricket Club. Unfortunately, that was in the late autumn so obviously there was no cricket to be seen. You will remember that I had developed a liking for watching cricket in Belfast, so I resolved to return to Hamilton Crescent during the season to see how the sport was played in Scotland.

On our walks, James would often stop and introduce me to people whom he knew. And, my word, he seemed to know a lot of people, all of whom smiled when they saw him. Not infrequently, he would stop and talk to young women making their way to and from church. He seemed to know a lot of them as well! With them he would be most polite, bowing his head slightly before engaging them in light conversation. When he introduced me and the young women bestowed smiles in my direction, I would turn brick red and find myself incapable of stammering more than a few words. Ah, the precious tenderness of youth!

But if you think that such a lack of social grace made me any less keen on meeting young women, you would be wrong. Not that I was a pavement philanderer of any sort, you understand, but there were always opportunities to meet young women thanks to activities provided by the local churches.

As you may imagine, there were numerous local churches of all denominations. I was told that there was a small synagogue and a Buddhist chapel not far away but, as I never came across them, I can't vouch for that. James and I did not attend one church in particular. When we did attend, and that was by no means every Sunday, we went to whichever one James decided on. I was happy enough to let him choose. After all, he knew our end of Glasgow much better than I did. Though, at this point, I must make a confession on behalf of both of us. Even at the time, and most certainly on reflection, there was no doubt that he made his selection not so much on the basis of the quality of preaching or singing, but more because of what a church might have to offer in different ways on any particular Sunday. Let me explain.

Some of the churches were very austere places where the sermons were long and gloomy and the doors shut as soon as the service was over. Other churches were rather more warmly welcoming places where, after the services were over, people would wait around and socialise either in the church itself or, if it had one, in the church hall. Experience suggested to me that such a difference had less to do with the denomination of the church than with the personality of the minister. You will not be surprised to know that James and I tended to visit the welcoming churches with something of a social life. I was never quite sure how James knew which churches were more amenable to our tastes, but, there again, he was a young man who knew many people and much of what was going on.

Some churches offered tea and cake after services. We were willing enough partakers of such generosity. Several organised picnic outings in better weather. There was a small fee for the hire of a large horse-drawn charabanc but it was worth every penny. I vividly remember days sitting on the banks of Loch Lomond and the Tail o' the Bank, eating, laughing, loafing and, on a few occasions, indulging in a little harmless flirting, at which James was much more accomplished than I was. Which reminds me of the greatest benefit of our occasional church attendance.

Following the service and a cup of tea, it would be time for the Sunday walk home. Most days, people like us walked in a hurry, heads down, on our way to or back from work. But Sundays were different. Sundays was the day of hard-won leisure and people were determined to treat it as such. They dressed their best and, even if that was less than finery, it was more elegant that their normal wear. The walk home from church would be a sedate affair, often taking a long way round with frequent stops for conversations on the way. It was common for whole families to walk together: grandparents, parents and children, half of whom were girls. James and I would pay a lot of attention to the composition of the family groups and were particularly interested in those with the prettiest daughters.

Older and more socially confident than I was, James was more adept at attaching himself to any family in which a young girl had taken his eye. But I watched and learned and became not too bad at it, even if I do say so myself!

There was one family I got particularly close to. They were the Reid family who lived some distance away. Some years earlier they had lived in our street but they worked hard, saved money, and opened a grocery store at the other end of the burgh. But they never forgot their old church and returned to it regularly. Mr Reid was tall and well built, as befitted an ex-plater. Mrs Reid was short and beginning to turn to plumpness when I met them. On the day, I'd gone round the church hall with the big metal tea pot, topping up everybody's drinks. When I clapped eyes on young Jessie Reid, I want back for the plate of cakes and made sure she got the choice of them. She was a few months younger than me, quite tall for her age, no doubt taking after her father, and quite lacking the plumpness of her mother. Her fair hair hung prettily underneath the Sunday bonnet she always wore. For reasons I did not understand, Mr and Mrs Reid took to me and allowed me to join them in their ritual Sunday walk home. My, how I loved those walks even though they were a fair distance out of my way and involved a long walk home. I would walk as close to Jessie as I could so we could have a good blether. She was my first girlfriend, I suppose, though it went little beyond walking and talking. Except that at the church's Christmas celebration during my second year in Glasgow, she gave me a kiss to wish me a Merry Christmas. Man, I can taste the sweetness of those lips to this day!

I left Brown's Foundry shortly after I'd spent six months there. True to his word, James had kept his ears open and heard that there were openings at Rowan's Boiler Shop, not far along the river from Brown's. One evening after work I called in enquiring about work and was hired on the spot. The ease with which I got a job should have set off alarm bells in my brain but I was too young and naïve for that. It turned out that the owner, Mr George Rowan, had once been a partner of Alex Archibald and, between them, they had run one of the biggest boiler shops in the city. I was never clear what had come between them but Rowan had left Archibald and was setting up on his own. He did not make a very good job of it.

You see, it's all very well owning a boiler shop, or any other business for that matter. And of course it helps if the workers you employ are good men which, by and large at Rowan's, they were. But when you manufacture things you have to be certain that there are people who want to buy these things. That's where Mr Rowan fell down. He left Archibald and Rowan with a full order book and failed to persuade any of his old customers to follow him. The old boiler shop was a large and long-established concern whereas Rowan's new shop was smaller and untried. I have no doubt that he tried hard to attract new customers, and he must have had some success because we were never entirely idle. But business was generally poor and I never picked up the whole 21/- wage I'd been promised. So after a few months at Rowan's I was again on the lookout for a new job. I dropped some hints to James but I didn't like to say too much in case he felt that I was letting him down. So, while keeping my eyes open for new work down near the river, I just continued to work as many hours as Rowan's could provide. By this time I was determined to buy my first major personal asset. I was saving what money I could to buy myself a watch.

It was at about that time, around May of 1873 it would have been, that James unwittingly caused me some distress. He had finally made up his mind to leave Glasgow and become a miner. It was not the shock it might have been. On my first night in Glasgow, he had hinted at it and, in our recent conversations, he had regularly turned the subject round to what was going on in the mines. To be frank, I could not entirely understand his attitude. Or should I say attitudes, because some of his views seemed to me to differ sharply.

'Without mines, there would be no Britain,' he often claimed. 'Coal is needed to provide the power to drive all important industries.' Which indeed to a very large extent was true. So, did he want to be a miner simply because it was a job in the national interest? Perhaps so, though he was never explicit about that. Instead, he usually took a different tack. 'Can't you see Robert?' he would demand of me. 'Can't you see the power that could accrue to the miners?' When I told him that I wasn't entirely clear on that point, he would explain. 'This country absolutely depends on coal. That makes mining the single most important industry in the land. There are thousands upon thousands of miners across Britain. And where would the coal industry be without them?'

Well, the answer to that was obvious enough, but he would not let it rest there. 'The miners have the chance to enjoy power in a way that no ordinary people have had before. Properly organised, and knowing their own value, they could secure for themselves and their whole class a position in society they've never dreamed of.' A zealous light would illuminate his handsome features and one fist would be thumping the top of our table. Then he would groan and slump. 'But with these unions we have today, these New Model Unions ... ' He almost spat out these words ' ... we will never get anywhere. Oh, a few shillings a week and maybe an hour off the day, if we're lucky. But control of their own destiny? Control of the mines?' His eyes would light up at that point, then dull over again. 'We will never see that until we see the mines of Great Britain joined together under the banner of Socialism.'

He had talked like that often in the year I'd lived with him. Of Socialism, weak unions, and the owners' abuse of the regulation of many mines acts. According to him, the owners could ignore regulations at will because there were so few inspectors and most of them were in the owners' pockets. These were constant thoughts of his, but by May of 1873 they had become obsessions and it was clear that he had decided to put in his lot with the miners and do what he could to help bring about the state of affairs which he held dear. One night, he showed me some papers from a pit in Larkhall, a small town some twelve miles south of Glasgow. The last page bore his signature. It was an employment agreement, the most formal I had ever seen. The die was cast. James was leaving.

Before he left he performed one more act of kindness for me to add to the ever-growing list. One evening, he brought home a young lad by the name of Sean Wilson, newly-arrived from Ireland and about to start work at Brown's Foundry. Sean needed lodgings, so he could take James' place. And that was that. For three nights, Sean slept on the floor then, the following Sunday, James was shaking my hand, vowing to write and visit regularly, and then he was gone. Away to Larkhall and the mines. I had lost my brother again. Yes, I would see him now and again but that would never be the same as living with him. That night, Sean moved into my room and I took over James' bed. With a tear never far from my eye, I wrote to Nan Smillie, telling her of our news.

In those last, lengthy conversations with James, I had continued to play my role as the uncouth youngster, knowing little and understanding less. But that was not the real truth of the matter. Or, should I say, not as true as it had been earlier. You see, after settling into Glasgow, I returned to something I had enjoyed in my later years in Belfast: reading books. I had brought a few of my treasured childhood books from Belfast, more for sentimental reasons than anything else. But since beginning to earn reasonable wages, I had added to my small library. In addition to a bible and a dictionary, there were more works of Shakespeare, some Milton and Chaucer, plus, most prized of all, a complete edition of Burns poetry complete with a biography of the great man's life. All of these were bought second-hand in a shop not far from Brown's Foundry. I read them avidly, particularly on dark evenings when walking was no great pleasure.

However, during the two or three months before James left, I had found myself more and more drawn to the books and pamphlets on the table in the main room. I suppose you could call these works broadly Socialist in nature and they came from all manner of places. There were pamphlets from miners' associations, unions representing all manner of trades, even translations into English of some very weighty works from countries such as Germany and France. Frankly, I did not understand every word I read, being only about sixteen years old and a fairly unskilled reader. But I found them intriguing, dealing as they did with big issues like the ownership of capital, the poverty of ordinary men, and the nature of power. Not for a minute did I necessarily agree with all that I understood but that reading material stimulated in me the greatest gift a man can have: the power to think. Without question, I began to feel sympathetic towards Socialism though, at that stage, I had not developed my own view of what form it should take.

So in my later conversations with James I undoubtedly knew and understood more than I was prepared to let on, mainly because feigning ignorance was the best way of encouraging James to talk at length. And by now you will know how much I loved to hear him discourse. After he left, the lodgings grew quieter for Sean turned out to be a very quiet lad. A decent lad too of no bad habits and a more regular and more devout church attender than I was. Not only that but he was on the small side and was usually exhausted when he got home from work. So it was that our conversations tended to be fairly one-sided with me doing almost all of the blethering. It reminded me of my early months in lodgings with James but now the boot was well and truly on the other foot. I received regular letters from James who seemed to be settling well in Larkhall. I'd read bits of those to Sean who, without family of his own, took an interest in our affairs.

A month or so after James left, I changed jobs once more. I simply followed two of our more experienced platers from Rowan's into James and George Thompsons' boiler shop where I became a plater's helper. A few of the older hands there muttered the opinion that I was 'over young' for the job, which demanded no little strength and stamina, but by then I was big and fairly strong for my years and soon proved to them that I was no child when it came to using a fore-hammer. With another new recruit, a shy lad called John Munroe, I was assigned to the charge of an experienced plater by the name of Gallacher. He was an Irishman and a very skilled worker, though not physically strong. He also had a reputation for being particularly surly and foul-mouthed after a night 'on the booze' which was a common event to him. I was soon to find out that that reputation was well justified.

As plater's helpers, it was up to John and me to prepare large sheets of metal for the plater to do the finishing work. His was the skilled work, ours was the heavier and more dangerous work. One day the task was to flange end-plates for high pressure boilers. These plates were thick and heavy and it was hard work to get them into the right approximate shape before the great heat cooled down. We had to prepare them to Gallacher's satisfaction and with some speed in case they cooled down too much for him to be able to do the finishing work. If we did not swing a plate from the heating fire to the work blocks with sufficient speed to satisfy him, we could expect an outburst of the foulest cursing ever heard outside the stokehold of a steam ship. Before that particular day, we had suffered his foul tongue on several occasions.

Though I was so young, I resented his foulness. It seemed unfair and unnecessary seeing that we really were doing our best. But John and I had nobody to complain to. The platers themselves had a union, though I was told that it was neither very strong nor efficient, but mere helpers had no trade union at all. We knew that we were the laughing-stock of the whole shop because of the way Gallacher was treating us, but there was nobody we could turn to for help or guidance. Our salvation from his blasphemy could only lie in our own hands.

Well, though I was only a boy, my dander was up, I can tell you, and I made up my mind to try to put a stop to this unjust bullying. I knew that Gallacher was not strong enough to 'knock down the heat' as we called it, although he could put on the finishing touches with a deft hand. So his weakness was that he needed his helpers: he couldn't do the job without our preparations. As John and I were the only two hammer men in the squad, that gave us some leverage if we could work out how to use it. At first, John was nervous of taking any action but, as he was as weary as I was of the constant abuse, he finally agreed to the plan I had hatched.

We agreed that the next time Gallacher began to abuse us when a heat was laid down, we would simply refuse to lift our hammers. We swore a sort of child-like oath to one another, in which we agreed to act together and not let anybody else know of our intentions. In the back of our minds there was the fear that the foreman might find out and then we would be in real trouble. On that day when the end-plates were being fashioned for high-pressure boilers, we did not have long to wait to test our resolve.

A plate came out of the fire and was laid down on the block perhaps half -an-inch off the mark. Before John and I could lift our hammers to begin the onslaught on the glowing iron, Gallacher's tirade began. He truly excelled himself that morning. In short order, he poured foul scorn on every relation either of us had from Adam downwards. During his rant, John and I had actually managed to slew the plate into its proper place but that did not check his outburst. I knew the time had come to test the very first Union I was ever associated with.

'Come on you f*cking b*stards!' Spittle flying from his mouth. 'Knock it down right, b*gger you!' I apologise for the use of his words but, believe me, that example is 'moonlight into sunlight' compared with the reality of his lengthy harangue.

John and I just stood there, our hands on our hammer shafts, and did not move. Gallacher swore again at us, calling us all sorts, but we refused to lift our hammers. He tore my hammer from my hands and began to shower blows on the plate, but it was no use. He wasn't strong enough and, breathing heavily, his eyes gleaming redly from the previous night's booze, he began swearing at us again before throwing the hammer to the floor close to my feet. He cursed us at length, using every foul word he could think of then repeating them, blaspheming every part of our bodies and our souls too. Still we did not move. I fancied that I heard John's knees knocking: mine certainly were. But having gone so far, we were not about to give up.

Gallacher would have loved to use physical force against is, but he didn't dare. No strongman, he was no match for either of us. The rumour of the row spread quickly and many pairs of eyes from every side of the shop were turned in our direction. Sensing that he wasn't getting anywhere with us, Gallacher changed his tone and started pleading with us to prepare the plate so he could carry out the finishing work. It was perhaps less unpleasant to listen to him wheedling rather than throwing curses at us, but we still refused to cooperate. He had to learn his lesson and the lesson was not yet over. We waited until the plate had cooled to the stage where it could not be successfully worked. Then I decided it was time to make our point.

'Listen here, Gallacher,' I said, with all the cheek of youth. 'We have been working our hardest and doing our very best for you, and you have given us nothing but abuse. I'm here to tell you that we are heartily sick of it and are determined not to strike another blow with our hammers until you have promised to stop swearing at us, and to treat us as free men and not as slaves.' Grand words, if you like, from a mere stripling, but they accurately portrayed how John and I felt.

For a moment, I thought that we had lost the game for his immediate response was to rave violently at us, using language equally as vile as anything that had gone before. But when he realised that we were not for bending the knee, his harangue faltered and the vile words ran out. Then he gave us his promise that he would not treat us that way again. We were not entirely convinced that he would keep his word because he would soon 'get fou' again and lose control. But for the moment, at least, he was quieter and tolerably civil, so John and I picked up our hammers and got back to work.

News of our action spread quickly and other platers turned it into a joke against Gallacher. They talked about the relative calm which descended on our part of the shop as 'the conversion of Gallacher'. For a time, things went smoothly enough and Gallacher more or less kept his promise to use. I was well enough pleased with myself, arrogant youth that I must have been. Not only had my first strike been a success, but it had been brought to a happy conclusion by refusing to strike. Alas, the relative peace that had broken out did not last long. Gallacher cared not to stay off the booze and, though his 'morning after' behaviour never quite plumbed the depths it had previously reached, it was bad enough. So, after only four months or so at Thompsons' boiler shop, I was keeping my eyes open once more for a better placement.

My brother James and I did meet several times during the year after he left for Larkhall. He had got in well with a drayman by the name of Watson whose round from a Glasgow brewery included Larkhall. James would cry a lift from him on an occasional Sunday and we would spend the day walking and blethering. He was as talkative as ever on the subject of Socialism but when he found out that I had been reading up on the matter and was busy developing some views of my own, he became rather less opinionated than he had been before. In our conversations there was the suggestion of an important lassie in Larkhall but, hard though I tried, I could not get him to say much about that.

On other Sundays, I still walked occasionally from church with Jessie Reid's family and went on occasional Sunday picnics with them but, young Sean in tow, I found myself spending more time down by the river, particularly round the quayside which I found fascinating. All those ships from all over the world, bringing goods in, taking goods out. There was something very exciting about it all. I soon learned the countries of origin represented by the various flags and, though never becoming an expert on the subject, I began to recognise more easily the many different kinds of vessels which filled the waterways. I also found the variety of human beings a delight to behold and listen to. I saw my first large numbers of negroes serving as deckhands on Baltimore clippers and Ivory Coast schooners. I saw and heard Brazilians, Spaniards, Portuguese and Africans. There were Yankees in stove-pipe hats, puffing furiously at huge cigars, Scandinavians with leathery faces, French officers wearing fancy wrist watches and heaven knows who else. My word, it was as if the whole world had come to Glasgow.

Though never as entertaining company as James, Sean was a pleasure to be with. Not only was he quiet and amiable, he was also a dab hand with a cooking pot, which made up for my lack of skill in that area. He was still very much the follower in our conversations. The nearest he came to leading was the first time he saw me with a clay pipe, which was only a few days after he realised that I had decided to grow a moustache. He made some weak joke about the wee boy trying to pass himself off as a man. Although it was not very funny, and at my expense, I laughed at it anyway for it was nice to hear him put a few original sentences together.

In the late spring of 1874, we found a common interest. One Sunday, I persuaded him to walk with me as far as Hamilton Crescent and visit the cricket ground there. It was a lovely, sunny day, though still with a hint of spring crispness in the air, and we sat down on the grass beyond the boundary rope some distance from the well dressed throng of ladies and gentlemen gathered around the attractive pavilion. As we watched play, we talked and it came to my attention how long the arm of coincidence is. It turned out that Sean had quite often visited the same Belfast park as I had some years earlier and that his favourite sight there had been not the fine ladies and gentlemen, nor the horses, not even the music from the bandstand. Instead he had most admired the cricket matches. A small world, is it not?

We watched cricket several times during the early summer and enjoyed it thoroughly until one particular Sunday when an incident occurred which annoyed me thoroughly and reduced Sean to tears. Each time we'd visited, we had bemoaned our lack of opportunity to play the game. That particular Sunday, as we once more sat on the grass some distance from the fine ladies and gentlemen, we saw on the grass only a few yards away a bat and ball. We had already been there for over an hour and nobody had been near us so I assumed that the bat and ball were lost play things. I smiled at Sean and he nodded back. Seconds later, I was lobbing the ball at him and he was knocking it back to me. We had hardly begun our little game when we saw a large man striding round the boundary rope towards us.

'You there!' he shouted. 'What the blazes do you think you are doing?' His voice was Scottish but not of the Glasgow kind I was used to. 'What are you up to, you pair of young rogues?'

'Only having a little game,' I told him, noting his immaculate whites and colourful cummerbund. 'We found ... '

'Found? Found did you say?' He grabbed Sean by the arm, very tightly to judge by my friend's yelp. 'That bat and ball belong to my son. You've stolen them!'

'I am sorry if they are your son's,' I said. 'We found them lying on the grass and ... '

'No excuses, you lying little devil!' In the background, people were looking on our direction to see what all the fuss was about. Two more men dressed in whites were moving toward us. 'I'll get the peelers to you,'

'No you won't!' I exclaimed, moving close to him. Growing bigger, I was almost his size and rather stronger. 'And if you do not let go of my friend, I will have to make you do so!'

'What! What's that you say?' He flushed a deep red, whether from embarrassment or fear, I never knew or cared. 'Go on, be off with you,' he said, sensing the approach of his two friends and feeling bolder again. 'And don't come back,' he added. 'This is a decent place and we don't want the likes of you here.'

For a moment, I came close to hitting him but sense prevailed and I led the sobbing Sean out of the ground and to the safety of the streets outside. We said little on the way home and were both mightily relieved when we reached our side of town. The incident had both shaken and upset me and I resented bitterly the tone which one man felt he could reasonably adopt towards another. I have no doubt that the stinging memory of that day fed into the political views I eventually developed.

What turned out to be my last job in Glasgow was at yet another boiler shop, Anderson's this time. Happily, there was no Gallacher around but there were still some characters in the shops. There were two platers and six helpers in our squad. The two platers were very experienced and generally considered to be the finest at their craft in the whole city if Glasgow. There were also most agreeable men to work with. However, Geordie and Pete as they were named, were not the most reliable of men because, like Gallacher, they were fond of their booze and were often 'guy wet' as we used to say. So wet in fact, that they were often late for work and sometimes didn't turn up at all. They only managed to hang onto their jobs because they were so good at it. When they were there, that is.

As mere helpers, we had to turn up every day, but we would be sent home if the platers had not turned up. That did no good to our wage packets, I can tell you. Now and again, even when Georgie and Pete did turn up on time, they were useless for half of the morning until their heads had cleared. Again, that meant a loss of wages for us. Then there were the days when they would come in late, desperate for a drink to settle their nerves as they put it, but spent out because of what they had bought the night before. If any one of us was foolish enough to lend them any money, they were as liable as not to walk straight out of the shop, make directly for The Crown which was the nearest public house, and have a wee drink just to 'settle their nerves'.

Then there was the infamous day of the pony. We were at the gate, waiting from them to turn up and, when they did, they were once more the worse for wear. They both tried to 'raise the win' or borrow money but we weren't for lending them any. They were in a bad enough way as it was. While we were standing around, waiting for their heads to clear so that we could begin work and make some money, a young boy arrived and asked if anyone knew Geordie. We pointed him out.

'Mister Geordie,' the lad said. 'Mister Smith from The Crown wants to know if ye're going to tak away yon pony you bought last night.'

'A pony?' Geordie replied, his eyes still not quite able to focus. 'Are ye telling me that I bought a pony?'

'Aye, ye did an' all, sir.'

'I cannae believe it,' Geordie said, shaking his head, then groaning. 'Tell me laddie, what did I pay for it?'

'Ten pounds,' the boy replied. 'And a right good pony it is too.'

'Ten pounds, eh?' A sly look came over Geordie's face. 'Do ye think Mister Smith would give me five pounds to take it back?'

'I'm sure he would, Mr Geordie.'

'Aye, well,' Geordie said. 'Pete and I will just go over and see him about it.'

As you might imagine, they didn't return that day, so the squad was sent home. Though I laugh about that incident now, it is an unfortunate truth that there were many very heavy drinkers in the boiler shops in those days. Perhaps it was due to the great heat in which we worked which could leave you feeling dehydrated by the end of your shift. But far too many men overdid it, causing misery to themselves and, no doubt, their families. Not to mention a loss of wages to their helpers. Things have improved since those bad old drunken times but back in 1874 I was beginning to find the boiler shop environment less and less attractive as time went on.

Then out of the blue a letter arrived which was to change my life forever. It was a letter from my brother James in Larkhall. The letter in itself was nothing unusual. He and I had been corresponding regularly with one another and with

Nan Smillie since James had left Glasgow. But the contents of his letter took me aback and gave me reason for some very serious thinking. If I was interested, there was an opening for me at one of the pits and he knew where I could find good lodgings too. The money was good, some way better than I'd been earning in the boiler shops, we could see more of one another and - knowing that he was dangling a fine piece of bait with this - the miners had a cricket club. What did I think? I had to let him know as soon as possible because he didn't know how long it would be before the job and the lodgings were taken by somebody else. Well, that letter sent me into a frenzy of thinking, I can tell you. To be honest, the idea of becoming a miner had no immediate appeal for me. It was well known that mining was a hard, dirty and dangerous occupation. When James had left Glasgow for Larkhall, I had rather feared for him. Now the thought of taking the same route myself rather filled me with dread. On the other hand, I asked myself, did I really want to stay in Glasgow?

It would not be true to say that I had outgrown Glasgow. In fact, it would be more true to say that Glasgow had outgrown me. In some ways, it was a wonderful place to work and live. There were always plenty of reasonably well paid jobs available, and there were certainly plenty of sights to see and things to do. But I think that the very size and frenzy of the city were beginning to daunt me. If I'd been a member of the other class as James called the owning class, perhaps I would have felt rather differently. I thought briefly of the well-to-do cricketers who had ejected Sean and myself from their ground. No doubt, they had ways of passing their time which make city life attractive. But that wasn't for 'the likes of me', as they would no doubt have put it.

Instead, I was working in an environment where heat, dehydration and an uncertainly over wages was normal. In which men were so hard-used that they turned to drink for comfort. They were good men, by and large, and there were some I was friendly enough with. But they were not how I wanted to be when I grew older. Working life shaped by the heat of a boiler shop, private life determined by the never-ending rows of tenement packed streets. To be honest with you, I was not entirely certain what I wanted from life. Does anybody at the age of seventeen? All that I was becoming more and more sure of was that I did not want my life to be confined by a great city and the nature of life in one.

Like James a year earlier, I decided that I wanted to live somewhere where the countryside was on my doorstep, where your workmates were also your neighbours, where there was a sense of an identifiable community. For me, those things could never be obtained in Glasgow, great city though it was. I was still far from certain that I wanted to be a miner, but from everything James had told me, living in Larkhall might well present me with the opportunity to live in a way that no city could offer. Besides, the wages would be better and there was the tantalising prospect of finally being able to play cricket. Two days after receiving James' letter, I wrote back to confirm that I would shortly be with him in Larkhall.

There was no long farewell to Glasgow. There was no time for that. I downed my fore-hammer on a Saturday, picked up my wages, and caught a lift on Watson's brewery dray to Larkhall on the Sunday. I did not forget young Sean's situation. A new boy had started at Anderson's that week and he was sleeping up a close near the docks. I brought him back to our lodgings and introduced him to Sean. From the start, they got on well. The new lad Hamish was a quiet Highlander who had come south to escape the fishing life which had been all his family had ever known. He had about him an air of quiet determination which I knew he would need if he was going to survive in the boiler shops of Glasgow. I believe that his and Sean's personalities were better suited than mine had been with Sean's. Hamish seemed to have no interest in politics so Sean would be spared the sermons I was inclined to preach at him. As I expected, Sean moved into the big room and Hamish had the smaller room. It took me a little time to pack my few belongings, the heaviest part of which was my library which had expanded somewhat over the past year. I embraced Sean, shook hands with Hamish and wished them every good fortune. On my way to the corner where Watson was due to pick me up, I made my last Glasgow decision. I dropped into Abbotsford's, the chandler down by the river. I reappeared moments later clutching a second-hand watch of the style they call a hunter. It had cost me a large part of my small savings but I was determined on it. I tucked it safely in my canvas sack and marched off to meet up with Watson.

As the dray rumbled slowly towards Larkhall, I reflected on the similarities between my coming to Glasgow and my leaving of it. On both occasions, I'd been carried, albeit by different forms of transport, and very much looking forward to a reunion with my dear brother. And the similarities did not end there. A mixture of excitement and apprehension, an uncertainty about what lay ahead, and a fervent hope what I would acquit myself well. Not that there was much profit in such reflections, of course. I'd made my decision. I was ready for Larkhall. Whether Larkhall was ready for me was another matter!

IV

Underground

OVER THE YEARS I was to become well known to the mine workers of Britain. And to other groups and individuals as well, though that is a story for later. It strikes me forcibly looking back that the miners in particular would have been surprised by the fact that I did not come from mining stock. As I have told you, my parents died when I was young but I have discovered enough about them to know that they had no connections whatsoever with mining. My father had been a crofter in Scotland before moving to Belfast where he worked in various placements but never as a miner. My mother's people had been agricultural workers and domestic servants. Nan Smillie was a country girl. Indeed, my only connection with mining was thorough my brother James, at whose suggestion I first went to Larkhall, and his reasons for becoming a miner were more political than anything else. So, when I took up lodgings with a colliery fireman named John McKnight and his family with whom I lived in Colliery Row, Larkhall, I had no more knowledge of mining than a new-born baby would have had. It is strange to think how mining and miners would come to dominate my life, given my total ignorance of the industry until I arrived in Larkhall.

My lodgings in the town were close to the Summerlee Colliery in which I was to be employed. Larkhall was spared the ugly developments of high-rise tenements such as I had become used to in Belfast and Glasgow and, if the rows of miners' cottages were hardly pretty, they at least allowed a man a view of the surrounding countryside. If I was only the second in generations of our family to descend a pit shaft, I had at least attained the age of seventeen, so I was not exactly a 'child-slave' as some writers have called children employed in British industry. It may seem hard to believe now, looking back from a distance, but the lot of working-class people, children included, was quite dreadful during the nineteenth century. It is instructive to remind ourselves of what life was like for the industrial working class in particular, not only in mining but wherever hard labour secured an owner's profit.

Throughout the century, factories and mines were dangerously unhealthy places. To an extent I had witnessed that in the boiler shops of Glasgow, but the reality was often grimmer than even those places. In 1832, a Parliamentary Committee Enquiry produced evidence to show that thousands of children, especially girls, were working in factories from six o'clock in the morning until half-past eight in the evening, with only thirty minutes allowed for eating. By the end of the day, many were so fatigued that they had to be beaten by the foreman to keep them awake. In the textile trade, it was common practice to use the smallest children to clean spinning machines and looms while they were still in motion and quite literally threatening grievous injury. The children were also used to crawl under broken machinery in operation to tie broken ends of yarn. Small wonder that there were so many accidents involving children. How could a system, even an owner's system, have encouraged dreadful working practices like these?

Being used for work at low levels, the long-term effects on thousands of children of bending for long periods was that they developed weak, curved legs and arched backs. Frequently, in the textile mills, there were dreadful respiratory diseases caused by working in a hot, humid atmosphere where the air was contaminated by clouds of microscopic cotton dust.

There was danger in other industries too, almost anywhere where working people were herded together in buildings to do their master's work. Consider the pottery workers, for example. Many workers began their working lives for a company at the age of six and remained there until they died which, in too many cases, was at a very young age. A report on that industry referred to the experience of one man who from the age of six had been a mould-runner and who, for a shift which could last up to fifteen hours, was paid a shilling a week. His job at that tender age was to light the fire in the store-room and spend the rest of the day rushing backwards and forwards bringing the raw clay to the potter and then running to take the plaster moulds into the hot store-room where the plates were hardened off. From the age of six! What kind of employers would treat a child like that? What kind of government would turn a blind eye to it?

Then there were the workers in the match factories, many of whom were young women. Many of them routinely developed a disease known as 'phossy-jaw' which caused teeth to fall out and the jaw bone to rot away. Up and down the country, in all kinds of employment, workers of all ages were put at risk. History tells us that there were good employers like the Wedgewood family of potters who were caring about their workers. But too often the owners had care for nothing but their order books. I always remember the words of a doctor from the Stoke-on-Trent area. Giving evidence to an enquiry, he wrote, 'The potters as a class are as a rule stunted in growth and frequently deformed in the chest. They become prematurely old and are certainly short-lived.' These words were the most awful condemnation of working practices in factories across Britain for much of the nineteenth century.

There was legislation passed in an attempt to improve conditions for workers. Factory Acts of 1802, 1819, 1831, 1833 and 1844 were all, in various ways, designed to improve conditions for workers and, in particular, young children.

But just in case you might think that all this legislation ensured some kind of golden age for the working classes, you might care to consider the main provisions of the 1844 Act. It provided that children might not start work until they were eight years old, that children between eight and thirteen could only work a six-and-a-half-hour day and that women (not girls you will notice) over the age of thirteen were limited to a twelve-hour day. In some ways, these provisions were more liberal than their predecessors but the harsh truth is that there was little in them which would significantly improve conditions for the majority, and children remained factory fodder. One provision of that act, the fencing-off of dangerous machinery, was potentially beneficial but the inspection regime was for many years so weak as to make it almost meaningless.

As far as the mines were concerned, the problems which affected factory workers were present, but there were other very severe problems too. As the demand for coal had grown, mine shafts went much deeper. This caused very real problems such as lack of ventilation and a considerably increased risk of flooding. There were frequent gas explosions, particularly at depth, because although it was available, the use of the Davy Safety Lamp was not compulsory. That depended on the attitude of the owner and many, perhaps most, were too cost-conscious to provide the Davy for their miners. Small children of both genders, sometimes as young as four years of age, were employed underground hauling trucks of coal along passageways which were too low for an adult. They were also used to sitting for hours at a time, opening and closing ventilation doors. Many of these iniquities were revealed by the findings of a Royal Commission report published in 1842. It told some dreadful stories. A twelve-year-old girl carrying a hundredweight of coal on her back, crouching and creeping through water in a low tunnel. Children climbing dangerous ladders up the pit shaft with huge baskets of coal strapped to their backs. Naked and semi-naked men, women and children all working together, which the report concluded was quite literally demoralising. And much more of the same.

That report led to the Mines Act of 1842 which forbade the employment of women and girls in mines, and of boys under the age of ten. But, as it only appointed one inspector to oversee the observation of these provisions, they were generally ignored. Further Acts of 1850, 1860 and 1872 did make some progress. More inspectors were trained and appointed, the employment age for boys was raised to twelve, all mines had to have two shafts to improve chances of escape if there was an explosion, and there was a requirement placed on owners to provide fan ventilators, stronger support timber, stronger ropes and safety lamps. In the round, these provisions represented improvements. However, these improvements could only be guaranteed by rigorous inspection. Although there were now more inspectors, there were nothing like enough. And beyond question, some inspectors were in the owners' pockets. These owners' interests were represented strongly in the House of Commons and even more so in the House of Lords where they did everything they could to halt or at least slow down legislation which intended to protect miners. Their collective attitude was rather well summed up by Lord Londonderry who described the 1850 Act's attempt to provide more inspectors as 'iniquitous'. Needless to say, the miners themselves had no direct representation in parliament.

It is impossible to describe accurately the conditions for miners across Britain in the 1870's. Conditions varied enormously not only from region to region but even from pit to pit. These variances were due to the attitudes of the owners. There were good owners around, men who made every effort to implement the meagre provision of the various Acts of Parliament. Equally, there were those owners who did as little as they could get away with which, if they successfully courted the local inspector, might be very little indeed. Such was the state of affairs for miners when I first entered Summerlee Colliery in Larkhall in the summer of 1874.

Those of you with knowledge or experience of mining will know what I mean when I say that I began my mining life as a hand pumper. For those of you who know little about mining, let me explain. You might think that at the coal faces there is a huge open cavern where hundreds of men might be hewing out the coal. Well, that was not the case in my early days in the pit and did not become the case until much later when large excavating machines were able to create large spaces for working in. When I started, each tunnel or gallery was dug out by pick and shovel, so the space in which the miners worked was typically small, low and narrow. Particularly at depth, water had to be continuously pumped out.

In most working spaces, there were what the miners called dooks or dips, places where water could gather and, at least, make the miner's task even more uncomfortable. At worst, if there was a sudden inrush of water, their lives could be at risk. That water had to be got rid of by means of a mechanical, hand-powered pump. That was my job. On any day except Sunday, there were three shifts for the miners. Each shift lasted eight hours. Imagine if you will, eight hours of continuous hewing at the coal face, usually crouching, often balancing on knees, dust filling your lungs at each blow of your pick. Add to that the continuous hazards posed by gases and potential flooding, and you might begin to understand how wearing the task of coal-getting is. In any given small working, there were six miners, only two at a time on shift. The job of hand pumpers like me was to make sure that they were safe from at least one danger, that of flooding.

In comparison with hewing out the coal, manning a pump was not particularly arduous. Certainly, I would never claim that keeping down the water was exhausting work. But in one or two ways, we hand pumpers were worse off than the miners themselves. For example, there were only ever two hand pumpers for each squad of miners. Given the fact that the mines would be in operation for twenty-four hours a day, there was an inevitable consequence. The hand pumpers' shifts were twelve hours long. Not only that but, while miners always worked in pairs at least and sometimes more, the hand pumper would be on his own. On his own for half a day!

There was an added problem for the hand pumpers. The pump itself was situated a mile from the bottom of the pit, and, crouching and stumbling, it took half-an-hour to reach it. Then, at the end of a shift, another half-an-hour to regain the outdoors and some blessed fresh air. So although the shift was nominally twelve hours, more than long enough you might think, the length of our shift was actually thirteen hours. That extra hour of walking to and from the pump, in the position of a half-shut clasp-knife, was really harder than our actual work. Not that there was any official recognition of that of course. We were paid for pumping, not walking! We were not even allowed time off to eat. We had to snatch a bite as and when we could, often in the presence of some very unwelcome guests, as I shall explain.

On top of all this, there was an arrangement when I was a hand pumper at Summerlee which made for a more trying experience than anything else. The miners worked six days a week, having Sundays to themselves. But that did not mean that the mines could be left entirely idle. What would happen if on the Sunday there was a gathering of water in one of the tunnels? Why, that would mean that there might be a delay in starting coal-getting on the Monday, and that would hit the owner's pockets. So the pumps had to be kept going even though the miners weren't there. Even worse, as there are seven days in the week and the hand pumpers alternated from day-work to night-work in turn, it meant that every second Saturday one of the hand pumpers went on his shift at 6pm and had to remain there until 6pm on the Sunday; believe it or not, a twenty-four hour shift! But it got worse than that. With the exception of a man in charge of the pumping station almost a mile away, the hand pumper would be the only person working in the pit. Twenty-four hours underground on your own! Little wonder that I did not look forward to second Saturdays.

I will be perfectly honest with you. Those twenty-four hours spent in the bowels of the earth with no human company could be quite frightening, particularly to start with when I wasn't used to it. Up to that point, my life had been spent in busy places with many people around. Busy streets, tenement buildings, boiler shops and all the rest. When I suddenly found myself entirely on my own below ground at Summerlee it came as a total and unwelcome shock.

I do not know for certain, but I think I might have been less distraught if I had been surrounded by total silence. But, you might be surprised to know, in the depths of a mine-working, there are always movements and their accompanying noises taking place. I was never down there but there was the constant drip-drip of water. That may not seem much but, when you are enclosed in a narrow echoing place, such an apparently minor sound can take on the significance of a waterfall. Then, just as I was settling into the hush of the grave, only interrupted by the occasional drip-drip, there might be a fall of stones which could make a terrifying noise. Oddly enough, it was less terrifying if such a fall occurred close by. I would jump and my heart would race but at least the noise subsided fairly quickly whereas, if the fall occurred some distance away, the effect on me was always more severe. It is often said that sound carries further at night, when the world is dark and still. Imagine how that sound might carry in the relative darkness of mine-workings, its harshness building and echoing as it ran through the tunnels, disused workings and shafts, then came at you. I hated distant falls and found my body tensing as the noise raced towards me.

It was easy to lose all sense of time down there on your own. I never took my hunter watch with me. It was far too precious to risk anywhere near tight rocks or the coal face. You well know that it can be hard enough to judge time without a watch when you are in company in daylight hours. Believe me, it is a hundred times more difficult underground and on your own for hour after weary hour. I am reminded of a line from a poem I read many years ago: 'The hours crept by on leaden feet'. Sometimes it became so bad that my nerves failed me.

I look back with shuddering disbelief to the frightful, waking nightmares of those double shifts when I started out at Summerlee. They were so dreadful that I regarded them as my fortnightly entombments. It is no pleasure to recall those dark times spent sitting there with hardly any illumination. Sometimes, I would try to take my mind off my lonely situation by thinking what I could do on the following Sunday, my next day off. And that would lead me to imagine what everybody else was doing. No doubt having a lie-in, then getting dressed for church. Following the service, a leisurely walk then home again for the best meal of the week. No doubt, some men would be at the booze, but others would be out and about, enjoying the fresh air, perhaps even playing a game of cricket. And would any of them be aware of me, standing or sitting on my own for hours on end down in the pit? No, of course they wouldn't. Believe me, it is very easy to become morose in such circumstances.

But if human companionship was scarce, there was always company of a less welcome kind, the four-footed variety. As many collieries were, Summerlee was infested with rats. Certain kinds of collieries were more prone to rats than others. Not every shaft of a mine is driven perpendicularly into the ground. A few, like Summerlee, not only have that kind of vertical shaft, but also have a sloping route from the surface all the way into the workings. Such a means was called a 'daylight mine' because, due to the relatively gentle angle at which the way moved from the surface to the workings, daylight was able to penetrate that much further inside. Unfortunately, as well as attracting daylight, such a means of access also enabled rats to gain access with great ease. At Summerlee they did exactly that, and in vast numbers.

Somehow, the rats seemed to know very well that I was alone and this knowledge emboldened them. Whereas they would normally wait on the fringes of human activity and wait for the humans to depart before foraging for crumbs and bits of crust, when they knew that you were the only human around they became positively impertinent. As I ate my pieces prepared for me by Mrs McKnight, they would come closer and closer to me, almost in military fashion in tight little groups of twos or threes. Then they would stand still, almost within arm's reach, staring at the food in my hands through their sharp, beady eyes. Let me tell you that rats' eyes staring at you in near darkness are by no means reassuring.

Once or twice during those lonely vigils, I made a great mistake concerning my rodent companions. Probably too tired to think clearly, I threw some crumbs just beyond them in the mistaken belief that that would satisfy them. Off they scurried into the darkness and there was a great squealing as they fought over the crumbs. Then after a few seconds they returned, taking up position again very close to me, those awful beady eyes once more fixed on the bread in my hands. I learned a valuable lesson on that shift. A rat may not be satisfied with a crumb. He will not give up until he has eaten the whole loaf.

A word of warning here if you are ever in a similar situation, forced to stay down a pit for twenty-four hours with only rats for company. Never fall asleep! I did, on only the second occasion I had to endure my fortnightly entombment. It was near to the end of my shift, my eyelids had grown heavy and I just couldn't help myself. I was suddenly awakened by a curious, echoing rattling noise. Leaping to my feet, in the semi-darkness I saw a huge rat making off with my oil flask. The devil had fixed his large incisor teeth in the cork and was hauling it away, no doubt to whatever dark fissure in the rock served as his hole. It was the noise of the tin striking the rails on which the coal wagons ran that had roused me from my slumber. I gave chase in that low tunnel but the determined fellow actually got that flask to the very entrance of the hole, a point where the dim light of my lamp hardly reached, before I was able to stretch out and wrestle the flask from him. He turned towards me, spat out the flask cork from his mouth then bared his teeth at me before, much to my relief, disappearing into the hole.

Now you may think that what I described was a trivial incident; that, in the great scheme of things as they were during a twenty-four hour solo shift, the meeting with that big rat was meaningless, just a minor irritation. Let me tell you that it was anything but minor. Imagine if you will the results if the rat had succeeded in stealing my flask. Or, just as bad, if the flask oil had spilled out on the floor of the pit as a result of the rat dragging the flask by its cork. If either of those things had happened, my plight would have been pitiable. The small lamp that I carried to the bottom with me was the only thing that stood between me and all-engulfing total darkness. If there was no flask or, for that matter, no oil, I would have been totally blind down there, perhaps for hours. And how much more difficult would that already hazardous journey back to the surface have been? I tell you, it doesn't bear thinking about.

Not only that, but the oil lamp was the only means by which I could roughly tell the passage of time. As I have told you, I never took my watch with me but what I did have was the knowledge that my lamp, fully-filled, would last for about two hours. Each time I refilled it meant that another dreary two hours or so had passed. That was not by any means a precise timing, of course, but over a mind-numbing shift of twenty-four hours I was always grateful for even the imprecise notion of time my lamp provided. Had the rat succeeded in his efforts, I would have lost that small contact with reality.

Sometimes, the things which keep a man from slipping over the edge can be trivial indeed. Let me assure you that, in the depths of Summerlee pit, the trivial matter of some lamp oil took on the mantle of great importance. It was not unknown for people, particularly younger boys, to emerge from a twenty-four hour shift shaking like a leaf and gibbering like a lunatic. On those awful occasions, a common cause was a failure of their lamps and the consequently dreadful experience of many hours of total darkness with only discordant noises and rats for company. I am glad to say that it never got quite that bad for me, in spite of the best efforts of those hellish rodents.

And that is what it was like for me during my introduction to the world of mining at Summerlee. From what I have written, you will see that the life of a hand pumper was neither easy nor agreeable. There were some men and boys who took up such a position and left within days, so affected were they, not so much by the work itself as by its attendant circumstances. Not that I have told you everything about the unpleasant aspects of the work: the fatigue, the cloying dirt and dust, the smell of gas, the acrid tastes in the mouth and all the rest of it. But those things were common to all men who worked underground, not just the hand pumpers, and I will have more to say about the miners' lot shortly. For the time being I was prepared, if not content, to make the best of things. I was certain in my mind that I would not be a hand pumper for long. I regarded that as being part of my apprenticeship, if you like. Not a pleasant experience, but necessary.

But life was not all doom and gloom. I had fallen in with the McKnight family who could not have been kinder to their new lodger. I felt that I was becoming part of a real community because, unlike Glasgow with its multiplicity of factories and industries, Larkhall was largely devoted to the one industry and people shared the local hazards and pleasures almost as one big family. I was growing stronger and felt as healthy as I have ever done in my life. Away from my work, I could look around me and see God's handiwork in the beautiful forms of the countryside. At long last, I was even getting the opportunity to play some cricket.

And, of course, I was closer to James. There was indeed, as I'd suspected, a lassie in his life. That meant that I saw rather less of him than I might otherwise have done. Still, it was a better situation than the separations we had previously experienced, as I explained in my letters to Nan Smillie.

So on the whole I was a satisfied young man moving towards my eighteenth birthday. I felt that I was becoming part of something that mattered. I had the feeling inside me that maybe I would contribute something. It was the vaguest of feelings at that time, but events would soon take a turn which would help to provide a clearer shape to that feeling. I still had an awful lot to experience and learn, and that learning was about to gather pace in ways that I could never have predicted.

V

Becoming a Miner

FROM THE PREVIOUS pages, you may well understand how hard life could be for a hand pumper. Perhaps you imagine that life got easier for those who worked their way from that lowly status to becoming a fully fledged miner. If so, I must ask you to reconsider your view. The miner has always had a very hard time of it, working in one of the most dangerous, life-sapping occupations imaginable. It did not take me long in Larkhall to understand that.

From my earliest days there, I became aware of the huge risks miners took every time they descended the shaft. Apart from the dangers of explosion, gassing and drowning, all sorts of injuries were commonplace in the normal run of events. I know of no other occupation in which there were so many mangled or lost limbs. Around Larkhall I lost count of the number of one-legged men on crutches, one-armed men with empty jacket sleeves flapping in the wind, and men so badly maimed they could hardly get around. Collapsed rib cages following rock falls were considered to be just another hazard of the job. If the man was lucky, he would lose weeks' or months' work. If he was unlucky, he would be damaged for life. I have no doubt that some of those so affected wished that the fall had been heavier and simply killed them.

Damage to the head and face was no rare event. The loss of an eye or eyes was all too common. All in all, miners led a very dangerous life. In spite of which and on the whole, miners will work hard given a fair chance and will hold their heads high among other workers, whatever their grade. But when I first started and for much of the time since, they have been the victims of culpable neglect by their employers. In addition to the burdens of incessant toil and the ever-presence of great dangers, the miners have had the domination of the owners as an extra cross to bear.

Besides issues relating to work, other aspects of their lives caused them great problems. Take housing, for example. There were three basic arrangements as far as houses were concerned. A few, a very few be it said, of the miners lived in their own homes. Men whose families had lived in Larkhall for generations and inherited the family home. Then there were those families who rented houses or parts of houses from private landlords. These properties were mainly in the old part of Larkhall, from the time when it had been but a tiny village. But the majority of miners lived in cottages like those in Colliery Row where I first lodged. These rows of cottages belonged to the Summerlee Iron and Coal Company, in effect to the owner of that company. Not for nothing were they known as tied cottages, because living in one of those meant that the company controlled important aspects of the miners' lives. As I will tell you shortly, in the event of industrial disputes there was no security in occupying a tied cottage.

Then there was the issue of income. Generally speaking, miners were rather better paid than some of their contemporaries in other industries. As a matter of opinion I would say that, given the nature and dangers of their occupation, they were entitled to that little extra. But just as there was little security in housing tenure, there was no great deal more as far as income was concerned. Demand for coal rose and fell. So too did prices. In good times, owners kept on a full workforce and paid the agreed wages. In less good times, men could get laid off or have their wages reduced. Sometimes, both these evils occurred. Then there were the many cases of injuries preventing men from going to work, perhaps for lengthy periods of time. And remember that this was in the days before Acts of Parliament dealing with national insurance and unemployment benefits. In these circumstances, there was little automatic support for mining families in financial trouble. It was at such times that the mining community was often seen at its best, closing ranks and supporting one another with money, food and, above all, love. However, it is impossible to over-emphasise the extent to which miners and their families were held in thrall by the mining companies and their owners who, if they wished, could rob a man of his job and his home.

While I was still a hand pumper, I saw at close quarters the kind of evil – I use that word deliberately – which could befall the mining community. It was while I was still lodging with the McKnight family who were so kind to me that it makes me weep to think of the privations they were to suffer. Mrs McKnight was a particularly Christian body, forever fussing after me, reminding me to write to Nan Smillie and giving me work pieces, which you would call sandwiches, of a much better quality than my rent payment warranted. It was the autumn of 1874 and I was into my fourth month of hand pumping which, as you know, I was barely tolerating. For some years, mines had been at peak production. There were fears at the highest level that the Franco-Prussian War of 1870 might embroil Britain in armed conflict so factories were on high alert, if you like, and the mines were producing coal to fuel those factories. However, by 1874 fears of conflict had abated, industrial output was cut back, and the demand for coal dropped. You may well imagine who suffered most cruelly as a result of that.

Wages had been reasonably high until that autumn. Even I, as a mere hand pumper, had been earning six shillings per shift or forty-two shillings a week. This was undoubtedly good money for a lad of seventeen just starting out on his mining career. But with the reduction in demand, the company was enforcing a reduction in wages. This was to produce the first miners' strike I ever experienced which, in its own way, was bad enough. But there was a second effect which was far, far worse.

The head of the family I was lodging with was a good man by the name of John McKnight. Many a night I used to enjoy a long blether beside the fire. Over a clay pipe, we talked about a lot of things for he was a knowledgeable man, but you will not be surprised to know that a constant subject for our conversations was the state of mining. I'm not sure that John was a political man in the sense of having a fixed affiliation to any hard-and-fast political beliefs. I found many mine labourers to be like that. In spite of the 1867 Reform Act, which doubled the size of the British electorate, miners living in typical pit villages were still ineligible to vote. So, most of them, like John, had opinions on all manner of things but no allegiance to any political party and its beliefs. But one thing became clear to me in our conversations. He was totally committed to the mining community. So much so that a disaster befell him and his family.

In protest against reductions in wages, a strike was called. Now John had no need to get involved in this because he was a colliery fireman rather than a miner and therefore not subject to the same regulations and obligations. However, his sympathy for and kinship with the miners was fully demonstrated when he decided to make common cause with them and he too came out on strike. I was aware of the fact that other employees who were not miners did the same but it was John and his family whom I knew best and it was their great sacrifice that I witnessed.

The McKnights were among that majority who were tenants living in a company cottage and, as I remarked earlier, that tenure could be precarious indeed. As soon as it became known to the colliery owners that John had joined the strike, the inevitable happened. He was served with a notice of eviction. Of course, I was also evicted, which was no great pleasure, but it did not so greatly affect me. After all, I was young and single. But what I saw happening along Colliery Row was heart-rending. The awful spectacle of miners' poor furniture being loaded onto carts and then hauled away to whatever refuge could be found was a sight which remains vivid with me now more than sixty years later. As far as I know, no family went without a roof over their heads. The great community spirit would not allow that to happen, and many a small cottage became overfull with unexpected guests. But it was a pitiable sight.

It seemed to me a total outrage. I have to confess that, at that young age, I found positive rage in my heart. Rage at a system and those who controlled it for allowing such an injustice, such an affront to humanity, to happen. My young blood boiled and my soul blazed with anger at the sight of so many good people just being thrown out into the street. In later years, I would often be accused of being an agitator. If I deserved such a name, and I will leave you to decide on that, then the sight of that grim, terrible, sorrowful procession of evacuees was what first inflamed me in that direction.

It was on that awful day that I first crossed swords with what you might call one of the masters. As the sorry procession wound its way along, a small knot of people stood on a small hillock just beyond the cottages. I was helping to steady the McKnight's cart full of furniture as it rattled its way along the uneven road. As we drew closer to the group of strangers, I recognised one of them. It was Rob Dougal, a company factor whose job was to do whatever unpleasant task the colliery manager gave to him. That day, he was supervising the evictions. He turned to one of the others whom I did not recognise but who, by the cut of his fine clothes and the silver-topped cane in his gloved hands, was obviously above the station of mere manager. He was fairly young, perhaps about thirty years old and, for reasons I never fully understood nor had confirmed one way or another, I took him to be an owner's son. I could not restrain myself.

'You, Mister, you with the fancy cane!' I shouted. 'Do you not think that these poor folk are of the same flesh and blood as you?'

'How dare you?' he replied, starting back as if hit. 'I have no time for simple sentiment, and I have no intention of discussing weighty matters with you. Away with you, and mind your own business.'

Almost level with him now, his smug features staring down at me, I was consumed with rage. I took a step forward, my arms cocked, fully intending to climb that hillock and give him a blow he would remember forever. But I felt a hand clawing at my arm.

'Wheesht, laddie.' It was John McKnight, looking as worried as I've ever seen a man. 'It'll do no good. Ye'll just cause mair trouble for everybody, yourself included.'

He was right, of course. I dropped my arm and returned to steadying the cart, aware of the smug look on the 'gentleman's' face. Even then, I realised that I had almost made a most dreadful error. If I'd punched the man, what would have happened? It would have been the police and jail for me, and no mistake. Rightly too, I suppose, because it would have been common assault even if I'd felt a sense of provocation. Even worse, given the already tense atmosphere caused by the evictions, might some of the miners have lost their heads and allowed trouble to erupt? If they had seen me being dragged away, how might they have reacted? And what would have been the consequences of them supporting somebody who had struck one of the masters? It just doesn't bear thinking about, so it was as well all round that John McKnight intervened when he did.

As I helped the McKnights along the street with their cart, we were joined by another man, John Kilpatrick, who I knew a little because he worked in the same pit as myself as a pony driver. I was slightly embarrassed but not a little pleased when he told me he'd admired the stand I'd taken against one of the masters. He expressed sympathy with the lot of the evacuated miners, told me his tenure was safe because he didn't live in a company house, then asked me if I had anywhere to stay. Of course, I had to tell him that I hadn't – at which he immediately told me that I was welcome to stay with him and his family. This was yet another example of the great community spirit which abounded at times of great difficulty. I thanked him profusely then helped the McKnights to their refuge with friends of theirs in the older part of Larkhall. I thanked them for their kindness to me and wished them well. Mrs McKnight embraced me, reminded me to keep writing to Nan Smillie, then I picked up my canvas sack and found my way to the Kilpatricks' home.

Quite a lot of miners' families bought the local newspaper, published in the town of Hamilton a few miles away. It was, I suppose, a typical local newspaper full of little stories about local people. It did not shy away from bigger stories like strikes either, though you will not be surprised to know that such stories were always told through the owners' eyes and I don't remember the miners' view of affairs being freely reported. But we also had a wee club going, of which I was a member, and once a week we would buy one of the national newspapers such as the *Scotsman* or the *Glasgow Herald*. When I read these, I was forced to conclude that all the awful problems faced by miners did not register in the minds of the great newspapers' editors.

If you looked really hard, you might find news of reductions in wages and consequent strikes, accompanied by the usual prejudiced phrases such as 'mob agitators' and 'colliery held to ransom' and such like. Usually, though, you would have to search particularly keenly to find much reference to events in mines other than production figures. Rather, such newspapers would be full of articles on what their editors considered to be the real issues of the day. Politics, and more politics which, at that time, usually meant reports of the latest bitter exchange between Gladstone and Disraeli. And overseas news, a great deal of that, almost always bearing down on the greatness of the British Empire. Frequent references to what we were about in India, how we intended to extend our influence in Africa and, a very warm piece of news at the time, how Britain might take advantage of the financial difficulties of the Egyptian Khedive and buy up shares in the Suez Canal.

In their reports on both domestic and foreign affairs, national newspapers were often equally narrow. Domestically, news was made by the rich and powerful, the rest of us mattering little. Abroad, only those things in which Britain had an interest made for real news. The rest of the world hardly existed. Nevertheless, I devoured these newspapers in spite of what I saw to be their limitations. I believed that by informing me of events beyond my immediate experience, they were part of my education.

I lived with the Kilpatricks for several months. Like the McKnights before them, they could not have been kinder to me. In spite of the fact that they lived in a small, single apartment house, they took me in and fed me, treating me as one of the family. Mrs Kilpatrick fussed over me and was as good to me as she was to her own child, in spite of the fact that I'd been a complete stranger to her. The strike lasted seven long weeks during which time I could not give them a single penny towards keep. It didn't matter to them. As they saw it, they were looking after one of their own. When I eventually got back to work, after a strike in which the miners won nothing apart from maybe a wee bit of self-respect, I gave Mrs Kilpatrick every penny I earned until I had paid off my arrears. It was the very least I could do, but I never felt it was enough to repay their kindness.

It was late in 1874 when we returned to work. I was still a hand pumper, though that would not last much longer. Instead of the usual young man, my mate for five days of each week was an elderly fellow by the name of George Currie. I was given plenty of warnings about George to the effect that, after changing his trade from hand-loom weaving to mining because the money was better, he'd found that he was no better off than he had been as a weaver, so I could expect him to be a bitter old curmudgeon, grumpy by nature, and liable to either ignore me or bite my head off. Which just goes to show that you should not treat people on reputation. Instead, take them as you find them. Because, as I look back, I remember only his kindness to me. Also, he must have had the gift of prophecy.

'See here, Robert,' I remember him saying one day, as we were making our way back to the surface after yet another long shift. 'There's better work for you than hand pumping, or I'm much mistaken.' Smiling as he said it, then grimacing. 'As for me, its aboot a' I'm fit for, and the money's no' too bad. But you, boy, you stick in and ye'll do fine.'

His prophecy came true more quickly than either of us imagined. As we moved into 1875, it was a period of frequent disputes. During a strike at Summerlee, I got work with the Millburn and Cornsilloch Coal Company. Bidding farewell to George, I began my career as a drawer. Which was advancement of a kind, if you like. The colliery itself was named by the men as the Monkey Pit. This was on account of the low head room at the workings, so low that the miners spent much of the day in a crouched position. At the end of their shifts, they were so stiff that, for an hour or more, they continued to walk in a crouched position, rather as monkeys do.

As a drawer, my job was to convey empty tubs from the pit bottom to the coalface. Once the tubs had been filled, I had to return then in the opposite direction. Needless to say, the return journey was considerably heavier work that the outward one. As a job, drawing was more tiring than hand pumping had been. On the other hand, the shifts were only eight hours as opposed to twelve, the pay was a little better, and there was more in the way of company.

My career as a drawer was relatively short-lived. That was due to circumstances rather than any great initiative in my part. Through illness, the coal-hewing squad was light and the colliery manager was desperate for immediate replacements. Without thinking too deeply about it, I remarked to some of the squad that I'd had a bit of practice during my time at Summerlee. That much was true. Sometimes when my hand pumping shift had finished, I had waited around the mines at the coalface. As much for company as anything else, to be honest with you, after the loneliness of the shifts I was experiencing. But I grew interested in what the miners were doing, marvelling at the dexterity with which they handled their picks, and asked a few questions about how they went about it. It wasn't long before they started to demonstrate because they realised that I was a keen lad. Then, after showing me how to handle the pick and how to use it effectively, they allowed me to practise with them until I became reasonably competent. At the Monkey Pit, I may have gilded the lily a little when I reported my experience because the news got back to the manager and, within days, I was a fully-fledged miner at the coalface. The money was better, the company was good, and I felt that I had made great strides in a short time. Ah, the vanity of youth!

I stayed at the Monkey Pit for six months. During that time, I realised that I knew considerably less about hewing coal that I had fondly imagined. But I stuck at it and became more or less competent. Then, during another period of general unrest, I returned to the Summerlee pit. Once back there, I rejoined my newspaper club and found that the nationals were full of praise for Disraeli who had borrowed £4 million on behalf of the Government from Rothschilds the bankers, and used the money to buy a 44% share of the Suez Canal. This was lauded as a great boost for British trade, which indeed it turned out to be. In a great huff, Gladstone called the purchase 'a ruinous misdeed' and predicted that Britain would eventually have to occupy Egypt. He turned out to be right about that. My own opinion, for what little it is worth, was that at least some of that money would have been better spent on improving conditions for miners and other industrial workers. Needless to say, no newspaper reported that view.

By this stage, you will be thinking that I had turned into a too serious, probably rather dull young man. Maybe you would be right, though you would have to seek others' views on that. Yes, I was serious about my work. And it was true that I was giving more and more thought to what you might call the politics of industry. And perhaps I did pay more attention to the serious newspapers and to books than other young men of my age though I can assure you that I knew others of the same disposition. But believe me when I say that my life was not entirely without fun and relaxation.

During my first two summers in Larkhall, I had finally realised a long-held dream. I began playing cricket. Perhaps because of my days watching cricket at a distance in Belfast and Glasgow, I took to it quite quickly and, though I was never up to much with the ball in my hand, I became a fair batsman. I smile when I think now that it would have taken a wee while for a member of the MCC to have recognised us as players of his club's sport for, until we had bat and ball in hand, we looked nothing like the sportsmen he would be accustomed to. You see, it was many years until any of us sported cricketing whites, as they are called. You will remember that I saved long and hard to buy my first watch. Well, it would have taken at least the same financial dedication for any one of us to have acquired enough money to buy white flannels and jumpers, because these were expensive items. And, as a rule, miners had rather more pressing financial obligations to meet in the forms of rent money and food. So it was that we played in our every-day clothes. Even basic elements of protective wear like pads were something of a luxury, with the result that there were many bruised legs after our games. But we didn't mind, well not too much, for we were young, enjoying the fresh air and playing a sport we loved.

I rather think that our pitch would have come as somewhat of a shock to the MCC as well. It was just a piece of farmland leased to us by a local farmer for thirty shillings a year. It was of a reddish clay, which is common enough in the area, and provided a firm surface. However, it was hardly an entirely flat surface. We had no roller, nor any source for borrowing one, so the playing area was, shall we say, on the bumpy side or sporting, as they say in cricketing circles. Knowing better than our opponents where the worst bumps were, we generally won our home matches. It would perhaps be only fair to record the fact that our performance away from home, where opponents knew the bumps on their pitches rather better than we did, was not nearly as strong.

Our opponents were from other villages near Larkhall, some of these mining villages, others more agricultural in nature. I remember fierce competition against teams such as Carfin, Quarter, Stonehouse, Shamrock and Lesmahagow. No doubt because all these teams were near neighbours, the matches were always hard-fought affairs which nobody liked to lose. I had acquired something of a reputation as a batsman in those early days shortly after I had helped to transform Larkhall cricket from a group of men just playing around with a bat and ball into a proper club with a real fixture list. I believe that that was rather typical of me even as a young man: I was always keen on making things better through good organisation. Whatever, I believe that it was against the Stonehouse Club that I achieved my first wee bit of local fame, a more pleasant memory than the notoriety I often had levelled at me later on.

We won the match and I was top scorer for Larkhall. To this day I can recall the drive which won the match and bought me my score of 29 not out. It was with a glow of pride that I read the brief report in the *Larkhall Press*. In that way, I was as typical a young man as any other. Particularly if we had won, a crowd of us would wait outside the paper's printing office for the paper to appear, for the simple joy of seeing our names in print. I still have a cutting somewhere of that match against Stonehouse. It makes me smile when I think of the rapture with which I greeted its printing and seeing my name mentioned without being called a 'rabid Socialist' or 'national peril,' merely a flannelled cricketer.

One of the beauties of cricket is that once the match is over, and irrespective of winning or losing and the number of bruises you may be sporting, time is made for good company with the team members and opponents alike. We often repaired to a local public house which boasted not only a fine local ale but also, wonder of wonders, a billiards table. We would sit with a pipe and glass, and replay the match in conversation. Many good friendships were struck up in post-match get-togethers. So, even if the MCC might not have recognised our dress, pitch or ability, we thoroughly enjoyed our cricket and the fresh air, sport and friendship it provided.

1876 was a year of continuing friction in the mines. Reducing demand, wage reductions, occasional strikes and all the rest of it. But that was not the burning issue of the day according to the national newspapers I continued to read occasionally. I remember a series of events that year which brought home to me sharply the values held dear by the owning classes and their total disregard for the lives of ordinary folk. Events which, oddly enough, were linked by a game of billiards of all things. Let me explain what happened as best I can remember.

The quality newspapers were full of talk about Queen Victoria who, by that time, had reigned for thirty-nine years. Of course, she lived in a world which ordinary people never experienced though the newspapers kept her subjects informed of her greatness by reporting such news as the palace saw fit to release. However, the great news of the day did not stem from royal circles. Rather, it came from the great showman prime minister, Mr Benjamin Disraeli. I did not understand the ins and outs of it fully but it seemed that Disraeli was concerned about Russian intentions towards British possessions in India and he was looking for a way to bind the Indian people closer to Britain. So he reviewed an old idea which had been born after the ruinous Indian Mutiny of 1857. In order to make the Indians feel that there were genuinely close ties between them and Great Britain and make them less likely to entertain Russian subversions, Queen Victoria should become Empress of India. The lady herself was apparently keen on the idea and so the Royal Titles Act was duly passed through parliament. There was some opposition to the Act, principally from Gladstone who described it as 'theatrical bombast' but most people who mattered seemed to be all in favour of it. It was the talk of the town and, of course, the quality newspapers. I was never sure what most Indians thought of it because that was never reported and it is unlikely that they had a say in the matter anyway. They had an Empress, God bless her, and that was that.

As I played a quiet game of billiards with some friends one Saturday night, I told them that the position of the majority of Indians reminded me forcibly of the position of the miners.

'How do you mean, Robert?' Dicky Rundell, a friend of mine, asked as he was chalking his cue.

'They never get asked what they want or need,' I replied. 'Like us they are told what they are getting and expected to get on with it.' Everybody laughed, and I was just bending to my shot when, from outside, the dreaded call went up.

'A fall! It's a fall!' somebody was shouting.

We dropped our cues and raced to the pit head. A fall meant only one thing. A working had caved in and somebody was in awful trouble. As we reached the pit head, we saw a group of miners staggering towards us carrying a man. He looked in a bad way.

'It's Andrew Kelly,' one of them said. Four of them were carrying Andrew, one of the oldest miners in the pit, an arm or a leg each.

I helped them get him back to his cottage. Covered in mud and not a little blood, he was moaning piteously. His wife Sheila cried out loud when we carried him in and laid him gently on the floor in front of the fire. Somebody - I don't remember who - ran for the doctor while Sheila boiled up some water. To my amazement, Andrew was struggling to his feet, breathlessly insisting that he couldn't see the doctor when he was in such a mess. Or that's what we were fairly sure he was saying but his face and beard were matted in blood and he was spitting out teeth as he was trying to speak, so his words were indistinct.

I'll never forget the sight of that proud old man, his back bent, his joints twisted, blood pouring from him as he shakily stood there. We helped him off with his clothes, noting with great alarm the bruises and lacerations on his body where sharp pieces of rock had cut through his jacket and trousers. Worst of all to our eyes, he was shivering violently. Down at the coalface, before the rock fell on him, he would have been pouring with sweat. Being carried all the way from there to his cottage meant a massive change of temperature being inflicted on his battered, old body. Now, in spite of the heat from the stoked-up fire, his body was still freezing and he was shaking like a gnarled tree in a fierce storm. At this point, the doctor arrived.

I groaned when I saw who it was. There was a doctor in the village, a good man who treated people well and equally, whatever their station in life. But this was Robertson, the company-appointed doctor. I would not go as far as to query his abilities as a physician, but it was felt by all the miners that he was none too caring about his treatment of the working folk, and he was only concerned to extract his fees from the company. He was in a surly mood. By the smell of him, he'd been called from a meeting with a glass of good whisky. As Andrew crouched before him, his examination was cursory in the extreme. As he was leaving, he passed some medicine to Sheila - a 'boatle' as mining folk called all medicines - and said that all that Andrew required was a bit of rest. He managed to imply that it was a waste of his precious time being called out. Then he was gone.

While Sheila washed her shivering, groaning husband, then dried him off, we found some blankets and cushions. When Andrew had got on some dry clothes and Sheila had taken away his filthy ones to wash, we got him into the chair beside the fire and draped the blankets over his body and legs. If anything, he was shivering rather less by then though I thought I could see the beginnings of sweat. Though he was obviously in pain, he insisted he was feeling better. Sheila made a pot of tea and we waited for a while until Andrew had settled down. He had virtually stopped shivering but his torn face was certainly sweaty and his breathing sounded coarse. I wondered if we should get Robertson the doctor back, for what little good that might have done, but Sheila said Andrew always made strange breathing noises when he was tired and about to sleep, though they weren't nearly as bad as the awful snoring he did when he was actually sleeping. We all laughed at that, then made for the door, saying our farewells.

'See you, lads,' Andrew called weakly from his chair.

On Sunday, as we were leaving church and making our way into the frosty outdoors, we heard from a neighbour of his that Andrew Kelly had died in front of his own fire. Sheila sat with him all night and, sometime in the early hours, had dozed off. She was awakened by a loud cough, followed by a long sigh. By the time she got a lamp lit, Andrew's head had lolled forwards and his breathing had stopped. In the mortuary, they discovered that Robertson's examination had been even more cursory than I had thought, so much so that he had missed the sharp shard of rock which had gone right through the skin on Andrew's back and embedded itself in a lung. During the night, he had quite literally drowned in his own blood. Needless to say, as an appointee of the company, Robertson had to face little retribution for his incompetence.

My shift pattern allowed me to attend Andrew's funeral. After a short but moving service, his body was brought to the cemetery where it was laid to rest, hundreds of his fellow miners in attendance. Sheila had done some borrowing and looked dignified in a black dress and veil. Her two grown-up sons, dressed as neatly as their relative poverty would allow, were close to tears throughout. Most of the miners present, on their way to or from shifts, were in their working clothes. As the shovels dropped the soil into the grave, it started to snow. For some reason I've never understood, I suddenly thought of London and the new Empress of India. Bitterly, I wondered if she knew or cared how her subjects, good men like Andrew Kelly, lived and died. Had her courtiers and her friends in parliament ever been tended by a doctor as indifferent as Robertson? Would any one of them, herself included, ever witness the kind of burial accorded to an ordinary working man? I rather doubted it. In a foul mood, but summoning the kindest face I could, I broke into my thoughts and walked over to offer my sincerest condolences to Sheila Kelly and her sons.

Both events made the newspapers of course. Andrew Kelly's death was reported in both the Larkhall and Hamilton newspapers, three lines each in the deaths notices. Victoria was rather more fulsomely treated. For months, the nationals were full of toadying praises for her, a serene monarch making bonds with India for the good of mankind, and other such platitudes. I felt the difference deeply. I bore no particular ill will towards Queen Victoria but I had known Andrew Kelly, liked him, and found him a good man. Yet, in the view of the world, or certainly those who ran it, his death mattered nothing in comparison with the further aggrandisement of somebody who already had power and wealth beyond any ordinary working man's dreams. It seemed to me that there was something dreadfully unbalanced about the world. I have no doubt that those oddly-linked events, strangely connected by a game of billiards, contributed greatly to my developing views of the world.

It was at about this time that I moved into the town of Larkhall itself and took up lodgings with the Rundell family. The son of the Rundells' happy marriage was an easy-going young man called Dicky. He was a workmate of mine, an occasional billiards opponent and my closest friend. His given name was John but everybody called him Dicky. I did not know the reason for that and to this day I still don't. We got on famously well even though, in some ways, we were hardly kindred spirits. I was that bit more serious that he was though, with an infectious spirit like him around, I was easily enough jerked out of any reflective mood. Also, though he was dedicated to his fellow miners, he never became active in what we now call the Labour Movement. Instead, he remained a miner all his working life, always in the employment of the Summerlee Iron Company, working in the pit where I had made my start as a hand pumper. You will know by now how commonplace accidents were in the pits and Dicky was one of the many victims. In an accident, he lost an eye. That did not stop him returning to the coalface. In spite of the differences between us, we were close companions, opposites attracting you might say, and I enjoyed my stay with his family.

By then, twenty years old and beginning to think more seriously about the politics of the mining industry, I decided that it was about time that I did something about the deficiencies in my education. You will know that I had little formal education and that the few skills I had were due to the loving attentions of my grandmother and brother; also that I tried to improve myself by reading as widely as my abilities would allow. But by 1877 I felt that that was not enough, not nearly enough. Vaguely as yet, I sensed that I would do rather more with my life than hew coal, delighted though I was to be part of the community that did so. Yet, what else was I qualified to do? Taking stock of myself, the answer had to be – nothing!

All of which might explain to you why I began to attend school. To no surprise on my part, Dicky declined to join me, saying that he had better things to do with his time. Knowing Dicky as I did, I was sure that meant the lassies and billiards. And good luck to him: God did not make us all in the same way. So off I went to night school which was at the Muir Street Board School where a Mr Beattie was the main teacher. Nothing on the night school curriculum was a great deal more than basic. However, over time, I did grasp more of the fundamentals of our language and of mathematics. Not that I ever achieved mastery of either, let me add. Perhaps that was in part due to the nature of the teaching. Mr Beattie's approach seemed to be that he felt he had done well if he managed to get us to understand the 'what' of something but never the 'why.' I remember vividly the evening when I was struggling with a sum of some kind. Memory insists that it was a multiplication but, in honesty, it may as easily have been a subtraction. Whichever, to my considerable embarrassment, I was getting into some difficulties. I asked Mr Beattie for help. Not a little impatiently, he showed me how the sum was done. Even more embarrassed now, I still did not understand. 'But tell me, Mr Beattie,' I said, 'when you moved those figures to that side of the line, why did the figures on the other side have to change as well?'

'Listen, young Smillie,' he replied, treating me more like an infant that the man I really was. 'For the present, all you need to know is what the answer is. You need not mind how that is the answer.'

'But ... ' I began, then gave up. Maybe I was just a nuisance, displaying the characteristics of the agitator I would allegedly be later. But I think it was just in my nature. I believed that knowing 'what' was better than knowing nothing, but it was more important to understanding to know 'why'. In that belief, there was an odd sort of parallel with my development within the mining community. I certainly knew the what of things, that the miners were ill-treated, hard-working slaves of the mine owners. But as to the why, I was less sure. Why we were in that position, why we seemed incapable of doing anything significant about it and why I was beginning to give so much thought to it all. Why, oh why? Such a small word, but such a very important one.

Looking back, I think you could say that by the age of twenty I had served an apprenticeship of sorts. In the mines, with my books, on the cricket field and in the classroom. I had even had my first argument with one of the masters. But the apprenticeship for life is another matter. Does it ever really end? Do we ever achieve mastery over our affairs? I certainly had not by the year 1877. Not that such philosophical concerns were much on my mind at the time. I had something else to occupy my thoughts. I had met a girl by the name of Ann Hamilton.

VI

Never So Good, Never So Bad

A FEW MONTHS after moving in with the Rundells, Dicky and I were much taken by two girls we met at a church social. Annie Fleming caught Dicky's eye while mine were enthralled by Ann Hamilton, a slim, brown-haired lassie with a lovely twinkle in her eyes. The four of us quickly became inseparable and Dicky and I squired Annie and Ann to local events such as church picnics, dances and the occasional birthday party, as well as enjoying long Sunday walks together. Although not a great socialiser, I felt greatly at ease with Ann. Typical of me, once I had made my mind that I wanted her, which I certainly did, there was no letting go. We were married in 1878 on Hogmanay, a time which many couples picked in those days. We rented a small house in the village, one which would mean home to me for over fifty years. By the way, Dicky married his Annie a short while afterwards.

Ann Hamilton proved to be an ideal Mrs Smillie. I honestly confess that, without her, my future work on behalf of the miners would never have been accomplished. She bore nine children, seven sons and two daughters, and my family proved to be the bedrock of my life. In future times, I always knew that wherever my duties called me, and however long they kept me away, Ann was looking after our children and our home, and would provide the warmest of welcomes on my return. She never complained about my frequent absences. She provided more love and devotion than I would have believed possible. There were times when I was called away on duty that I cursed myself for my absences and I can truthfully say that I never spent an unnecessary hour outside the home circle, even if I now realise that too many hours and days were spent away. When I later attained some higher offices which demanded many prolonged visits to London, I never considered leaving Larkhall. It was always my home. In the course of this narrative, I will have relatively little to say about family life. Not because it was not important, because it certainly was. But my narrative about mining and politics is for the world. The story of my family life is for Ann, our children and me only.

Our marriage was one of the few pleasant events of that time of my life. Otherwise things were bad and only grew worse. Only a few months after we married, I got the most dreadful news in a letter written in a very poor hand, so poor that I could not read the signature of the writer. But the message was clear, horribly clear. Nan Smillie was dead. That dedicated, loving woman who had done so much for James and myself was no more. Suddenly, the world seemed a much colder place. That night, I searched out the packet of letters which she had written to me over the past six years and read all of them, my eyes brimming, Ann by my side. Had it not been for Ann, I believe that I would have broken down altogether. As it was, she helped me through my despair.

Shortly after that, there was another personal hammer blow. My dear brother, who had attended our wedding on his own and seemed somewhat out of sorts, though he had tried to hide it, sought me out and told me he was leaving Larkhall. I could not prise out of him all the reasons for his decision, hard though I tried. I suspected that it might have something to do with a lassie, but I wasn't sure of that then and never did find out. Embracing me, he promised to keep in touch, which he did by letter for several years. He seemed perpetually on the move and I was never certain that he received the letters which I wrote to him. It was one of the saddest affairs of my life.

As if personal loss was not enough, the following years were to prove to be some of the most arduous experienced by the mining community. Low demand for coal, low coal prices, a series of tragedies and a number of lengthy strikes combined to make it the most wearying of periods. It was a time when owners took even less care than usual of their employees, citing difficult trade circumstances as justification for pitifully inadequate safety precautions in the pits. It was not particularly for that reason, but I almost became a victim myself.

My partner at the coal face was a young Cornishman by the name of Mitchell, an intelligent young fellow with more education than I had. We were at the stage of the shift when we were gathering together the heap of dross to sit on when we were undercutting the coal. I turned round to pick up my shovel, then heard an ominous dull thud. A huge stone, weighing somewhere near a ton, had fallen from the roof and was lying on the heap of dross we had just piled up. If it had been just a few seconds more before falling, it would have been me it had fallen on! I was quite shaken by the incident but decided to say nothing to Ann about it in case she became unduly fearful each time I went out the door to work. Most miners were like that, never saying much to their wives about the daily hazards they faced. The problem with that being that their silence only increased the pressure on themselves, and it was not as if they did not have enough pressures as it was.

I was becoming increasingly angry at the tremendous inequalities of life. A social system which produced class cleavage with indifferent arrogance on the one side and deep bitterness on the other. Rightly or wrongly, I took the view that the workers were the wealth producers and that it was an abysmal failure of our industrial system not to distribute equitably the wealth which was produced. I suppose that I was both hot-blooded and warm-hearted, these being different things, and the differences in the lives of owners and employees at the same time filled me with rage and pity. The ever-present spectacle of certain types of employers grinding their workers to the extreme limit of existence, and feeling no compunction in doing so, while they themselves lived in luxury, stirred my compassion for the one and my fierce resentment against the other. Without a doubt, out of such feelings the views evolved which would eventually make me a Labour leader.

It was in 1880 that I took my first faltering steps on the path that would see me play some part in industrial politics. I was appointed as a check-weighman. That appointment came not from the company but my fellow workers and filled me with pride and satisfaction. It was as if the hundred and fifty of my peers had said, 'We can trust Bob!' You see, for the miners the role of check-weighman was very important. The owners based wages on the amount of coal produced and we knew that it was in their interests to under-weigh the coal. It was contended by the miners that employers 'kept back part of the price'. This was not just a local grievance – it was common to all mining districts.

For many years, the miners had badgered owners for the right to appoint one of their own to double-check the weight of the coal produced. As Burns wrote:

If self the wavering balance shake,
It's rarely right adjusted.

As usual, Burns had it right. But the employers did not agree and fought tooth and nail against the idea until one of the provisions of the 1860 Mines Act stipulated that it was the right of the miners to appoint 'one of their number' to supervise the weighing of the coal brought up and to keep a register.

You might have thought that that would have brought an end to the dispute about the weighing of coal, but it did not. Too often, an owner would find a reason to dismiss the man selected as check-weigher by his fellow miners. Nothing in the Act prevented that happening and it took years of further agitation to establish the right to elect their own check-weighman, without let or hindrance from employers. It might seem strange that any employers could take exception to this, but they did. For years, the miners were helpless in the face of the owners' intransigence over this matter and could only resort to strike action to make their point. But strikes actually strike the striker harder than they strike anybody else.

The phrase 'putting on the block' came into use at that time. In despair, the miners developed a new way of fighting back. In a ballot, the name of a colliery was drawn out and went 'on the block.' In other words, that colliery struck on behalf of all the collieries and suffered for the sake of all other colleagues. In this way, the miners in the collieries which were not on strike could support the miners in the one which was. Of course, the employers responded. They put on their own block. They issued instructions that no miner would be employed who had previously worked in a colliery which had been put under the block. In effect, this struck against the miners' right to strike. For miners as well as other workers, this right had been enshrined in the 1871 Trade Union Act, though it was weakened by the Criminal Law Act of the same year. Employers used every tactic they could to exploit that weakness.

During block strikes, the striking men had to be supported by those still at work, which was a great strain on very limited incomes. Then after several weeks what commonly happened was that the owners, knowing how stretched the resources of all the miners had become, issued notices of a reduction of sixpence per day in wages, unless the men capitulated and the 'block' was raised. I remember only too well the time when we stayed out until forced with a third sixpenny reduction, and had no choice but to yield to superior force. So, having fought them and lost the battle, we were once again crushed under the yoke of their bondage. During the strike, we were not even allowed to gather in the surrounds of the striking colliery which was laying down the block. To have done so would have meant breaking the law as laid down by the provisions of the 1871 Criminal Amendment Act which had, among other things, proscribed picketing. Common criminality for supporting and encouraging our fellow miners would have been the outcome. Those who ran our industries always enjoyed greater support from the law makers than those who laboured endlessly in these industries.

One strike was particularly hard to bear for all of us. It was locally known as the 'Tattie Strike' owing to the fact that we were reduced to a diet of potatoes towards the end of the dispute. It was to prove to be one of the hardest-fought battles in the history of Scottish Mining which, heaven knows, had more than its share of them. In fact, it was an epoch-making crisis which, appearing to end in disaster, eventually led to something good. In particular, it proved that not even the best of good causes can succeed without the backing of funds and strong organisation. It was a hard-learned lesson but a valuable one in the long run.

As always, the women and children suffered most. I must give praise to many local tradesmen such as butchers, grocers and bakers. In the time of our privation, they gave credit to an extent which must have risked their own security. Of course, they knew who they were dealing with. After previous strikes, debts had always been repaid in instalments on the resumption of work. However, during the Tattie Strike, the leader of the strike intervened and, instead of individual families running up debt, the leaders contracted a huge debt for the mass purchase of bread and potatoes to be provided to the most needy families.

The leaders laid down a guidance rule. If a family was in need, it would receive the assistance of the strike committee. Families could apply for assistance at appointed centres where potatoes and such bread as was available would be doled out in quantities proportionate to the size of the family. So there was a never-ending stream of poor folk carrying baskets and bags filled with potatoes. It was the sight of them which gave the strike its title. This awful state of affairs went on for several months before the strike eventually collapsed. For all the suffering, no gains had been made. When work re-started, efforts were made to clear off the debt owed to local tradesmen, that debt which had been arranged by the strike leader. But the strike had been so long, and was followed by yet another wage reduction, that though contributions were levied and the miners gave what they could, a portion of the debt remained unpaid. I believe that remains the case to this day. It demonstrated clearly to me that, to make a success of any industrial action, much better organisation was required and a contingency fund had always to be available.

The only really positive thing which happened during that ugly saga was that I became acquainted with a man with whom I was destined to share much over the years. Because of the employers' attitudes and trickery, I was no longer a check-weighman and I was back at the coal face when the strike took place. Leaving the pit on the day before the strike began, I met a group of men making it their business to talk to the miners coming off shift. These were mainly elderly and middle-aged men who had been striving for two years to re-organise Lanarkshire's miners so that they could present a more united and effective front against the power of the employers. I immediately recognised one of them, Alexander MacDonald. He had been a strong supporter of my earlier appointment as a check-weighman.

'Robert, come over here, if you please,' he said, in that grand old way of his. 'There's somebody here I would like you to meet.' He pointed to a younger man standing beside him.

'Evening, Mr MacDonald,' I smiled at him, then nodded at his companion who nodded back. In that brief exchange of looks, I knew that this young man had something special about him. It was my experience that you can often tell these things.

'Here for the last shift for the moment?'

'Aye,' MacDonald replied, grim-faced. He sighed deeply. 'I fear we are in for the long haul this time.' He shrugged. 'But where are my manners? Bob, let me introduce you to Mr Hardie, Mr James Keir Hardie.'

And that was the first time I met a man whose name would be indelibly linked with the Labour Movement, initially through trade unionism, then as a founder of the Labour Party and a Member of Parliament. But even in those early days, before I got to know his as well as any one man can know another, I recognised the inner strength in him.

Hardie started off as a pony driver before becoming a miner at the Quarter Colliery in Hamilton. I saw a fair bit of him during that dreadful Tattie Strike and, perhaps recognising kindred spirits in one another, we developed a close friendship, though that took time to mature. One odd thing arose during our increasingly regular conversations. It turned out that we had met before, on the cricket field of all places!

'So you were that batsman with all the luck in the world,' he said to me, laughing, as I regaled him one evening with tales of my cricketing prowess.

'And you were that Quarter Colliery bowler who never bowled a straight ball,' I joked back.

The real truth was that neither of us remembered the presence of the other on the cricket field. Whatever we might do in the future to earn recognition in unionism and politics, we clearly had not impressed one another as sportsmen.

At that stage in his life, Hardie was already an accomplished public speaker. In part, that was no doubt due to natural gifts but he had honed his skills as a speaker in the service of the Independent Order of Good Templars. Whatever, listening to his speaking was never a hardship. He always seemed able to find the right words to have an audience 'eating out of his hands,' as the saying goes. When you bear in mind that his audience was inevitably made up of miners vastly more experienced at mining than he was, and that miners on the whole are not easily impressed, his performances as an orator were all the more impressive. Perhaps it helped that he was known to be a tolerant man, accepting of the world and its weaknesses. For example, he was a total abstainer from alcohol himself but never thought to lecture anybody who was fond of a drink, an attitude that went down well with many miners.

Even back then, he was diligent in everything he did. I was told that he had been like that at the coal face though I never saw him in that capacity. But in his work on behalf of the Lanarkshire miners, he was better prepared than any man I met. In fact, I never met a man who worked harder. I am reminded of the fact that John Wesley, the great preacher, used to make notes while riding on horseback for fear of losing time. Keir Hardie was another of the sort. While I doubt if he ever wrote on horseback – the very thought of that makes me smile – he certainly made notes for speeches while walking and, in later years, when on a train and everybody around him sleeping, Hardie would be writing, writing, everlastingly writing.

Like myself, and others of our class, his education was very limited, but he made up for that; in addition to his natural gifts, he studied voraciously. He had one particular skill which was very rare. While still a young lad working in the pit, he began to study Pitman's shorthand. He told me that he used to pick up flat pieces of stone or slate down in the pit and, when he could find a spare minute, he would smoke them over the flame of his oil lamp. With the pin which miners used to adjust the wicks of their lamps, he would then trace the shorthand characters on the flat pieces of slate and stone. He acquired considerable skill in shorthand and I often saw him making shorthand notes in meetings. I was so impressed that I tried it myself but I lacked the patience to master it though some colleagues in the Labour Movement, men like George Barnes and John Robertson, fared better with it than I did.

That first acquaintance with Kier Hardie hardly outlasted the Tattie Strike. For reasons connected with the miners' debt to local tradesmen, Hardie and Alexander MacDonald fell out. During the strike, I had been aware of the fact that Hardie had not approved of the strike committee's decision to purchase a bulk of food stuffs, then take responsibility for its allotment to the strikers. He felt that the organisation was not strong enough and that there was certainly not the guaranteed funds available to make a success of the process. In my opinion, he was right on both counts. I believe that he and MacDonald argued strongly over the matter to the extent that they could no longer work together. Indeed, MacDonald was reported to have said, 'If Hardie will leave the county I will undertake to see this money paid.'

The upshot was that Hardie did leave. He talked to the tradesmen to whom money was owed, apologising for the fact that they had not been fully paid. He promised them that the miners would do all in their power to make good the difference and was pleased to discover that the tradesmen did not hold him in any way responsible for their loss. That was a measure of the esteem in which Hardie was held. No claim was ever made against him by any shopkeeper.

'I'll be sorry to see you go, Keir,' I told him on the day of his leaving.

'Our paths will cross again,' he replied, smiling. I doubt if even he realised just how prophetic his words were.

At that time, very few miners were overtly political, there being no body they could attach themselves to. However, there was a great deal of what I would describe as unwitting Socialism, communism even, among them. There was certainly a very strong sense of brotherhood, of sharing life's struggles and making sure that everybody was looked after. One illustration of this was the way in which they tried to ensure better medical cover for all miners and their families. You will remember the awful story I told you about the elderly miner Andrew and the incompetent, uncaring Dr Robertson? Well, that was a quite typical outcome of the arrangements made by employers in those days. They insisted on appointing what we called a 'club doctor,' and our experiences of them were none too positive. In the late 1870's, the 'club doctor' was a Dr Marshall who lived in Hamilton, nearly five miles away from the Summerlee pit in Larkhall where he was responsible for all the miners and their families. He visited Larkhall twice a week, whether he was needed or not. It was almost as if he and the employers believed that colliers and their families would only be unwell on some kind of fixed rota basis. None of the miners lived in the district where the doctor lived and, if sudden or serious illness occurred, it was often impossible to secure his prompt attention. In which case, we would have to run to a local doctor, one not employed by the pit, to get his help. Though I don't remember any doctor like that actually refusing to attend a serious case, I often enough heard the words, 'Why don't you get your own pit doctor?'

All of this explains the Socialist streak in the miners' thinking when it came to medical cover. By the last 1870's, they all clubbed together, paying into a fund which paid for local and immediate medical attention for themselves and their families. Naturally, there were those, robust in health and fortunate enough to escape injury at work, who made little or no use of this service, but I never heard one of them complain. They contributed to the collective fund because they believed that it was good for all members of the mining community rather than just for themselves.

In this connection, my wife Ann and I had a bitter enough experience of our own. In 1879, married for only a year, Ann was taken seriously ill. She was shaking violently, sweating severely with a fever, and in great pain. Marshall, the pit doctor, lived miles away and, though he had a fair reputation as a physician, I was certain that the hours it would take to find him and get him to our house could only result in one thing: Ann's death. So I called in the local doctor, and he was able to control Ann's condition and set her on the road to health. His services to us continued until her complete recovery. I decided not to make use of the funds to which we had all contributed. That was a limited resource and there were others in greater need than us. The doctor's bill was relatively light as these things went, being only £3. But that was more than a week's wages to me then, and the bill seemed as huge as Mount Everest! It was a sad reflection of the times that we had only a choice between using a pit doctor, who was rarely readily available, exhausting a relatively small fund of collectively saved money, or paying out individually what seemed a small fortune for professional services rendered.

My experience, and that of others, led us to try to go some way beyond simply having a fund to pay for emergency medical services. At a mass meeting, we discussed the possibility of raising sufficient money to actually appoint our own local doctor. We had nothing greatly against Dr Marshall other than the fact that he lived too far away, but that was reason enough. We took a vote on the matter, with me appointed to count the poll, and by a majority of more than five to one, we voted in favour of appointing our own local doctor. But we had reckoned without the attitude of the colliery company. When news of our decision reached them, they became angry beyond reason. In a written statement issued to us, they said, 'We are not prepared to change the doctor, and these workmen who do not wish to contribute towards the continuation of Doctor Marshall's services may leave the colliery.'

What purpose such an attitude served would be hard to fathom if you knew nothing about the general view held by our employers. To put it simply, they wanted to control as many aspects of our lives as possible in order to keep us tied to them. So even the apparently trivial question of who was to be our doctor mattered to them. They saw the issue as a factor of the power they wished to maintain over us. This was all part of the same, old, sad story. The process of gaining justice in any part of their lives has always been difficult and slow for miners. This accounts for the long-lived feeling of mistrust held towards employers and suggests why many of the strikes which took place were so bitter. In the future, concessions would be made, but it is tragic to reflect on the fact that what was eventually granted to us because of our increased strength might have been granted earlier by human decency. I believe it shows how dangerous it can be when one hand is always holding the whip.

Another serious grievance during that grim period arose as a result of that we miners called 'Blind Saturday.' No doubt to those of you ignorant of the ways of the mining industry that must seem an odd use of words, but the meaning was very simple and the use of the word 'blind' very appropriate. You see, it was very often the custom that collieries paid wages fortnightly rather than weekly. So one Saturday in two was blank or 'blind' as far as money was concerned. On the 'blind' Saturday, a workman could ask for a pound to tide him over until the next Saturday, but that came at a cost. For any money he elected to draw against his next wage, he was charged a shilling in the pound. Therefore, if he drew a pound, his next wage was debited to the tune of twenty-one shillings! I'm afraid that our language, rich though it is, is not rich enough to describe meanness of that kind. A parsimony on the part of the employers which, of course, represents a profit for them. Sometime later, the Truck Act would make this employers' trick illegal, proscribing deductions of this kind from a workman's wages but, at the time, it was yet another cross to bear.

There will be those of you who will wonder why all miners would not simply divide their fortnightly wage in two parts and budget accordingly. Which would be a reasonable enough question in favourable circumstances. But our circumstances were far from being favourable. It was a time of generally low demand for coal and consequently low prices. The owners, anxious to maintain their profits, frequently reduced wages. That often resulted in strikes that were rarely successful and usually resulted in further wage reductions, the usual 'sixpence-a-day less' tactic from our employers. So, as the 1870's became the 1880's, the truth was that miners were being paid a pittance. If you budget with a pittance, dividing it into two parts because it will be two weeks until your next wages, you end up with a half a pittance for each of the two weeks. Little wonder that so many of us had to draw down a pound on 'blind' Saturday to tide us over.

By the 1880's another issue arose which led to great controversy and considerable bitterness. It was one of those arrangements which, at first glance, seemed reasonable but which, with experience and on closer inspection, presented problems. With the demand for coal low, the owners decided to stockpile coal in anticipation of better times to come. So, the mines were kept more or less fully open and the men kept their jobs. Around the collieries there grew up huge heaps of coal, known as bings, aggregating tens of thousands of tons. In this way, in bad times most jobs were preserved so, on the surface, it seemed like an excellent idea. Time was to prove otherwise.

You see, these huge reserves of coal proved to be a great impediment against us if any dispute arose. Threatened by strike action, an owner could survey those huge bings of coal, shrug, and meet the threat of any industrial action with total indifference. If displeased by even the suggestion of action on our part, he could enforce a lock-out, effectively shutting down production, and rely on his huge stocks of coal to see him through. Given that strike action was our only recourse against habitually deaf employers, this meant that our only weapon was removed from us.

There were two general circumstances in which an owner might begin to use his coal reserves. If we went on strike, he had a ready supply. If trade improved, he had a surplus to sell. In either circumstance, we were the losers. In the case of a strike, we would have had to be away from the coal face until hell froze over until the reserves were exhausted. And when trade picked up, that surplus could be sold at enhanced prices while we were still working for wages which did not reflect those increased prices. As ever, the control and the advantage lay with the employer.

The plagues which befell ancient Egypt never produced seven leaner years than those which we experienced in the pits between 1878 and 1885. At that time in my life, I did not have what you might call a bird's-eye view of the whole industry. I only really knew Lanarkshire. The national newspapers which I still occasionally saw sometimes carried small pieces about the mining industry but, as ever, these tended to centre on production figures and said nothing about us, the miners. I remember a story about the failure of the City of Glasgow Bank and the dreadful effect that failure would have on colliery owners who had invested heavily in it. That was in 1879, I believe, at a time when miners were suffering yet another round of 'sixpence-a-day less,' but there was no mention of that, of course.

The whole industry was in turmoil, we were bearing the brunt of it, and yet we were powerless to defend ourselves. The mining trade unions were in disarray. Even in Larkhall, which had been recognised as one of the best organised districts, hardly a vestige of trade unionism was left. It was very clear to those of us who discussed these matters that a trade union revival was necessary for our self-defence, and was long overdue. Among others, I was determined to see this happen. If it did not, we would continue to be totally in the power of the owners and, with a few honourable exceptions, they were only interested in their balance sheets and had little or no regard for their employees. In such desperate times, we had to climb out of the pit of serfdom and establish ourselves as a unified, determined band of men.

But, as I remarked, throughout that desperate period, although strikes did take place, there was no really effective combination among our ranks. Then a particular issue arose which eventually had the effect of changing the situation. Since the beginnings of mining, the men of Lanarkshire had been at their most combined when the question of a 'five days' working policy' was raised. Indeed, most attempts to organise Lanarkshire miners had been centred on that policy. Without question, it was one of the most important issues to them, the sheet anchor of their inclination to combine for collective purposes. In the past, Thursday had been regarded as a weekly holiday. Miners' leaders liked it because it regulated the output of coal and reduced the opportunities for owners to build up coal bings to be used as weapons in times of unrest. Of course, the coal face workers employed the Thursday break as a necessary respite from their physically demanding work. But those Thursday breaks had become things of memory. The problems in the industry, the low wages, the unsuccessful strike actions and the intransigence of the owners had all conspired to produce in most men a total weariness leading to apathy. A belief that the world was against them and there was nothing they could do about it. So they became used to working the six days each week demanded by their employers and the Thursday break became a rare event indeed.

Then came the day that changed it all. On one of those rare free Thursdays, the older men of Motherwell, men who had known better trade-union days, convened a meeting in their district. It took place at Camp Wood, which had been the scene of many momentous miners' meetings in the past. At that meeting in 1885, the veterans urged us to reorganise ourselves and, among other things, reestablish the weekly Thursday break. The best speaker was Robert Steel, an elderly man by then, but still with 'fire in his belly', as the saying goes. He invigorated me and many others there, and we left the meeting determined to make ourselves stronger. Indeed, the resolutions passed at that meeting were historic in nature. Those of us from Larkhall agreed to form a local branch and pursue the reinstitution of the Thursday break. Not only that but it was decided to use picketing strategies. Previously outlawed in 1871, Disraeli's act of 1875 made picketing legal, as long as it was peaceful. I saw that as essential as a tool of support and persuasion and I determined to become heavily involved in it. Little did I realise how far it would eventually take me.

A crucial role in the redevelopment of the Lanarkshire Union was played by William Small. A small man, heavily-built, red-faced, he had never been a miner. He was nevertheless our authority on trade unions in general, and mining matters in particular. He was a tireless worker, ever prepared to sacrifice himself for the cause of the miners.

'You will be Robert Smillie,' he said to me, smiling broadly, when he first met me at a meeting in Hamilton when, with two others, I was representing the Larkhall miners.

'I am indeed, Mr Small,' I replied, feeling somewhat confused that he had known who I was. 'But how did you know me?'

'You have been pointed out to me,' he said. 'And I also take note of up-and-coming men. I have been told that you are both committed and admired by your friends in Larkhall.'

'You are too kind,' was all I could think of by way of reply. I have to admit that it was very gratifying to be told that I was held in some esteem.

It would not be an exaggeration to say that William Small lived his life for us. His routine was demanding and intensive. Five days a week, at least, he left his house in Blantyre at four o'clock in the morning to conduct early meetings up to twenty miles away. No horse and trap: that would have been far too expensive. So, apart from an occasional lift on a cart, that devoted man made those long journeys on foot at all seasons of the year. Frequently, after summer evening meetings, he would be far from home and it became a common sight to see him sleeping out in a field or wood with only a newspaper for a blanket. That way, he could be at the next colliery meeting early the next morning. Sometimes, I attended his meetings and would meet up with him by arrangement at some point on the road. When I asked him if he had been home the previous night, he would show me the spot where his newspaper blankets lay scattered. It was ironic in its own way. Those newspapers were usually the *Scotsman* or the *Glasgow Herald* which were no friends of the miners but they afforded shelter to the Union's General Secretary.

'But how did you manage to get here so early, William?' I would ask him.

'Man,' he would laugh, 'I was so tired that I just lay down in the lap of mother earth.'

'Take care you don't catch a chill or worse,' I told him.

'No, no laddie. I'm well looked after.' And his eyes would raise to the sky as if he knew that a higher authority was protecting him. He truly was a dedicated and pious man.

I worried over his outdoor sleeping habits many a time because he seemed not very robust. But he never complained and, in all that time I knew him, never seemed to catch a chill. Maybe that higher authority really was looking after him!

Much later, he would accompany me on conference visits to London and he would prove a delightful companion. We often visited the British Museum where, to his delight, he unearthed some old Scottish mining laws which he copied out and had published as articles in several newspapers. He became such an expert on the subject that John Davidson, well known in Fleet Street, often quoted him as a source. William Small's research work on mining laws would later play a significant part in the deliberations of the Coal Commission when noblemen were called in to prove their ownership of the land they claimed to possess. I was to play a part in that Coal Commission and often felt indebted to the work done by William Small. But in the 1880's I was just delighted to acknowledge him as my friend and occasional walking companion.

Though loved by the miners, William Small was shown scant respect by the Lanarkshire mine owners. His efforts to inform them of any grievance of ours were met with petulance. His letters went unanswered and, when he tried to call at their homes to reason with them, he was turned away. This attitude on their part prevailed during the early 1880's.

'You must be in despair, William,' I suggested to him after yet another letter went unanswered.

'Despair, Robert?' he replied. 'Not at all. Despair is for non-believers.'

The owners might on occasion talk to a miner representing all the miners in his own pit. But they held no truck with union representatives, full-time officials, who might represent an area but were not employed by them. They considered such people to be agitators rather than miners, and simply would not deal with them. However, their obstinacy in this matter simply strengthened our determination to make them yield, which they eventually had no choice but to do. In many ways it was a small enough concession, and grudgingly made, but at least a principle had been established.

At last, the union was beginning to rediscover itself. As Russell Lowell remarked, 'We had a damned long row to hae,' but progress was being made. Still a young man, albeit the proud father of two wee bairns, I was nevertheless aware of the need for a degree of patience. So much had been wrong that it was bound to take time to set it right. Most events have a small beginning, often not noticed at the time. The day that the Motherwell pickets visited Larkhall was one of those apparently small events which had significant consequences.

At the Camp Wood meeting, the Motherwell men had agreed to send out pickets to try to persuade men from other districts to reorganise and try to re-establish the Thursday break I told you about. The pickets duly arrived at Larkhall and began spreading the word among our miners. For a morning I became a Motherwell man because, having attended the meeting, I knew what had to be said and I said it. The miners at the Summerlee pit, in common with others in Larkhall, took Motherwell's advice and convened a mass meeting on Boyce's Green that very afternoon. The men asked me to preside, and I was happy to do so. The main speaker, an older organiser by the name of Daniel Cunningham, talked to the men about the main issues of the day. In particular, he pressed home the advantages of the Thursday break and the need there was to get back into effective union. A skilled speaker, he carried the meeting with him and the decision was made to call our reformed union 'The Larkhall and Upper Ward of Lanarkshire Miners' Association'. The reason we included the words 'upper ward' was that we hoped to include and organise the mine workers in the Coalburn District, at that time fairly small-scale but with the promise of considerable mining development.

A committee was selected and, much to my surprise, I was appointed as Secretary. To be perfectly honest, I was rather taken aback at being given that role. After all, the secretary in any organisation is usually, and quite literally, a man of letters and I was not. In fact, I was acutely aware of my limitations, and embarrassed by them. I didn't actually tell anybody, but I rather dreaded the task for I feared that my poor education might let me and everybody down. You might say that I took on the role as Secretary in full knowledge of my shortcomings, with my eyes wide open to the difficulties. And I would not be a paid official at that stage, able to make up for lack of skill through putting in a great amount of time. No, I would still be working at the coal face while attending to my secretarial duties. But how could I have turned down the role? I had been selected by a unanimous vote in spite of the fact that I had not sought the office. You could say that it had sought me. And if I had turned it down, how would that have helped the development of our branch? In all conscience, I could not have done that. My misgivings were somewhat eased as a result of a conversation I had with Daniel Cunningham in the aftermath of the meeting.

'Well, Robert,' he said, 'this means that you're on your way.'

'Aye, but on the way to what?' I replied, smiling as best I could though, as the truth of my appointment sank in, I was feeling more apprehensive than cheerful. 'Sleepless nights perhaps,' I added.

'Oh, there'll be a few of those no doubt,' he chuckled. 'But as the union grows and gains strength, so will you. Mark my words.'

'I just hope I'm up to it,' I told him. 'All that writing, I mean.'

'Don't worry about it, laddie. In this union, the Secretary will be no mere scribe. He will be a leader. That's what you've to be ready for. How do you feel about that?'

'I will do my best,' I told him, meaning every work of it. He seemed satisfied with that.

It was at that time that a rather odd and disturbing event took place. Again, it was one of those relatively little things which seem of no importance at the time, except to the people directly involved, yet which provided a lesson for the future. Only days after my election as Secretary, Rebecca Scobie sought me out and told me that her husband Tam was anxious to meet me. I knew Tam well enough, having shared shifts with him, and was aware of the fact that he was laid up at home with a broken ankle suffered in one of those frequent rock falls. Mrs Scobie wouldn't or couldn't tell me what Tam wanted me for, simply saying that Tam was desperate to have a word with me. I hurried along with her to their tied cottage in Colliery Row and there found Tam sitting by the fire, his right leg propped up on a stool. He went to get up as I arrived, but groaned and flopped back down in his chair.

'Stay where you are, Tam,' I said, taking the chair opposite him. 'You've no need to stand up for me.'

'What, with you being Secretary an' all?' He grinned. 'Man, I thought I'd have tae bow tae ye.' Originally from Glasgow, Tam had one of those quick, harsher accents.

'I'll away and make a pot of tea,' Rebecca announced, and disappeared into her scullery.

'You wanted me, Tam.'

'They're efter me. Those buggers is efter me.' His heavy features turned into a scowl. 'Ah've a broken ankle an' the buggers want me oot.'

'Who wants you out, Tam?'

'The colliery factor, the fat wee bugger,' he spat out. 'Ah've been aff work for ten days wi' this bluidy broken ankle of mines an' it'll be at least two weeks mair afore ah can gae back. An' the buggers want us oot o' here.'

'Have they served an eviction notice?' I asked.

'No yet,' he replied. 'But they said it widnae be long. The buggers! Twelve years ah've worked here an' now they want rid o' me like I was a clapped-oot horse. The buggers!' In his dark mood, 'buggers' seemed to be his favourite word. Not that he could be blamed for it.

'Settle down, Tam. Settle down,' I told him. 'I'll see what can be done. But why did you send for me, anyway?'

'Well, you bein' Secretary an' all,' he explained. 'Ah thocht ye might be able to arrange something. Onyways,' he added, 'you've always had a good heart.'

Well, I drank tea with them, promised I'd see what could be done, then left. Knowing that Tam's main problem was that, out of work, he couldn't pay his rent, I got a few of the shifts together and organised a collection. We raised enough to pay not only the back rent but also the following few weeks as well. I delivered the money to the colliery office and got the factor's assurance that Tam and Rebecca would be safe in their cottage, at least for the time being. Within the fortnight, Tam was back at work and, over the months which followed, repaid his workmates every penny they had raised on his behalf.

That small event taught me two things. First, that Daniel Cunningham had been right. Throughout I'd been organising things and hadn't had the need to write down a single word. Second, that it was important to make the union strong as soon as possible because miners were still very vulnerable to the whims of their employers.

Well, what a tempestuous period that was! In so many ways, it reminds me of Dickens' 'best of times and worst of times'. There were some very low points. The death of Nan Smillie, the disappearance of Robert, my fears for Ann when she was seriously ill, and the never-ending struggle of those of us employed in the pits against the attitudes and actions of our employers. Too much illness, too many deaths and a lot of hunger. The faces of desperate wives and starving children haunt me to this day. The feelings of helplessness and despair as we staggered from one day to the next.

But there were the high points as well. Getting married and starting a family, forming friendships with men like Keir Hardie and Andrew Small, being elected as Secretary of our branch. It was that last thing which perhaps pointed most significantly to the future. It was a crucial time for miners, as well as other workers and some things were moving our way. For example, the 1884 Parliamentary Reform Act was significant. Gladstone's Act extended the electorate by some two million people. Previous acts had denied the right to vote to workers outside the towns and cities so very few miners, who mainly lived in pit villages, had been eligible. The 1884 Act to a fair degree changed that, giving the vote to all householders in the counties. Still, for a variety of reasons, almost a third of British men were not eligible to vote but, at least, for the first time many miners enjoyed that right. The inevitable consequence of that was, in future, the legislators would have to pay rather more attention to the interests which we held dear.

That change was also important to the redevelopment of trade unions. Only through strong organisation could working men make collective views known to the legislators. Only by speaking together could our voices be clearly heard. At that time, only trade unions could provide that organised, clear voice. I was convinced of that and determined to redouble my efforts to ensure that the Larkhall and Upper Ward of Lanarkshire Miners proved to be a success.

There was one other development that I was becoming increasingly aware of. Miners and workers in other industries were developing the view that the existing political parties, both the Liberals and the Conservatives, were unlikely to represent our aspirations for the future. On the whole, the Liberals had been more friendly towards the working men, though the Conservatives had passed some legislation in our favour. But there were those of us, myself included, who likened both parties' attitudes to 'grannie handing out sweeties' – prepared to be kind to us on occasions, but in the attitude of an adult condescending to a child. We were beginning to believe that it was high time that working men had their own representation, men of their own class who would work with us, not just for us. In 1884, the Social Democratic Federation and the Fabian Society had been set up, both with Socialist aims. But again they were run by people not of our class, however admirable their intentions. We were in a mood to place our own people in positions of power. For some of us at least, this became an important aim in its own right.

In early 1885, the national newspapers were full of the death of General Gordon in Khartoum and defaming Gladstone for his mismanagement of what was popularly called the Sudan Affair. Previously, Gladstone had been called the GOM (Grand Old Man) but suddenly he was the MOG (Murderer of Gordon). In April of that year, Gladstone further outraged public opinion, or at least that opinion which was voiced in the newspapers, by withdrawing British forces from the Sudan and leaving the territory open to Muhammed Ahmed, known by his people as the Mahdi, the saviour of Islam. All of which mattered in its own way, of course. General Gordon was dead and the newspapers made much of that. So too were British soldiers of the ordinary type, though there was little mention of them. No doubt, there were Sudanese and Egyptian dead as well but, if our newspapers were anything to go by, they didn't count at all.

In the same newspapers, there was precious little mention of the miners or other industrial workers. That's how things were then. An obsession with Empire and territorial gains and losses. Full reports of matters political and the affairs of great men. But of the work, lives and struggles of those whose work made others great, a deafening silence. There were those of us who were committed to seeing that lack of balance change.

VII

Learning the Ropes

IN MY NEW role as branch secretary, which included attending many meetings not only in the district but also around the county, I quickly became aware of an unpleasant truth which I was going to have to face up to, and face up to quickly. If I wished to play a leading and influential role in union affairs, and I was certainly committed to that intention, I would have to become used to public speaking. I found the oratory of some of the veteran union leaders not only impressive but, I have to admit, rather frightening. Not because of what they said, but because of the apparent ease with which they said it.

I measured my speaking skills against those of men like Robert Steel, James Harley and Daniel Cunningham, and found myself sadly wanting. I almost blush now when I think back to my first attempt at public speaking, long before I held any union position. It was in 1876, I was barely nineteen, and I was attending the weekly meeting at the Miners' Hall. Some leaders were reporting on the business of a conference which had taken place in Hamilton a few days earlier. For some reason which is now lost in the mists of time, I didn't think much of the report. Somehow, I got it into my head that the leaders were heading in the wrong direction and trying to persuade the men to go with them. Totally unprepared for saying anything at all, I caught the secretary's eye and he beckoned me to my feet.

You won't believe it but I remember almost nothing of what happened next. When I got to my feet, I began sweating and the hall began to swim, then dance. The faces turned towards me were all just a blur. There was a lump in my throat blocking my voice and my mind was a total blank. I don't even remember sitting down. By the time I had regained my composure, the conversation had moved on and, thankfully, I was no longer the centre of attention. Later, somebody told me that I had made what he described as an impassioned speech which lasted several minutes. Well, that was news to me.

At the end of the meeting, the pit lads sitting near me congratulated me warmly for getting on my hind legs and daring to disagree with the older men. More than one of them remarked to me, 'Man, Bob, ye did fine.' Which was all very well in its own way, but it would have been even better if I could have remembered what I had said. On the way out of the hall, my pleasure at my workmates' congratulations was shattered when I was cornered by one of the veterans whose views I had challenged. It was Hector McNeil, one of the 'grand and revered seigniors', as one of my friends had called the older men.

'Young Mr Smillie, I believe,' he said, in a tone of utter condescension. 'You young ones might better leave matters they ken nothin' aboot tae their elders.' Then, nose in the air, he left.

'Pay him no mind,' Jimmy Souter said to me. 'He's an arrogant bugger, yon.'

Well, I can tell you that McNeil's rebuke, added to the terror I'd felt getting up on my hind legs at the meeting, made me desperate not to court any form of publicity for some time. Though I chuckle now when I remember that, from that time on, if I was showing any signs of making public utterance, the lads would shout, 'Come awa, Bob! Up an' at them!'

When I became branch secretary, and recalled that first effort at public speaking, I did so with no great pleasure. Daniel Cunningham had warned me that, as Secretary, there would be more leading than writing. But what use could I be as any kind of leader, even a relatively junior one, if I was apprehensive about speaking in public? Well, none at all, of course. So I resolved to try to do something about it.

One measure I took was easy enough. I took great care to study the style of experienced speakers like Steel, Harley and Cunningham. They were all different, of course, but they had certain characteristics in common. I noticed that they were usually well prepared, holding a piece of paper with notes. None of them actually wrote out speeches because they believed they would sound over-rehearsed and unnatural, but they also had those notes ready in case memory failed them. Another thing was that they stood in a fairly relaxed fashion. You can always tell a nervous speaker, who will stand as stiff as a ramrod, muscles taut and then, inevitably, with sweat starting to appear on his forehead. My models didn't go in much for constant gestures either. You see some speakers waving their arms or clenching their fists with every sentence. Not the great speakers, though, who believe that too many gestures deflect attention from their voices and what they are trying to say to their audience. One other important thing I noticed was the way they allowed their gaze to wander slowly round their audience. No jerks of the head, no attempt to look at everybody at the same time.

'Pick one man or maybe a small group,' Daniel Cunningham once told me. 'Fix on him or them for a few seconds. Make it seem like you are talking to a friend and you are really interested in him. Then move to the next man or small group and let your eyes fix there. In the course of each speech, you will cover many people in your audience. You will have contacted them, not just spoken to them, and that really matters.' It was excellent advice.

In addition to studying my betters, I increased my efforts at self-improvement through reading. You know that, apart from my watch, my earliest prized possessions were my few books. Well, in addition to reading good newspapers and attending night school, I had also been building up my collection of books to the extent that by the mid-1880s I had my very own small library. Nothing that would ever compare to the library of books, often unread, you would find in a great house, but sufficient to aid my development.

The greatest boon to my improvement as a public speaker was my small collection of Shakespeare's works. I originally bought a few second-hand copies to improve my reading. Then I obtained more because I loved reading them and found so much wisdom on the pages. I read and reread those copies of his great plays. It was a new and illuminating world. Used as I was to being 'cribb'd, cabin'd and confin'd' by the iron clutch of industry, Shakespeare's works were a revelation. I found much of what he wrote so memorable that the works stuck with me and, to my surprise, found myself able to quote extensively some of the best passages, particularly from the tragedies, but from the comedies as well. I became so immersed in his work that I frequently visited Larkhall Library to read those texts which I could not afford to buy for myself. There are those who scorn public libraries. So-called 'superior persons' argue that such places have no educational value. Well, they are wrong. That library, housed in a little room in a very ordinary building, lent light to my life. It cost me 2/6d a year for membership, and it was worth every penny. I was also a keen supporter of the concerts they put on to raise funds for the purpose of buying more books.

But if my original intentions in reading Shakespeare were to improve my reading and expand my knowledge, I also discovered a strategy for improving my public speaking. Shakespeare's works are full of great speeches. Some of the soliloquies are particularly memorable. I used those to what I hope became good effect. Often, instead of just reading them, a rewarding joy in itself, I would actually perform them, read them out loud to Ann and our bairns. Had anybody seen us in our one room, me on my hind legs spouting, Ann and the little ones in front of the fire listening, no doubt it would have struck that observer as quite a comic scene. But it was anything but that for me. It was part of learning to be a speaker. Later, as our children grew older, I continued to read to them. Not just to improve my speaking, but just for the sheer love of it. Listening to those readings opened the minds of the children, gave them a love of good reading, and gave them a better educational start than many enjoyed. I would commend the practice to any father.

As well as Shakespeare, I read the work of many other writers. Burns, of course, who along with Shakespeare had more to say than any of them and had been a favourite of mine for years. I also read widely from the *Bible*, *The Popular Educator*, and the *Standard Royal Reader* in which I first met the poets Gray and Goldsmith. A real treasure, purchased from the barrow of a Hamilton second-hand book vendor, was an out-of-date edition of the *Encyclopaedia Britannica*. That proved to be a rich source of information for my enquiring mind. With these, and other purchases, I built up my small library. This began on one shelf, but many more were added as time went by.

These were the ways in which I prepared myself for a life of public speaking. I studied other men, read as widely as I could, and practised reading aloud from great dramas. It did not come naturally to me, I freely admit, and I recognised early on that I would never become a great orator. But over time I did improve, which was no bad thing given some of my early efforts.

I made what I think of now as my maiden speech before the time when I deliberately set out to improve my speaking. The occasion was that meeting at Bryce Green which I referred to earlier at which we established our local branch and I was elected Secretary. As Secretary, I was expected to say a few words, and I did. I was used enough to expressing my opinions, pretty strong ones at times, to small groups of fellow workers, but this was the first time I had tried to address a large meeting. There were almost a thousand men present. As I rose to my feet, I was horribly mindful of my poor effort in front of Hector McNeil at a much smaller meeting years earlier.

You will no doubt want to know how I got on. Well, in the words of my own people, I was maybe not 'just fine' but perhaps I was 'no too bad.' I spoke rather haltingly, no doubt due to my nerves. But as I knew my audience and my subject, the need for a strong union, I managed to keep going. I voiced some of our grievances, and that struck a chord, because they were common grievances. I can't claim that I ever relaxed, but knowing my audience were on my side helped considerably. I even managed to use a tactic I'd admire in other speakers: I told a wee story.

It was a sort of clerical tale, and entirely true. A minister, newly-appointed in the locality, told a miner with whom I shared shifts that the miner's wage of three shillings and sixpence a day was a good rate of pay provided that the work was regular. Not only that but, in a sermon, he informed his congregation that he believed that the wages were actually too high if the miners had enough money for cards and other forms of gambling. Shortly after that as it so happened, the new minister was making the rounds of his 'flock' and called in at our home. By then, we had four bairns and the six of us were living in one room with a small scullery attached. It was on that visit that the minister began to change his views about the lives which miners led.

Like many folk ignorant of the mining community, he had fallen for the stories of miners' liking for drink and gambling. There were a few, a very few, who were prey to such vices but the vast majority were sober men with no interest in gambling, a vice that few could have afforded anyway. Even if the hoary old stories about miners' cottages boasting two pianos and lads tossing horseshoes for pound notes continued to be told in ignorant circles, our new minister discovered that truth that day he made his first round. Seeing families like mine living in cramped conditions, with enough money to put food on the table and little more, was a more eloquent response to his sermon than anything I or anybody else could have said to him. We parted amicably, with him apologising for any hurt his earlier sermons might have caused. For years, I would meet him on good terms and, for a time, serve with him on the local school board.

Well, I told this story to my thousand-strong audience. There was many a shaking head when I talked about the minister's sermon, then many a nod of approval when I pointed out how the incident resolved itself. Then I finished my speech with a strong condemnation of owners' frequent habit of reducing wages, and urged the men to stay loyal to one another in our attempts to regain our Thursday break. At the end, there was some cheering and a good round of applause.

So that first real speech had gone reasonably well. But I cautioned myself against over-confidence in the light of it. I had been playing at home, as it were, and was very familiar with my subject matter. I realised that it would not always be like that. That there would be times I would be on opponents' ground and less used to the matter in hand. Which was the reason I practised and watched, then watched and practised some more. I did everything I could think of to improve my public speaking.

But who would be a Labour Secretary? That is no idle question. Believe it or not, it is one which I laughingly applied to a parlour game. Round the fire, we were fond of playing a word game which involved changing the character of the parson's cat so that it might start off as 'an amiable cat' and end up as 'a one-eyed cat'. One evening, I started off the game saying 'The Labour Secretary is a laborious secretary.' I will not reveal to you how Ann finished off the game but it reduced me to very small significance indeed. I could afford to laugh at that but, in reality, the role of Secretary turned out to be very taxing.

Looking back, I must have been a real bundle of energy in those far-off days. If I hadn't been, I could never have carried on: I would have broken under the strain. Each week was a very full one. I worked ten hours a day in the pit, exhausting enough in itself. On Tuesday nights, there were committee meetings. On Wednesday nights, there were district meetings. Once we had regained the right to our Thursday break, these days were given over to meetings of the Federation Central Board to which I was a delegate. Those meetings were at ten in the morning in Hamilton. Then at noon on the same day there were more meetings to consider the resolutions passed by the Board. Friday evenings brought more of the regular meetings then, Saturday evening, the branch treasurer and I spent several hours going over the books. Sunday was supposed to be a day of rest but I devoted much of that day to clerical work, such as keeping the ledger of names which by the late 1880s held 1500 names.

Believe me, that was a typical week for several years. In return, I received a secretarial fee of fifteen shillings a quarter – £3 per annum. Luckily, I was not expected to pay my expenses out of my fee. For example, when I went to Hamilton on those Thursday break days to attend the Federation Central Board meeting, my delegation fee was met and I got a sixpence for my train fare. For occasional business outside my area, I might sometimes be reimbursed to the tune of one shilling but, in all, I believe that the union got a lot of my time for very little money. That was entirely fair, in my opinion, because we did not believe in squandering the union's limited funds.

As the union grew in size and, therefore, importance, the demands on my time increased further. In truth, I had little more of my own time left to give and, if I was called upon to hold morning meetings at any of the various pits, I had to absent myself from my work at the coal face. Naturally, the employers stopped my wages for that, denying me the pay for a whole shift even if I had only been away at a meeting for an hour or two. I did not wish to complain about this for I believed that the work of the union was more important than my own comfort. On the other hand, I had a growing family to look after.

As 1887 was racing towards 1888, Ann and I were living at 40, Miller Street. By then we had eight children. There was Jeanie, Mary, John, William, James, Robert, Daniel and Alexander. Not only that but Ann was carrying our ninth bairn who would be born later that year and christened Joseph. So it was with great relief that I greeted the news that the union would pay me 3/6d for any shift I had to miss due to union business.

I can scarcely believe it now but I allowed even more of my time to be taken away from family matters that year. To my surprise and delight, my friend Keir Hardie got in touch with me. With the support of several unions, he was standing as Socialist candidate in the Mid-Lanark parliamentary election. This caused quite a buzz of interest in our circles for here, at last, was the ordinary man standing against parties which, in spite of the occasional nod in our direction, were inclined to view us as lower specimens to be helped now and then, rather than the men we were. Mind you, the Liberals and Conservatives were being a wee bit more tactful by then in their election addresses, because they knew that the 1884 Reform Act had given the vote to many more working men. Even so, many of us were of the view that they were still talking down to us.

It was in these circumstances that Keir Hardie asked me to help him with his campaign. You might well imagine that, with everything else that was going on in my life, I would find it difficult to find the time to provide as much support as I would have wished. And so it proved. I was able to arrange some meetings for him, rouse a fair number of men to demonstrate on his behalf, and help to distribute campaign leaflets which were not, I have to say, of great quality. In comparison with his opponents, his funds were very limited, and campaign literature cost money. Nevertheless, we all did what we could to help him. It was to no avail, and Keir Hardie lost, rather badly as it turned out. We had failed to galvanise the newly enfranchised workers to turn to our cause. The main reason for that, apart from our lack of funds, was that Hardie was passionately advocating Socialism at a time when most men were still thinking along traditional Liberal or Conservative lines. Perhaps I should have realised that it takes a newborn baby a long time to find its feet! I think I took it rather more badly than he did. I remember clearly a conversation we had a few days after the declaration. It was a Sunday and he caught me at my clerical work. His visit was a good excuse to go for a walk and enjoy some fresh air.

'You're looking tired, Robert,' he remarked as we walked through Larkhall towards the pit.

'I confess that I am, Keir,' I admitted. 'Though with less cause than you after what you have just gone through.'

'It was a setback, that's all,' he said. 'You didn't think it would be that easy did you?'

'Hardly that,' I replied. 'But I thought that more of the ordinary folk would have voted for you.'

'I didn't,' he told me, as we paused by the low metal fence which divided the town from the pit. 'Take a look at the winding wheel, man.' Above the main shaft, it stood gaunt and silent, it being a Sunday. 'That wheel tells you everything,' he added.

'I'm sorry, I don't understand,' I told him.

'That great circular lump of metal represents a hundred years of misery and exploitation. As it moves, it sends the men down and brings them back up again. Down into the bowels of the earth and back up again, if they're lucky.'

'I still don't understand.'

'That wheel dictates our fate.' Then he smiled and looked at me. 'What's it doing now, Robert?'

'Well, nothing,' I said. 'It's Sunday.'

'Exactly.' As if I'd said something wise. 'And tomorrow it will start up again, won't it?'

'Yes, of course it will. But ... '

'There will come a day, Robert, when we decide how that wheel works. How many men go down, how long they stay down.' He sighed, then smiled again. 'For now, that wheel is like history itself, cold, unfeeling, and very heavy. But the men don't question it because it's always been there. It's all they know. And however bad reality may be, people don't give up on it easily because it's what they know.' He gripped my shoulders. 'It's our job to make our friends see that there is a different reality possible. My job, Robert, and yours too. It will be a long, hard struggle, almost like fighting against nature. But it's a struggle which we have to endure and which we must win, for the sake of decent working people everywhere.'

His words heartened me considerably and I vowed to him that I would carry on the struggle. He left, telling me that he intended to put himself forward for election again and suggesting that I should consider doing the same thing. That gave me food for thought, I can tell you. But in the meantime I was still a mere branch secretary with plenty of other things to do. There were times when, quite frankly, I would have preferred to be simply full-time at the coal face.

In particular, having to button-hole the first shift of miners before they went down into the pit meant the earliest of starts to my day, a day in which my responsibilities would stretch into the late evening. I had to leave home at 4:30 in the morning to catch the men before they started work. Many a time I breakfasted in the early hours from a collier's flask and with a share of his bread. I have enjoyed more delightful meals, but never with the same satisfaction as that sense of sharing with fellow miners. Even if I have to smile now as I remember that the men sometimes weren't in much of a mood for early morning union business. Hardly to be wondered at if it was 4.30am on a chill, dark, winter morning. Some greeted me with a smile: others with a scowl.

'We're no' goin' tae stop this morning, Bob,' somebody would growl.

'Aye, away the hell, you an' your bluidy union,' a less polite voice would offer.

But I understood the truculence of the minority. They were miners like myself, and there's little joy around at that time of a cold morning. I believe that they knew how enthusiastic I was to run good meetings, and they realised that I never spared myself, which put them on their mettle. Whenever I had something big to put before them, perhaps issues to do with the Truck System, the eight-hour day for miners, or a demand for an increase in our low wages, the men came in large numbers. In this day and age, with telephones at people's disposal, that may seem no great thing. But back then, getting news of meetings to men could mean hours of tiring legwork going round the pits and colliery cottages, because the only way available to me of passing on messages was by word of mouth. I do not care to think of how many weary miles I walked for that purpose.

We called our larger meetings demonstrations. In later years, that word would come to have a rather different meaning but, in those days, we thought that it was just a bigger word than meeting and sounded much more important. If a report of our activities appeared in the local newspapers, they sounded more significant when described as a demonstration rather than a mere meeting. Fondly, we imagined that the use of that word might have more impact on the owners. Perhaps that was just a particularly good example of wishful thinking on our part!

To give added impressiveness to those demonstrations, we often engaged the local brass band many of whose members were miners so the fee involved rarely stretched our funds. We also put up a fine display of banners, many of them old and weather-beaten affairs which had fluttered to many a miners' march in by-gone days. With those held high behind the marching band, we managed to give our demonstrations the air of gala days, though those of us who organised them were always mindful of their more serious purpose. That purpose was served by the speech makers.

Younger men like myself were often not very keen to speak at these larger meetings attended by upwards of a thousand men and, sometimes, their families. As I have already suggested to you, speaking in front of such a large number could be a formidable experience. Most of us preferred to leave the speaking to fathers of our movement such as Robert Still, James Harley and Daniel Cunningham. But in their wisdom, those men who had learned to make speeches the hard way, would not tolerate our reluctance.

'Ye must go an' face them, my laddies,' Daniel Cunningham told us. 'If ye dinna the noo, ye never will. Ye'll only learn tae speak by speakin'. Confidence will come by degrees. Ye'll no be an orator in just a wee minute.' Then the warning. 'For wha's tae tak oor places when we're gone?' It was excellent advice, even if some of my peers found it difficult to take on board.

As for myself, I still felt nervous before addressing any large meeting, but I steeled myself by getting in lots of practice. Most mornings of the week, I was talking to groups of miners on their way to work on the early shift. As I told you, sometimes they were receptive and, on other occasions, they were less so. But for me it was all good experience of talking to an audience. I was also running at least two meetings a week at local level and finding my way on the formal stage by that means. This meant that, in my role as local secretary, I was gaining considerable experience as the 1880s came to a close.

I'm reminded of an experience at that time which was serious in itself but, because of an unexpected outcome, makes me chuckle when I think of it. It involved old Hector McNeil, the veteran leader who had embarrassed me when I had spoken, or should I say, tried to speak in public for the first time at the age of nineteen. Our paths had crossed a few times since them but neither of us had referred to the earlier incident. Besides, on the whole he tended to talk to the more experienced men which meant that I rarely had any direct dealings with him.

Let me make it clear to you that I detest the idea of 'getting one's own back', because it is rooted in revenge and that never did anyone any good since the beginning of time. However, thanks to the Lord Provost of Glasgow and some action on my part, I quite unintentionally returned to Hector McNeil the 'favour' he'd done to me all those years earlier.

It was like this. Glasgow's Lord Provost convened a meeting of mine-owners' representatives and Lanarkshire miners in an attempt to settle a county strike being held in protest against low wages. However, in the notice sent out to call the meeting, the owners introduced the thorny old issue of who they were prepared to talk to. They flat refused to talk to anybody who was not employed by them. This caused a real problem. You will remember that one of our leading advocates was William Small. He had never been a miner, having been employed by a Glasgow drapery, but he was a most able speaker, an advanced thinker on land and labour matters, and had spoken on our behalf for years. But the owners would not have him at any price. Many of us were enraged by this. We had not tried to insist on who should represent the owners, so what right did they have to insist on deciding who should represent us? In truth, they were apprehensive of William's presence. He was a gifted speaker and more knowledgeable about the relevant issues than many of the owners were.

In the event, two delegates were selected to represent Larkhall. I was uncomfortable with the fact that I was one of them because, as I resented William Small's exclusion, I had decided that I would not attend. What finally convinced me that I was right in that decision was the fact that the notices convening the meeting in Glasgow had been issued not by the Lord Provost, but from an address in St Vincent Street, Glasgow, on behalf of Mr Baird who just happened to be one of the delegates representing the Mine Owners' Association. It was clear to me that the owners wished to have control of the affair from top to bottom.

I tried but failed to persuade our branch to take no part in the conference until such time as the county was permitted to nominate whichever representatives it wished, William Small included. I lost that argument but felt no bitterness about it. The men were desperate to obtain a satisfactory settlement and, though no happier than I was about the conditions for the meeting being laid down by the owners, were anxious for it to go ahead. So two delegates from Larkhall were sent. William Phairins was one and my old sparring partner, Hector McNeil, was the other.

The employers' representatives were led by Mr A.K. McCosh – from what I heard of the details, our side sadly missed the presence of a speaker like William Small. McCosh made the owners' rigid stance very clear. First, all miners had to return to work immediately. Second, we should drop all requests to re-institute the Thursday break, which would never reappear. Third, a sliding scale of wages' regulation should be established thereby negating the need for future negotiations. If we agreed to these three strict conditions, then the owners would concede to us the small increase in wages which we were demanding. Not one but two full meetings went by without our representatives being able to make the slightest dent in the owners' position.

At the end of the second meeting the two Larkhall delegates, Phairins and McNeil, called a meeting to inform our miners of the Glasgow meeting's progress. Or should I say, lack of progress. It so happened that I was playing my role as secretary at a branch meeting at the same time as that impromptu meeting, so none of us on the Larkhill committee could attend. Towards the end of our meeting, Hector McNeil suddenly appeared to tell us what had been said at his meeting.

'No Thursday break perhaps?' I ventured.

'Aye.' Looking grim at the gasps from the committee members.

'And a sliding-scale to regulate wages?' Somebody else asked.

'Well, yes ... '

'No future negotiations then?' I added.

'Not in the immediate future,' he admitted. Then he squared his shoulders. 'The Larkhill miners have accepted the owners' terms, so the matter's settled as far as this district is concerned.'

'No, Hector,' I said, as calmly as possible.

'What?' The worthy veteran stiffened as if I'd hit him.

'Such a decision can only be made by this committee,' I told him. 'You had no right to advise the settlement without consulting us.' I was taking no great pleasure in reprimanding him, but it had to be said. 'We will convene a mass meeting of the Larkhill District next Wednesday. Then, we will be glad to hear of your report of the conference proceedings.'

'But ... but I ... ' McNeil looked round and saw the determination on our faces. 'Very well then,' he said and left straight away.

The meeting duly took place at Shaw's Road in the open air with over eight hundred men in attendance. Hector made his report and used all his powers of oratory to try and persuade them to accept the Glasgow agreement. He was civilly received, but with little enthusiasm. I followed him and spoke for about thirty minutes. I urged rejection of the agreement and its provision for the loss of our Thursday break and our ability to negotiate our wages. When I had finished, we moved to a vote. Twenty-nine hands were raised in support of Hector McNeil's argument for the agreement. It was unnecessary to count the cloud of hands which went up for non-acceptance.

In the event, Larkhall miners would retain their Thursday break. They would not be bound to a wages' sliding scale and could continue to negotiate over pay. In the short term, they were awarded the extra sixpence a day they had been looking for. Other districts gave in to the owners' demands, lost their Thursday break and their rights to negotiate, and all for the extra sixpence a day. This event marked the passing of Hector McNeil's role as a miners' leader.

So, was my public speaking better than Hector's? Not a bit of it. Even in old age, he was twice the orator that I would ever be. But I knew my subject better and I knew the minds of the men. Facts which Hector admitted later because, in spite of what happened over the Glasgow agreement, he and I became good friends. But I don't think it would be too much to claim that those events led to a new dawn in mining affairs. The men of Larkhall had shown what could be achieved by being organised, sticking together, and refusing to be browbeaten. Things would never be quite the same again. Not easy, far from it, but never the same.

On reflection, I am certain that that victory for the Larkhall miners marked a beginning for me, a period in which I was more sure of my ability to lead. I had improved beyond measure as a public speaker and, even though I knew I would never be a great orator, I felt much more secure in my increasingly frequent role as public speaker. More than that, and in common with many others, I had learned how we could win. There were many trials to come but, by my mid-forties, I could see the path ahead with more clarity and optimism.

VIII

Of Men and Malevolence

LIFE IS NOT a simple path. It rarely runs straight and is often subject to diversions, some of those turning out to be cul-de-sacs. At any given time, a man may be involved in any number of things, apart from his main task of putting food on the table. Events, too, may be short in duration or rumble on for years. Some friendships grow and last forever while others wither on the vine. The same could be said about enmities. In other words, any person's life is complex, full of twists and turns, often made up of threads of experience, some of those threads being short, others never-ending. My life has been like that. It was particularly complicated during the later years of the nineteenth century.

Up to this point, I have been able to tell you my story in more or less chronological order. Though often fraught with difficulties, it was simple enough. But by the time when I became branch secretary, it was as if I was living several lives rather than just the one. Not just because I was filling each day with work, as I have tried to describe, but more because of the different directions in which life was taking me. Not only was I a miner, husband and father, which in combination was a life in itself, but I was becoming more and more heavily involved in various aspects of the Labour Movement. My role was demanding, taking many hours of my time every week. I was becoming a regular contributor to county meetings. There were calls on my time to attend conferences, not only in Scotland but across Great Britain. I had dabbled in politics in Scotland through my support for Keir Hardie's election campaign and was allied with a number of others in plans to create a new political party to represent the interests of working men.

Looking back, I find it almost incredible that I could have been immersed in so much – with more to come! – and perhaps you will think the same. But I was young then, full of vigour and commitment and, though my days were extraordinarily full, the demands on my time were something I gave little thought to.

However, the fullness and complexity of my life in those days present me with something of a problem as a chronicler of that life and the events surrounding it. That is why, and with apologies, I find it impossible to deal with the next period of my life in clear, chronological order. Instead, in the pages which follow I will deal with some of the major themes of my life at that time. I will begin with some of the men I worked closely with in those days, referring to the places in which I made their acquaintance. I will also tell you about some events which reveal the darker side of mankind.

My first major meeting outside Lanarkshire took place in 1886 while I was still a humble branch secretary. The conference took place in London and I can only assume that my invitation to attend was due to the recommendation of my good friend Keir Hardie who, along with Chisholm Robertson, were among Scotland's main delegates. Since my voyage from Ireland many years earlier, I had hardly ventured more than fifteen miles from home, so you might feel able to excuse the childlike excitement with which I anticipated my maiden trip to the capital.

The business of the meeting, which was attended by mine owners and miners' delegates from across Britain, was the proposed Mines Regulation Act, eventually enacted in 1887, which included regulations providing legal protection for miners while at work. Obviously, this was important stuff but, given my junior status, I was not called upon to make any major contribution. Which was probably just as well, given one particular aspect of my behaviour!

Each day of the conference, the chairman provided a stand-up luncheon of sandwiches and various drinks. Unfortunately for him, he did not know that I had a voracious appetite. Two-inch-square sandwiches should, I presume, be eaten one at a time. I managed to pick them up and eat them in twos and threes. Perpetually hungry in those days, I made a right meal of them. Hardie and Robertson ate rather less, perhaps because I did not leave much for them.

'Bob,' Hardie said. 'I'd rather keep you a week than a fortnight.' He had a point.

Between sessions of the conference, I was keen to see as much of London as possible and we managed to visit Fleet Street, The Old Curiosity Shop, the Tower, St Paul's and, of course, the House of Commons, among other sites. We were lodging in a small house near Euston Station. It was the upstairs of a newsagent, whose little shop we had to pass through when going in and out. Keir knew the newsagent well through the Good Templars' Movement. Indeed, he knew many people in London so it was no great surprise to me when he secured a seat in the House of Commons in 1892, representing West Ham.

What should have been the social highlight of that visit to London was a trip to the Crystal Palace arranged by Hardie who claimed to know London like 'the back of his hand'. He got us onto a bus at Westminster and, in the course of the next hour, we found ourselves at various places such as Liverpool Street Station and Ludgate Circus. So much for Hardie's knowledge of London! To add insult to injury, when we did eventually alight at the Crystal Palace, it was closed for the day! Those journeys and counter-journeys cost us in fares almost 2/- each out of a daily allowance of 7/6d.

'Man, man,' I said to Hardie, 'I could have bought a decent dinner for that amount of money.'

After our visit to the Tower, I was feeling thirsty. Not only was it a warm day but I was discovering that a huge city like London, swarming with people and enclosed by never-ending buildings, draws the moisture out of a man. Outside a rather rough public house, I proposed to Hardie and Robertson the benefits of a glass of beer and a clay pipe. Hardie did not drink alcohol and, taking one look at the place, Robertson claimed that he wasn't thirsty, so I went in on my own. It took me three attempts to get the barman to understand my accent, but I eventually got my glass of beer which was palatable if rather sweeter than I was used to. I also got my clay pipe but it was not the softer kind I used in Larkhall, which turned my thoughts to home, the fireside, Ann and the bairns. As the bar filled up with a crowd of very rough Billingsgate labourers, I was delighted by the thought that I would be catching the train back north later that day.

In 1888, I had the honour to attend the National Union Conference in Birmingham where I came across some of the great names of the Labour Movement, men in late middle age who had given years to the cause. I met Thomas Burt MP, Benjamin Pickard, Sam Woods, John Wilson MP, Enoch Edwards, Thomas Ashton and many others, including one wonderful Welshman, more of whom later. I regarded these men with reverence, knowing that they had been the pioneers who had suffered every kind of prejudice, dismissal, black-listing and all the rest of it.

Thomas Burt made a particular impression on me. It would not be going too far to say that he was loved by his colleagues. He had been a pathfinder for the Labour Movement, a missionary if you like. Yet, in spite of the awe in which we younger men held him, he was among the most unassuming men I ever met. He was quiet, genial and kindly, always having time and words of encouragement for those of us in the 'new generation.' He opened that conference with a well judged speech but had to leave when news filtered through of a wages dispute in his home area of Northumberland. He left to take part in critical negotiations, and his place in the chair was taken by Benjamin Pickard. There then followed what I can only describe as the Pickard-Wilson bout.

Outsiders have often believed that delegates at conferences are like sheep, easily led by shepherds in the form of veteran leaders. Believe me, nothing could be further from the truth. I have heard exchanges among fraternal delegates which were more bitter than those which took place between unions and owners. And that was healthy enough. After all, how would absence of argument serve democracy? All that mattered was that once the arguments were over, however vitriolic they had been, a united front was presented to the world. And that's what normally happened.

But that day in Birmingham, it was more than just a heated argument. It was personal. Benjamin Pickard was a large, bluff, outspoken Yorkshireman. His opponent on the day was John Wilson, MP from Durham, one of our most able men but with the unfortunate habit of deriding those with whom he disagreed to a point which smacked of the highest arrogance. To say the two men disliked each other would be an understatement. There was no love lost whatsoever. I do not remember the precise point they were making, but I do remember the styles in which they did it. Pickard used words like bludgeons, while Wilson used them like the lightest of terpsichoreans employs dance steps. Pickard's insults were direct, almost brutish. Wilson's were like the swordsman's thrusts, in and away before Pickard could form an adequate reply. Wilson won on the day, no doubt about that. But if I could admire his quick-witted oratory, I cared rather less for the way he set out to humiliate his opponent rather than his argument.

At that conference, I had a minor verbal joust with Wilson myself. Daniel Cunningham, one of my Scottish colleagues had spoken and, in reply, Wilson had taunted him over his poor grammar. He concluded his vitriolic statement by observing the old chestnut, that it required a surgical operation to get a joke into the head of a Scotsman. Which was not only insulting but also, for a clever man, totally illogical as no joke had been told on either side. Poor old Daniel looked totally crestfallen at Wilson's unpleasant words and, on the spur of the moment, I decided I wasn't going to tolerate such personal viciousness. Due to follow Wilson, and feeling not a little nervous, I got to my feet.

'Mr Wilson has claimed the need of a surgical operation to enable my countrymen to see a joke.' I paused for a moment for effect. 'I have no need, I suppose, to observe that Mr Wilson's remark is far from original.' I must confess that I enjoyed seeing his face redden with anger. 'But he has forgotten the second part of that time-worn story. Let me remind him of it. It is this. It is perfectly true that it is difficult to get a joke into the head of a Scotsman, if that joke is a poor English one.' As Wilson stiffened then tried to pretend that my words had had no effect on him, the rest of the delegates roared with laughter. Not that I'd said anything particularly witty, just that they were delighted to see the arrogant Wilson taken down a peg for once. I noticed a huge fellow slapping the table in delight. I had not noticed him before. He was called Mabon, and he was the wonderful Welshman I referred to earlier.

Unsurprisingly perhaps, Mabon's favourite song was 'Land of My Fathers', which he sang in Welsh. Even though Scots like myself did not understand the words, we certainly recognised the passion and eventually learned enough of it to join in at the chorus. Mabon would seek any audience for his singing. I remember the time when the new Usher Hall in Edinburgh opened and was about to host a Miners' Federation Conference. After admiring the hall's wonderful circular shape, Mabon wondered if the contours of the arena would add something extra to his singing voice. So he went up onto the platform, leaving us in the rear of the hall, and gave a rendition of his favourite song. His fine voice resonated through the empty hall with a tonality and volume which startled us.

'Bravo, Mabon!' we shouted at the conclusion of his performance. He seemed well enough pleased by our reaction.

After the conclusion of a national Welsh Miners' strike some years later, I was invited to take part in a series of demonstrations along with men like James MacDonald, Enoch Edwards, Thomas Ashton and Benjamin Pickard. Naturally, Mabon was among our number. We held many meetings at which I spoke, but the big events were the demonstrations, or rallies, attended by anything up to 20,000 miners. It was at these vast gatherings that I discovered the secret of Mabon's influence over the Welsh miners. If any dispute arose, he never tried to restore order in the usual way. Instead, he immediately started singing a Welsh hymn or 'Land of My Fathers' then, with arms uplifted, he would have all the assembly joining in by the end of the second line. The vast numbers seemed to drop into their respective parts and accompany him like a trained choir. It was magnificent, magical and thrilling. It also showed what a shrewd man Mabon was.

During that week in South Wales, we found some time for fun and games. Our opponents would have been amazed at the sight of allegedly dull, serious, wooden agitators actually taking time for trivial amusements. But we were men like any others and enjoyed occasional relaxation. Mabon was always the first to join in. No athlete – how could he be given his weight? – he was nevertheless keen on rounders and he excelled with a bat in his massive hands. He could hardly run and always found a young delegate to run for him. A truly crafty man, that Mabon!

He was also very fond of swimming. We took the plunge, as you might say, at a pretty beach near Swansea. I believe it was called The Mumbles. None of us had a costume so Mabon's son provided us with some from a local shop whose owner he knew. But he couldn't find a bathing suit large enough to fit his father. He got round this by pinning two together, to our great amusement. But the last laugh was on us. It turned out that Mabon was by far the best swimmer of all of us. I doubt if he was capable of sinking. He simply rolled in the water like a porpoise!

It was during the last of that series of meetings in South Wales that I came across a man you will have heard of. A very young man at the time, Winston Churchill was to be one of the main speakers. I was struck by two things. First, far from being the sullen youth as he was so often depicted as by cartoonists, he was actually keen to smile and be pleasant. Second, when he spoke he did so with a slight lisp. Years later, when I had considerable dealings with him, I did not notice that at all. Did he grow out of it or was it a performer's affectation? To this day, I cannot make up my mind about that.

The last session of that final meeting saw me speak for only the second time on a subject that was dear to my heart and got me involved in the formation of the Independent Labour Party. It was an evangelical statement, if you like, and alluded to the nationalisation of land and the eventual establishment of a Socialist state. I was followed on the platform by Professor William Jones. I was told later that he had countered all my principles, upholding the orthodox Liberal creed. Not that I knew that at the time because his speech was entirely in his national tongue, Welsh!

On the day of the last session, before Winston Churchill arrived, Professor Jones and I were on the platform again, ready to continue our argument about Liberalism and Socialism. I was due to speak first but, given what had happened at the previous meeting, I was none too pleased about that.

'I wish to follow Professor Jones,' I told the chairman. 'After all, he had the opportunity to speak after me last time.' Adding darkly, 'And he spoke in Welsh which I do not understand.'

'No, no, Mr Chairman,' Jones tried to insist. 'Mr Smillie must go first. After all, the people are much more anxious to hear him than me.' Which was laying it on rather too thickly.

'Mr Smillie?' the chairman asked.

'Well,' I replied, 'I am willing to speak first if the Professor will follow in English rather than Welsh. If not, he must speak first and my friends will translate as he speaks so that I have the opportunity to reply to his arguments.'

Given that option, Professor Jones said that he would speak second but in English. Which he did and spoke in the most beautiful idiomatic English. I totally enjoyed the purity of his diction, but insisted on the right to reply. We might well have been arguing to this day had Winston Churchill not arrived, at which point the chairman called us to order.

Let me make a final comment on the many meetings of that time. As well as their lighter moments, they were also characterised by serious debate, the outcomes of some of which greatly disappointed me. For years, Scottish delegates pressed on the issues of a guaranteed minimum wage and the Eight-hour Day. Neither gained much in support for many years, which must seem incredible now. Outside Scotland, only Sam Woods of Lancashire and good old Mabon of South Wales offered support. Men like Fenwick, Wilson and Burt opposed them for years. They had their own local reasons for that no doubt, but it led me to feel on occasions that one's foes can come from within one's own household.

Over those years, and outside the conferences with their fierce debates and occasional levity, there was still a real world. A world starkly described by Lord Macaulay in a book in which workers' children of the generation are enabled to speak to the child-slaves of the past. That book was, at the same time, engrossing and chilling. It told of little ones under five trapped in the mines, their mothers employed too as beasts of burden, harnessed to the coal trucks by belts and chains. I could never read that book without feeling the prick of tears.

My memories are not as grim as those, bad enough though some of them were. But in one way at least they were the equal of those dreadful earlier times. You will remember how I told you about the eviction of the McKnight family, those kindly people I lodged with when I first arrived in Larkhall. Perhaps you imagined that, after those dark days, things had improved and such evictions became a thing of the past. I regret to have to tell you that, if you thought that, you would be wrong. Evictions of families continued for many years after the McKnights were thrown out.

The worst period of evictions that I can remember took place as a result of a dispute at the Eddlewood Colliery. Those were as late as 1897, twenty-two years after the eviction of the McKnights. The dispute was over ton rates, worth not more than ten shillings a day to the company. I was one of the miners' leaders who approached the owners to say that the ton rate reduction was unjustified. We were wasting our breath. The masters believed that they were strong enough to enforce submission as they had done so often before. Our organisation was going through a relatively weak period and we felt that, unable to make any progress through negotiation, we had no option but to call a strike and some seven hundred and fifty men withdrew their labour. The owners' position was reported in the newspapers as that of good Christian men being forced into unchristian methods. Needless to say, our position was not reported and our views were never sought.

The sanctimonious cant of the owners beggared belief. Through their friends in the national press, they managed to convey to readers the mistaken idea that they were enveloped in grief at the necessity of employing dire weapons, by which they meant starvation and evictions, against workers who dared to put a decent price on their labour, and to stand up for just and equitable terms. However, the masters made it very clear that they believed the main duty of the miners was to 'learn to labour and wait'.

The owners found it easy to obtain eviction notices from the sheriff court and soon the miners who occupied tied cottages received those notices. We had no weapon with which to fight them so we called a meeting of those threatened with eviction and advised them to barricade their doors. We felt that at least some of the sheriff officers might hesitate when faced with the need to break into houses. What else could we have done? The owners had on their side the powers of ownership, control, housing tenure and even the law. We had nothing other than a determination not to let our people be thrown out onto the street. While many of the men barricaded their doors, a large number of us hastily constructed a series of wooden huts to house those families who would eventually and inevitably be evicted.

Briefly, we thought that the barricades strategy might work because the local sheriff officers did indeed refuse to act. At that point, the owners persuaded the authorities to station a company of about twenty policemen in the district. Their presence led to an incident which almost caused a riot. A small boy was throwing pieces of cinder. It is not clear whether he was aiming at the policemen or merely playing a game. Whatever, the piece hit a young constable on the shoulder. He drew his baton, his fellow officers did the same, and they charged a small crowd of defenceless women and children, several of whom were struck to the ground. I was passing, talking to a local parish priest, and we ran into the middle of the mêlée. He was a brave man, that wee priest.

'Stop! Stop!' he shouted as the batons flailed around him. 'For the love of all that is holy, think what you are doing.'

Amazingly, his words served their purpose and the policemen backed away. Their officer turned up and we persuaded him to withdraw his men to the colliery office. It was as well that we did because, moments later, up to fifty miners turned up in a rage, armed with staves and pick shafts. Had the policemen not withdrawn, I fear that murder would have taken place.

The temporary huts had just been completed when the evictions began. I talked to Bell, the chief sheriff officer and, warning him that there would be trouble, I found it easy to persuade him to let me accompany him. The first cottage due to be evicted belonged to Henry Burgoyne, a branch official at Eddlewood and an intelligent, upright and determined man.

'Open the door in the name of the law!' Bell shouted, me standing by his side. There was no reply which was no great surprise to me. Bell tried again. 'Open up, Henry Burgoyne, or it will go worse for you.' Again, there was no reply.

Just then, Mrs Burgoyne came along the street, carrying a small bag of messages. She took in the scene and quickly stood on the doorstep between Bell and the door.

'Mrs Burgoyne, you must move aside,' Bell said firmly but in a reasonably civil tone.

'This is my ain hoose,' Mrs Burgoyne snapped back at him. 'I'm entitled to stand on my ain doorstep.'

'Sorry, Mrs Burgoyne,' Bell said, 'but I have my duty to do.' He raised his hand to push her aside.

'Now, now, Bell,' I told him, 'it would not do to lay hands on the woman.'

'But I must get in,' he protested, but he brought his hand down.

While he and I were arguing, Mrs Burgoyne reached into her wee message bag, drew out a handful of something, and threw it at Bell's face. He immediately began to moan. A small piece hit near my nose and I recognised it as pepper. For a few minutes, nothing happened. Bell was too busy with his discomfort. Understandingly he was also becoming extremely angry.

'Mrs Burgoyne,' I said, 'it would be safer if you let the man do his work.' I watched her begin crying as she stepped off the step, then saw Bell swinging at the door with a great hammer. As it crashed inwards, I jumped past him and met

Henry Burgoyne coming forward, his big hands clenched, obviously ready to do battle to save his home. I grabbed hold of him. 'For God's sake don't injure the officer, Henry,' I shouted.

'Let me get at him, Bob!' he shouted back, struggling with me, Bell hovering behind us.

'Calm down, Henry,' I tried to tell him, 'or they'll have you in the jail.'

In spite of his defiant rage, he eventually saw the sense in what I was saying. Massive shoulders slumped, he staggered to his wife and embraced her. They both began weeping as Bell and his men began to remove the furniture and deposit them in the street. I found it sad enough to see Mrs Burgoyne crying, but the sight of big honest Henry Burgoyne with tears streaming down his red cheeks almost made me cry myself. An hour later, they and their possessions were inside one of the temporary huts we had assembled.

Later, a charge was brought against the Burgoynes. He for obstructing the sheriff officer and she for throwing pepper in his face. The strike then over, I appeared as a witness in their case which was held before Sheriff Davidson in Hamilton Sheriff Court. I managed to persuade the sheriff that Mrs Burgoyne's had not been a premeditated act. Eventually, Mr Burgoyne was fined £1 and Mrs Burgoyne £1.10/-. No small sums to be repaid but a lot better than imprisonment which was common enough for poor folk resisting eviction.

Numerous people were evicted in that year but one other case is particularly fresh in my mind. Charlie Menzies, his wife and baby child were to be evicted from their home. They lived in a newer type of tied property, two storeys, more robustly built, the entrance to the upper floor where Charlie and his family lived being by means of a narrow, iron-railed, stone staircase. Again, I went with Bell in order to try and prevent trouble. We went up the steps and, at Charlie's door, Bell knocked and shouted for the door to be opened. There was no reply then, to our astonishment, we heard music coming from inside, the unmistakable strains of a melodeon being played by a skilled performer. Even Bell smiled at the sound of it. But he had a job to do and, with a few blows of his hammer, removed the door lock from its fastenings.

We passed inside, Bell probably expecting to be assaulted by an enraged Menzies. Nothing could have been further from the truth. Mrs Menzies was going about the household chores, while Charlie was sitting by the fire, melodeon in his hands, one foot rocking the cradle in which their tiny baby lay sleeping.

'Why, it's yourself, Bob,' he said smiling. 'Come away in, and your friends too.' If you are surprised by his cheery attitude, I wasn't. I knew who was due to be evicted, talked to them all, and persuaded them to be peaceful. Even if Charlie was carrying it a bit further that I'd expected. 'It's cold out and we've got a grand fire on.'

'Did you not hear us knocking, Charlie?' I asked.

'I thocht I heard a noise,' he replied. 'But ah was gien' it laldy with ma melodeon, so I wisnae sure. Whit's the matter onyway?'

'Ye'll have to turn out,' I told him. 'The sheriff officer is here to take your belongings down the stair for you. You had better quit, for peace's sake, and let him remove your things. There's space for you and your family down at the huts.'

Quietly and in the most obliging manner imaginable, Charlie Menzies took his wife's hand and led her down the steps. Behind them, his face glistening with tears, one of Bell's men carried the cradle with the sleeping bairn. Soon afterwards, the Menzies and their few possessions were yet another family condemned to live in a crude hut.

There was an odd postscript to that story. In 1912, James Seddon and I visited the United States as fraternal delegates to the American Federation of Labour Congress. We addressed a number of meetings in the mining districts of Illinois, on our way to Chicago. One place was called Hamilton which, as the name suggests, was home to a large colony of Scottish miners. We addressed an enormous gathering, mainly of miners and their families. In the course of my speech, I referred to the Eddlewood evictions of 1897 and told them about the sleeping infant being carried away in its cradle. That story affected the whole audience, none more than a man at the back who jumped to his feet.

'Aye, Bob,' he shouted, 'that's the God's truth you're telling. An' here's the lad that was carried doon the stair in his cradle.' It was none other than Charlie Menzies who had emigrated in 1899. Sitting beside him was his son.

Everybody was astonished by the coincidence, nobody more than me. I beckoned them to the platform amid a great round of applause. After the meeting, I had the time to talk to them and some other past friends from Scotland. It was a remarkable occasion. At the end they got me to part with some Scottish clay pipes which they couldn't get hold of in Illinois. I didn't mind in the slightest. It was worth the sacrifice just for the chance to meet up with old friends again.

The Eddlewood evictions were a stain on our industrial history. Not that you will read much about them in the history books which would deal with that period in terms of Salisbury, Chamberlain and other great men, as well as the grand subject of imperialism and the subsequent Boer War. But we were there as well, we miners, living as under-trodden and precarious a life as ever. And bear in mind that Eddlewood was but one dreadful example from our country. Across Britain, there were countless more. For all the various reforms introduced by governments, we were still largely under the owners' heels.

From all of this, you may believe that I hated our employers. I did not. Hatred is a useless thing which has never done anybody any good. The worst I have ever felt towards an employer is contempt. That must seem a strange word for me to use but I can explain why I do so. Not all miners were good men. The vast majority were but there were some who, with a few shillings in their pocket, would drink too much and gamble beyond their means. I never approved of such practices but, to an extent at least, I could understand them. An ill-educated man, worn down by a life of toil, subject to the abuse of an uncaring employer and with no better future in prospect, can be forgiven for seeking refuge in a bottle or the fleeting chance of greater riches through laying a bet. But what about the owners, our employers? Almost all were educated, living lives of relative luxury and with no doubts about where the next loaf of bread was coming from. So what excuse can be found for the ways in which they often persecuted their employees, squeezing every last drop of sweat, sometimes blood, out of them in the name of profit? There is no excuse for such behaviour, none at all. Which is why I felt such contempt for them.

But, of course, not all employers were like that. There were those who at least had the grace and civility to treat us like human beings. In truth, I have good memories of decent men on both sides in many disputes. It may sound odd to say this, but on occasions parties in a dispute undergo what I can only call a test of honour. You see, legality and morality sometimes clash. What may be right in law is sometimes unjust, law and justice not being the same things. When such a clash of ideas occurs, the man is often revealed. I would go so far as to say that a man who decides against his own interests in the greater interest of natural justice is a real gentleman, in the best sense of that word, whether he owns a colliery or works in it.

Sometimes, even, men can change. I remember the case of Thomas Thompson, general manager of a group of collieries of which Eddlewood was one. For many years, including 1897 and the Eddlewood evictions, he had been impossible to deal with. Arrogant and dismissive, he refused to discuss the issues of any dispute with the men's trade union representatives. What caused the change in his disposition towards us was unclear to me – I am certain he had never visited Damascus! – but maybe it was due to the influence of James Keith, Provost of Hamilton, who arbitrated a number of disputes between us. Whatever, in his later years he seemed to have come to an understanding of the folly of his earlier arrogance and consented to deal with us. He became one of the fairest of negotiators and, when his son eventually replaced him as general manager, he followed the good example set by his father.

One of the shrewdest yet most honourable men I ever negotiated with was James Morrison, owner of a neighbouring colliery. The dispute, as it had been on many previous occasions, was over a claim by the colliery's miners for an increase in ton rates. The colliery manager accepted that the men's earnings were very low, but absolutely refused to give the increase demanded. A stalemate set in and a prolonged strike looked to be the likely outcome. On behalf of the men, I bypassed the manager and, with his reluctant permission, was granted an appointment with the owner, the aforesaid James Morrison.

With a deputation from the workmen, I met Mr Morrison in the colliery manager's office. Morrison told him that he need not stay, at which point the manager looked peevish but left. A well spoken man, dressed in well cut clothes in the country style, Morrison opened the batting, if you will excuse the cricketing metaphor.

'Mr Smillie, I'll be grateful for your opinion on something,' he said politely. 'What is the legal position in this case, according to our standing agreement?'

'I have to admit that if we consider only the legal position, we do not have a strong case,' I told him. 'But I would like to put to you what I believe to be a stronger one, a moral case.'

'Carry on, Mr Smillie.' Many an owner would have had me thrown out by this stage. 'I'm listening.'

'The men and their families are in great difficulty,' I said. 'Their earnings are so low at present that starvation for some is the only likely outcome.' He seemed to be listening intently so I pressed on. 'That is why an increase in ton rates is essential to them. It is not the difference between comfort and luxury. Believe me, Mr Morrison, in many cases it is the difference between life and death.'

'I see,' he said when I had finished. 'Yes, Mr Smillie, I really believe I do see.' There was the suggestion of a smile. 'If the claim is acceded to, it will be a fairly serious matter for us. As you know, the industry is not in the best of health at the moment.' His eyes twinkled. 'And as you have admitted, your legal case is weak. However, the moral case you have set before me outweighs the legal one. Therefore, I give you my word that the concession will be made.'

That concession, wrung from a very fair and honourable man, had an odd repercussion. Some time later, the same miners made yet another claim for an increase in ton rates. I was not convinced of their case because Morrison had already increased the rates and the argument in favour of another increase was thin, to put it mildly. Nevertheless, I was anxious to avoid a strike, so I arranged another meeting with Mr Morrison, who received me as courteously as he had on the previous occasion. He politely asked me to state our case which I did, though I have to confess, with no great amount of fire.

'I see,' he said, after hearing me out. 'You perhaps have the glimmer of a legal case this time, Mr Smillie, but what about the moral position?'

'That's harder to say, Mr Morrison,' I replied in some confusion. Other delegates were with me and no doubt expected me to make some kind of impassioned plea. But, in all honesty, I did not feel justified in making one. 'In all justice, and considering the moral position, I do not believe the men have a strong claim and I will tell them so.' At which point I left, some very puzzled delegates beside me.

'That was a damned fine thing to do,' Michael Moore snapped at me once we had left the office. 'What are you up to, Bob, eh? Ach, you and your moral law!'

'We will discuss it at the meeting with the men tonight,' I said as we made our way back. 'We will let the matter rest with them.'

At the meeting, Moore made it very plain what he thought of my handling of the brief negotiation. At best I had been daft, at worst weak. The chairman halted his flow of complaints against me and asked me to state my case. I told the men exactly what had happened and openly admitted that I had not pressed their claim with any great enthusiasm. That drew a few murmurs of dissent. Then I went on to explain that Morrison had previously behaved honourably towards us and, given the weakness of our claim, we should now reciprocate with honour on our side. The matter went to a vote, my recommendation was approved by ten to one, and the men dropped their claim.

Before or since, I never felt so proud of any body of men. Honour had been demonstrated on both sides and, for years afterwards, disputes were always settled amicably and fairly. James Morrison had provided a model for owners. What a pity that only a few paid any heed to it. Of course, disputes and strikes are very serious matters but, oddly enough, if you look hard enough you can sometimes find a grim vein of humour running through them. Such was the case with a wages dispute at Auldtonhill Colliery in Larkhall. Before negotiations could take place, the men came out on strike, believing that they held the trump card of all trump cards. And what a curious trump card it was.

In my naïveté, I thought that a lengthy intervention on my part had saved the day. I negotiated with the owner, a Mr Hamilton, and persuaded him to abandon his intention to reduce the ton rates by two pence. He gave me his word, I accepted it, and I thought that was that. I reported back to the men to recommend that they return to work. All was going well until one of the men, Danny Finnin, put a spoke in the wheels.

'Nah, nah, Bob,' he said. 'We're no' gaun' back till some ither matters are resolved.' He then spoke for five minutes, castigating all employers for past grievances, some of which had been resolved years earlier, and generally portraying them as a collection of 'hertless buggers' as he so eloquently put it.

Well, whatever the merits of any particular dispute – and bear in mind that the main matter of this one had been resolved – there's nothing a body of miners likes better than to hear tales of the injustices of employers. Danny had the meeting in an uproar. I tried to reason with the men but Danny came straight back at me.

'Bob, you're a clever mannie,' he told me, 'but though you might ken a lot, you dinna ken everything.' That drew laughter from the meeting. 'That old bugger Hamilton cannae beat us this time. Besides being a coal master, he's also a big grocer in Stonehouse. You know fine that he sends oot vans as far as oor hooses here.' He laughed slyly. 'An' what would happen tae his grocery profits if we're on strike an cannae pay oor grocery bills, eh? Tell me that, Bob. Well, ah'll tell you. The old bugger would be bankrupt in nae time. You see what ah mean, Bob?

He cannae afford tae hae us oot on strike so we should screw him for all the pennies he's got.'

Well, that was a new one for me. A strike against a colliery owner, threatening the failure of his grocery business as a strike weapon! As it turned out, Hamilton was sharper than Danny because he sold out the grocery side of his business interest. Perhaps he had heard how Danny intended to fight him and decided not to take any risks!

In life, you meet all kind of people and, in my days as branch secretary in Larkhall and delegate to numerous conferences, I probably met a wider cross section than most people of my humble background ever did. Naturally, I liked some more than others. In that regard, I was no different to anybody else. And honesty forces me to admit that I liked some of the owning class rather more than I liked some of my own people. However, on the whole I always preferred the company of my 'ain folk'. On the other hand, I think that I learned some valuable lessons about mankind during that period of my life.

There's an old saying which tells us that you cannot judge a book by its cover. I was discovering that you can say much the same thing about men. Whatever a man's station in life, however he dresses, no matter what kind of speaking voice he has, he also has the capacity to surprise you. Sometimes for good, sometimes for ill. Not only that but I rarely came across any man who was wholly good or, for that matter, wholly bad. I found goodness in some surprising places, and badness in places where I expected none. All of which led me into thinking that we are all compendiums of good and bad, and that it is circumstances which encourage the rising of the one rather than the other. In short, I had learned never to judge by appearance, nor for that matter by reputation, but to treat each man on his merits as I found them.

IX

Disaster and Triumph

WHAT'S IN A name, as the question goes? Sometimes not much. Whether you call it a bannock or a flat cake, it tastes much the same, does it not? And you would not waste energy or cause yourself any mental anguish in deciding which name to use. But sometimes names go beyond mere anguish into real pain and, when a choice is available, you don't really want to use either of them. For me, and many of my generation and background, Uddingston and Blantyre are two such names. They are simple enough names, the names of two small places separated by a wee bit road and not much else. In the history books, they are sometimes confused, often treated as synonyms. But whichever place name you use, and most histories tend to Blantyre, they mean only one thing to me. The worst disaster in Scottish mining history.

It should never have happened. Its principal causes had been known of for some time. Various enquiries and several Acts of Parliament had identified the major problems. It was well known that various gases derived from coal dust built up to dangerous levels underground and that these gases could cause or propagate explosions. For that reason, among others, provision was made by Acts of Parliament in the appointment of inspectors to ensure that all reasonable precautions were taken and greater safety was ensured. But that did not happen everywhere. There were too few inspectors, some of them were in owners' pockets, and too many owners resented the cost of ensuring safety procedures. One awful result of that was what became known as 'The Blantyre Calamity'.

The disaster occurred in 1887. Only a few years earlier, Thomas Burt, secretary of the Northumberland Miners' Mutual Confident Association, had taken such a positive view of the progress made in miners' legislation that he had written, 'No class of working men are better united than the miners ... one voice, demanding in tones clear and strong, that the life of the miner should be protected.' Many agreed with him that great progress had been made, that never had so much been done to ensure miners' safety. I was not convinced. I knew of the provisions of various acts, I heard the rhetoric with which they were greeted but, around me on a daily basis, I saw the reality. That while it was true that some progress had been made, it was patchy at best and too often notable for its absence. Thomas and I clashed on this issue at a number of conferences. He would later admit in private that my view had been nearer the truth than his.

The Blantyre Calamity, caused by an explosion triggered by the build-up of gases, claimed 207 lives. Men from neighbouring pits and districts further afield poured in to help as soon as the news came through. Unfortunately, the only help which could be given was in the transporting of dead, often mutilated, bodies to the surface. I will spare you the gruesome details of much that happened. Such horror stories would serve no purpose now. I will confine myself to saying that the funerals, many of them mass funerals with bereaved women and children in their hundreds present, were among the saddest sights I have witnessed in my entire life.

Blantyre's disaster was not unique. In a period of only nine years, in addition to smaller scale loss of life, some 1,280 miners were killed in eight disasters, including Blantyre. The locations raged from the North of England to South Wales. In each case, the principal cause was the same as in Blantyre. A principal cause which had been known about for years! What a condemnation of owners these tragedies were.

You could say that some good came out of those tragedies, though I doubt if any of the thousands of bereaved would have agreed at the time. But at least a more dedicated enquiry into mine safety emerged. Ironically, a Royal Commission had reported in 1886, a year before the Blantyre Calamity. Even more ironically, one of its members had been the same Thomas Burt, now an MP, who had written the 'great progress' statement years earlier. As a result of the Commissioners' Report, a great deal of scientific interest was stimulated. The 1887 Mines Regulation Act incorporated a number of compulsory safety regulations. Further Acts of 1894, 1896, 1900 and 1905 further strengthened these regulations. All too late for the miners of Blantyre and other places, of course.

The other positive move was political. As I have already said, many of us were totally frustrated by the attitudes of the Conservatives and Liberals who, though they passed an occasional piece of legislation, could never see the world from our point of view because they were not of our world. Many of us had recognised for some time that we needed political representatives who shared our background in order that the views of working people, miners included, could be heard at national, governmental level. The formation of the Social Democratic Federation and the Fabian Society, both in 1884, had been a start of sorts but members of those groups were intellectual Socialists rather than working people. We needed representatives of our own.

You will probably not be surprised to know that Keir Hardie provided the stimulus for action. Originally a supporter of the Liberal Party, he had become disgusted by what he considered their complacency and their social and business ties to industrial owners. As you know, he had unsuccessfully challenged for a parliamentary seat some years earlier but had not been discouraged by his rejection. Now, the memories of Blantyre and another dreadful tragedy at Swaith Main in

Yorkshire fresh in his mind, he urged the mining unions and others to close ranks in the name of self-protection and to create a new political party to represent working people. I needed no persuasion. It was music to my ears. Many others felt the same way. Thus it was that in 1888 the Scottish Labour Party was formed. Its original members included many trade unionists, but thinkers from other traditions as well.

I will not conceal from you the fact that I felt a great surge of excitement when the Scottish Labour Party was formed. A number of our men had fought parliamentary elections but failed. Of course, that was partly due to the old factors of lack of funds and people's early doubts about Socialism. But another major weakness had been a lack of organisation, the absence of a political base from which to operate. Now, at last, we had one.

At its birth, the Scottish Labour Party could not have been described as a group with a single set of beliefs. There were many interpretations of what we believed a 'people's party', as I liked to think of it, should be about. However, all of us were clear about two things. The interests of working people had to be promulgated and this was best done by working people themselves. From the outset we all understood that that would only be achieved by our own people becoming parliamentarians. That was our mission.

Though miners rarely featured in the national newspapers, the formation of the Scottish Labour Party did make some headlines. You may well imagine how our existence was presented. We were portrayed by and large as semi-literate agitators whose only interest was the destruction of the status quo which had made Britain great. Keir Hardie had predicted this and told us not to be disheartened by it. It was inevitable, he told us, that those who had or were related to power would fight against anything which they believed capable of upsetting their cosy existence. He also had two messages for me. First, he would be away campaigning across the length of Britain much of the time, so I had to make sure that the good work was carried on in Scotland during his absences. I heartily agreed to do my best. Then, for the second time, he told me I must seriously consider standing for parliament. Through my union work and considerable experience of conferences, I was well enough qualified. Or so he thought. I was not entirely convinced that I was ready for such a role but I told him I would consider his words, and we shook hands on that.

What with the never-ending toil and the frequent tragedies, you might well wonder how we miners kept going and managed at least a semblance of ordinary life. In truth, for the majority of us there was little option. Mining was what we knew. A few men I knew did move out into other work. Mainly they drifted towards the heavy engineering plants in Glasgow. But from what I heard at the time, conditions in other industries were not hugely better for workers than they were in the mines, and some industries had no great amount of union protection.

So what was the point? Except perhaps for that old human hope that the grass was greener on the other side. Which, for labourers, it rarely was.

Besides, most of us were firmly embedded in the communities in which we worked. The majority of men had wives and bairns to support and, poorly paid and dangerous though mining was, it at least offered a man the chance to put bread on the table. Also, even if some industrial workers earned a little more than we did, they had to find somewhere to live and that could be expensive. Even if miners in tied houses had no great security of tenure, they did at least have roofs over their heads. Add in the fact that most mining communities were tight-knit and families' relatives lived nearby, and you might begin to understand why, in spite of the toil and the danger, most men simply kept their heads down, did their work, looked after their families, and enjoyed whatever few simple pleasures they could gain from life. We were ill-equipped for much else. What choice did we have?

My family was my constant source of pleasure. Before the end of the century it was complete. There were nine bairns, seven boys and two girls. I loved them all dearly but, as a typical father I suppose, my wee girls always found it easiest to raise a smile on their tired father's face. Because of my work at the coal face and the increasing demands on my time as a branch secretary and conference delegate, I believe that my dear wife Ann probably put in more hours most weeks than I did. As well as keeping a tidy house, which she always did, she had the bairns to look after as well. As any woman will tell you, that's a full-time job in itself!

We were sometimes hungry, but we never starved. When wages were low and food in short supply, Ann made a little go a very long way indeed. She turned out to be as good at making soups as dear old Nan Smillie had been. After a hard shift, it was a joy to walk into our sitting-room, see the big pot on the fire, and smell the rich odours of a good broth. Somehow, she usually managed to get a wee bit of meat to add strength to the broth. How she managed that on the money I was able to give her I never knew, but like all the wives she proved remarkably resilient and creative when it came to putting food on the table. Oddly enough perhaps, it was over food that we had an occasional disagreement.

'Ann,' I'd tell her, sitting by the fire, the bairns tucked up like sardines in the three home-made beds they shared, 'you've short-changed yourself again.'

'Whatever do you mean?' she would ask, all innocence, darning away furiously at something-or-other.

'You made sure we all had a wee bit of meat in our broth bowls tonight.' Trying to sound angry, but finding it impossible. 'But you only had vegetables in your bowl.'

'I didn't really feel like having meat tonight.' Her usual answer.

'Well, it's not good for you, woman.' Playing at being the stern master of the house, but no doubt failing miserably. 'Tomorrow night you must take some of my share of the meat, do you understand?'

'If you say so, Robert,' as she carried on with her darning as if I hadn't said a single word.

There were no proper toys for the children, of course. There were some home-made bits and pieces I had contrived for them, and they seemed happy enough with those. Now and again, when I was visiting big cities for conferences, I would pause by the splendid toy shops, gaze in the windows and see the spinning tops, beautiful models of ships, grand hobby-horses and all the rest. I would curse myself for not being able to provide my children with such delights, the sort of things that children of better-off parents took for granted. But what could I do? What could any miner do? We had what we had and it wasn't much. During my life, I often heard my opponents describe Socialism as the politics of envy. If that means wanting better for your children so that they can enjoy the same quality of life as other children, then I'm guilty as charged.

In our wee house, the sitting-room was packed with people: Ann, myself and nine children. In that golden hour after our evening meal and before the bairns were packed into their beds, I would often read to them. From a barrow in Hamilton, I had bought two used volumes of verse and stories for children. The fact that there were years difference in age between the oldest and youngest never seemed to bother them. They just loved being read to. Sometimes Ann would read a wee bit, but mainly it was me. So, while she went through to the scullery to peel vegetables for the next day's meal, I would read to my captive audience. I could see their imaginations soar as they listened to tales of worlds beyond their experience. More than ever, those sessions reading to my own children became not only my most precious moments; they also reinforced my conviction that a good education was, second to a loving home, the greatest gift a child could receive. Much to my surprise, I was about to get the chance to test that idea in practice.

Given my views about the importance of education, I came to the decision that I wanted to be involved. To have any influence at all, that could only mean one thing, becoming a member of the Larkhall School Board. However, I knew that would be easier said than done because the board, which managed the five schools in and around Larkhall, had never had a miner elected to it. There were seven members of that board, all of them educated people, and I knew that it would be very difficult to become one of them. Nevertheless, when it was due for re-election in 1888, the miners of Larkhall asked me to run as a Labour candidate. Given my desire for involvement, I could hardly turn down such a request and I allowed my name to go forward. On the day of the election, I visited the polling station with the other candidates. It quickly became clear to me that I was, at least, an outsider in the race.

'Name!' snapped the polling clerk, who obviously did not recognise me, and clearly imagined that I had just turned up to vote.

'Robert Smillie,' I told him, then added, 'and I am one of the candidates.' As his face reddened in embarrassment, I tried to inject a little humour into the situation. 'One of the unfortunate candidates, I fear.'

'What, you?' snapped the man nearest to me. A local doctor, he had been a member of the board for years and was again a candidate. 'It will be your own fault if you are one of the unfortunate candidates. You should have known better than to stand.' He said this with great relish. He did not quite say 'you ill-educated miner, you' but his opinion of me was quite clear.

To my joy and no little surprise, when the result was declared that night, it was the doctor who was one of the 'unfortunate candidates' while my vote was among the highest of the candidates. I rarely came across that doctor around Larkhall after that, and I made sure that, if any one of my family was unwell, we sought medical help from one of the other local practitioners. I was to serve for twelve years on the Larkhall School Board during a period when I became well known in the Labour Movement across Britain. Yet there was something we managed to accomplish as a board which made me prouder than almost anything else I ever achieved.

It was the practice in those days for children to pay for their own school books. The feeling was that they would look after them better if they had to be paid for. I railed against this practice, pointing out time after time how it disadvantaged the poorest of children whose families could not afford to buy books. Those children were forced to share books in school, sometimes three or four children to a book and, of course, had no copies of their own to take home. I also told the other members of the board how beneficial to children it was to read and be read to at home, as I often did for my children. But that could only happen if books were provided by the schools, free of charge to all children. Well, that put the cat well and truly amongst the pigeons, didn't it? Some of the other recently appointed members had some sympathy with my opinions, but the longer-established ones were of the opposite view. The board did not have enough money, children would not value books which were given freely and, besides, weren't my ideas just examples of creeping Socialism? I hammered away at them for the best part of six years without success, became entirely disgusted by their attitude, then decided to put my ideas – as well as my membership of the board – to the test.

1894 was another re-election year. Tired of banging my head against the proverbial brick wall, I told the other members that I intended to make that election a fight on the free-books issue. I further gave them my opinion that no anti-free-book candidate would deserve to be re-elected. As you may imagine, that did not go down well with some of them. During the run-up to polling day, several other members told me that they had come round to my point of view. In the event, five of us who campaigned for the free books issue were elected which meant that, on a board of seven members, we would always be in the majority.

So it was that Larkhall became only the second town in Scotland to adopt a free-books policy. Other places followed though, in some cases, they later reverted to a charging policy. That retrogressive step tended to be as a result of the changing political colour of board membership. But in Larkhall the free books policy was to stay. We appointed a small committee to talk to parents about the importance of keeping school books in good condition and instituted a prize-giving system to reward children for the best-kept books in a school year. It even astonished me to see how well kept the vast majority of these books were. Often, mothers covered the books with paper or cloth and there was very little evidence of stains, turned-down leaves or any other damage. The teachers in all five Larkhall schools were unanimous in the view that the books were better-kept than they had been when the children had had to buy them. It was music to my ears!

There was one other educational issue which became of great importance to me at that time. I knew that four out of five of the boys in our schools would find their way into the local mines. Yet the school curriculum as it was then hardly referred to the mines at all. I thought that was wrong. Not that I expected schools to turn boys into miners: that wasn't my idea at all. Rather, I thought it would be wise for the boys to pick up at least an elementary knowledge of the kinds of gas which abounded in mines, mine ventilation and various other issues to do with mining dangers and safety in general. I believed that such knowledge could only improve young miner's attitudes towards safety precautions and, in some cases, give them a taste for the study of the technical side of mining.

Among the members of the board, there were some fears that the Scottish Education Department might not approve of this addition to the curriculum but I persuaded them that we should take that risk, which, in the event, proved to be no risk at all. Enough of the teachers were in favour to make it work and, with the procurement of a simple text book, we introduced mining issues into the curriculum for the oldest boys, mainly twelve years old, for an hour each week. I persuaded an assistant inspector of mines to set an examination paper for the last session of the school year, then prayed that all went well. My prayers were answered!

In his report on the examination, Mr McLaren the Inspector told the board that the majority of the examination papers had been completed to an excellent standard, and that some of the boys had demonstrated a knowledge of elementary chemistry that had astonished him. He concluded his report by writing, 'If this result can be achieved with one hour's teaching, what could be done if these were made school subjects?' The boys in question swelled with pride when they were presented with their prizes, books bought by subscription, and a number of them went on to become mine managers. But I doubt if their pride in their own achievements was any greater than my own when I considered the progress made by the Larkhall School Board.

Of course, during those twelve years when I was serving on the School Board, there were other things going on in life and the greater world. Oh my word, weren't there just! One major event was in the shape of startlingly good news. My good friend Keir Hardie, became the first Labour man to win a seat in the House of Commons. I believe I told you earlier that, on a conference visit to London, I had been amazed to find out just how many people there knew him, and saw at first-hand how well liked he was. Well, he had obviously become even more deeply entrenched in the heart of Londoners because, in 1892, he was elected as Member of Parliament for West Ham South. In their delight at the news, the Lanarkshire miners decided that somebody should represent them and be present on the day when he became the first of our men to take his seat in the house. You will not be surprised to know that, because of my closeness to Hardie and my relative familiarity with travels to London, I was absolutely delighted to be the one selected to attend.

From the visitors' gallery, I watched with great pride as Keir was sworn in, then took his seat on the opposition benches. Now, let me set the record straight about an often misreported fact of his first appearance as an MP. Members on both sides were astonished by the fact that he entered the house wearing a peaked cap. There were mutterings of disapproval and the press, predictably enough, portrayed him as wearing that cap as a badge of working-class solidarity, an act of bravado if you like. The truth was rather different, as I found out later that day when I asked him if he was aware of how much interest, most of it negative, his choice of headwear had generated.

'Ach no, Bob,' he laughed. 'It was no act of bravado. In fact, I had no intention of wearing a cap at all. I had a hat which I intended to wear but my supporters crowded beside me all the way to Westminster and things got so excited that I lost the hat. Couldn't find it anywhere. So I just put on the cap that I always have with me on train journeys between Scotland and England.' He laughed again. 'So, as you can see the cap was an accident. No political statement at all.'

'Well,' I told him. 'The press have made a real fuss of it. The evening papers are full of you and your cap.' I grinned at him. 'So, what will you do in the future?'

'Well, I've no doubt the press and many politicians will be calling me all sorts for wearing a working man's cap in the House.' He gave me one of those mischievous quick grins of his. 'Maybe I'll just let them have a wee bit of fun at my expense. If the worst they can do is pick on my cap, I'll be happy enough. Maybe it will stop them talking nonsense about my politics!'

Hardie continued to wear his cap while an MP and, strangely enough, the only time I ever fell out with him, albeit briefly, was also on the subject of headwear. A year or so after his election, I was elected myself. Not to the house, you understand, but to the Presidency of the Lanarkshire Miners' Federation, which mattered to me rather more at the time. I can remember the great pride I felt at the trust invested in me and the real lift it gave to my self-confidence. At yet another London conference I met up with an ex-Larkhall man by the name of Archie Hunter, once a miner but, by then, a commercial representative. Because of his job, Archie was expected to wear a top hat. Due to meet Keir Hardie at Westminster one evening, we reached the lobby where Archie decided to play a joke on Keir. He took off my hat and placed his 'chimney pot' on my head.

'He'll no' recognise either of us now,' he laughed as we saw Hardie at the other end of the lobby, staring about him but obviously not recognising us.

'Hello, Keir.' I went forward to him, holding out my hand.

'What?' He stared at me for a moment before realising it was me. 'Bob Smillie? Well I never. In the name of the wee man, are you wearing one of those bosses' hats too?' And he turned away and started walking off. He was clearly disgusted, maybe because some of our leading representatives had recently taken to wearing what he called 'lum hats' and he was none too pleased about it.

'Keir! Keir!' I shouted after him, pulling the hat off my head. 'It was Archie's idea of a joke, that's all.' I was relieved to see him turn round and head back towards us.

'A joke, eh? Is that what you call it?' Then his frown dissolved into a smile. 'Well, let me tell you that Archie looks respectable enough in a lum hat, but there's nothing that could make you look respectable, Bob Smillie.'

And those were the only cross words I ever had with Keir Hardie. During our conference days, we often shared a bedroom, sometimes even a bed, in cheap lodging-houses and, in the evenings, would talk and talk. You may imagine our usual subject matter. Oh, we talked of other things as well, but inevitably the conversation would turn to questions of Labour and our commitment to Socialism. We would talk until the wee small hours, both of us being more and more convinced that Socialism would mean the establishment of a new order of things which would uplift mankind to a higher life. We were also certain that that transformation was but a few years away. The one subject we never broached was that of top hats.

Keir Hardie was a later version of William Small, more influential but of the same ilk. He was an incessant worker. He did an enormous amount of speaking all over the country. He was also a writer, making regular contributions to an Ayrshire newspaper and also to the *People's Journal*. But he was not just a wordsmith. He was also a man of action, an organiser who actually got things done. He was the driving force behind the formation of the Independent Labour Party. This Britain-wide organisation was an ideal he and I had held dear for some time. It is ironic to think that the stimulus for its formation was actually provided by our political opponents.

You see, there was a dreadful slump in the Yorkshire woollen industry in the early 1890's, largely caused by foreign competition and increased American import tariffs. The whole area was badly hit first by wage reductions and then by widespread unemployment. At the time, Hardie and his associate John Burgess were running a newspaper called the *Workman's Times* and they used that newspaper to launch scathing attacks on mill owners and the whole system of capital. Wool workers at the Manningham Mills in Bradford went on strike against wage cuts but the mill owners and local politicians used the police to prevent the workers from holding public meetings. The newspaper again blasted the authorities for their high-handedness. Many of the local mill owners were Liberals and the Liberal Party had tended to enjoy the support of the mill workers. But now disillusionment had set in and Hardie seized his chance.

The Bradford area bristled with Labour clubs, descendants of the old Chartist tradition. Bradford alone had twenty-three of them. Hardie organised a conference in Bradford in 1893, a meeting which several other Scottish Union Representatives were pleased to attend along with like-minded colleagues from the North of England. Needless to say, though others spoke, Hardie was the main speaker and attraction. Judging the mood of his audience to a hairs-breadth, he was in as good form as I'd ever seen him. He was simply irresistible. He berated the owners and their system, alternately blasted and poked fun at the Liberals and, throughout, pressed home his message that only a working man's party would ensure a decent future for working men. Thus the Independent Labour Party was formed.

'My word, Bob,' he said to me before we left the platform, sweat pouring from his forehead, 'warm work this political business, eh?'

Of course, we both realised that this was merely a beginning and that much remained to be done. While it was true that the formation of the party had attracted the support of some of the Social Democratic Federations and the Fabian Society, many of whose members were middle-class southern intellectuals, the bulk of our support was Northern and working class. This was not only inevitable but also well and good in its own way. But Hardie, myself, and others knew, as was revealed in the frequent meetings we had in the immediate aftermath of Bradford, that we had to cast our net wider than that if we were to become truly influential. We would have to persuade people of more than just one class across the whole of Britain that our principal stated aim, the collective ownership of the means of production, was in the national interest.

As you can see, Keir Hardie and I were busy men back then. In 1894, I was to be the cause of him becoming busier. For a change, he was going to have to speak on my behalf. After a long period of consideration, I had decided to bite the bullet. No doubt spurred by the excitement of the formation of the Independent Labour Party, I was determined to offer myself as a candidate for the House of Commons. If only I had known what I was letting myself in for!

X

Learning from Defeat

PERHAPS IT'S SIMPLY the passage of time that clouds the mind. Or maybe it's because I'm in my eighty-third year now and not keeping so well. Whatever, as I look back at the busiest time of my life – and heaven knows there were plenty of them – it becomes increasingly difficult for me to be precise about some of the details. Events, places, faces: they are not so sharp in my memory as they once were. And another thing I can tell you is that some things, which at the time seemed so very important, live on less clearly in my recollections than other events which I recollect with much more clarity but which, back then, seemed of only personal significance. A strange thing the human mind, is it not? Or perhaps we remember most clearly those events which, for one reason or another, were a wee bit different. Maybe there was a wee bit of humour or human drama involved, even the involvement of somebody close to you. Certainly, my memories of the 1890's are at their sharpest where people who mattered to me were concerned.

So it is that I will not try to offer any great details of the particular circumstances in which several great honours came my way. Having been branch secretary for a number of years and the President of the Lanarkshire Miners' Federation since 1893, I was elected to the office of President of the Scottish Miners' Federation in 1894. This was an honour indeed for somebody only recently appointed to the presidency of his own district. It is not for me to say why I was elevated to this position. I do know that Keir Hardie was active in securing my nomination. I tell you, that great man had a finger in every Labour Movement pie! If I were to offer an opinion, I would say it was perhaps because I was known to be a hard worker and somebody who believed in bringing people together. Certainly that was needed during yet another bleak decade for miners, but I will have to let history be the judge of that.

It was only two years later that a number of us with more Socialist leanings brought most of the main unions together to form the Scottish Trades Union Congress. At a time of uncertain employment, generally low wages and largely unsympathetic governments, this was a very important step forward for the Labour Movement in Scotland. Whether my election to the chairmanship of that new body was as important is perhaps a different matter! However, following on from the formation of the Independent Labour Party in 1893, the birth of the

Scottish Congress could be seen as yet another step on the way to securing a powerful national presence for the Labour Movement. Not that we were strong in 1896 – far from it. We still did not enjoy the cooperation of all trade unions, some of whose leaders remained Liberal in their outlook and dubious about Socialism. Not only that, but in 1895 Keir Hardie lost his seat in West Ham. Typically, he was less upset about that than I was.

'I'll come again, Bob,' I remember him telling me. 'They can't keep Socialism at bay forever.'

So you can see that the Labour Movement, though growing, was still some way short of being truly influential. Hardie impressed on me the need to keep 'battering on the doors,' as he put it. He was also clear in his view that, although my work at union level was important, the greatest contribution any of us could make to our cause was to become overtly political: in other words to challenge for a position in parliament. He was right, of course. The trade unions had some influence, but it was in parliament that real power lay, as we knew to our cost.

So it was that I allowed my name to go forward as Labour Candidate for Quarter in Mid-Lanark. The Lanarkshire Miners were all for it to the extent that the Bog Colliery in Larkhall raised more than £20 in a fortnight for my election fund. By today's standards, that may not seem a huge sum, but remember that at that time a typical mining dispute would have been over a proposed reduction in wages or a demand for more wages to the tune of 6d a shift. So £20 was a great sum by the standards of our people, and it was enough to provide me with a fighting fund. You see, it was the case then, and still is now, that the purse paved the way to parliament. Keir Hardie had found that, quite literally to his cost, at his first attempt.

As I have suggested, some events stay fresher in my mind due to the fact that people important to me were involved. My dear Ann, when she heard of my intention to 'enter the lists', at first said very little. Which is not to say that she had no opinions on the matter. I found out about those that night. Bairns in bed, we were sitting by the fire, me with a clay pipe, she with her darning. There was a slight cough, always a sign that she had something important to say.

'Are you sure about this, Robert?'

'Sure about what, Ann?' Even though I more or less knew that was coming.

'You know fine well what I mean.' Needle moving faster.

'The election I suppose.' I laid down the old copy of the *Glasgow Herald* I'd been reading. 'What's on your mind, then?'

'You can make enemies in an election,' she told me.

'Indeed you can, Ann.' I tried to laugh it off. 'Mind you, I've made a few of them already.'

'But the Liberals and Conservatives have friends in the industry,' she said. 'Powerful friends. What if they turn badly against us?'

'Turn against us?' I couldn't help laughing. 'I didn't know there were any of them for us.' Which was true enough, but I could see that I hadn't said enough to mollify her. 'Listen, Ann, do you really believe that if I didn't stand, our employers would suddenly start treating us any better?'

'No of course not. But if you publicly stand against their people ... it's you I'm worried about, Robert.'

'Me? Worried about me? Whatever for, Ann?'

'I've heard stories,' she said, laying down her needle and looking at me. There was just the suggestion of tears. 'Awful stories.'

'Awful stories? What kind of stories?' I had an inkling of what she was talking about but I needed to be sure. 'Come on, Ann, you must tell me or it'll be me getting worried about you.'

'Lizzie MacLennan's man ... you know Lizzie who works at the bakery?'

'Aye, I know her,' I replied. 'And her husband, Alec. I know them both.' I also now knew what was coming next. 'What about them?'

'Well, Lizzie was saying what Alec had told her.' More than a hint of tears now: they were fresh and real. 'How yon man in Glasgow was killed after speaking up for Socialism in a public meeting.' She clasped her hands and shook her head. 'Robert, oh Robert, I don't want that happening to you. What would happen to me and the bairns if ... '

'Shoosh, shoosh, woman,' I said, as gently as I could. She'd heard a real story alright. The McNair case had been the talk of the steamie a few weeks earlier. I knew the man or, should I say, I had known him. Not only was he a Socialist of sorts, he was also a few shillings short of a pound upstairs. It was true that he had interrupted a Liberal rally in Glasgow and shouted loudly for several minutes until he had been removed from the building. It was also true that, several days later, he had been found dead in a dark alley in the east end of the city with more blood on him than a slaughtered pig. The likelihood that he had been killed by political opponents was about as high as me becoming Tsar of Russia. The truth was that McNair owed about as much money to bookkeepers as would have paid off a country's national debt. There was no doubt in my mind that he'd been killed because of gambling debts but the political assassination rumours made for better gossip. That probably wasn't the best line to take with Ann. I took her hands in mine. 'You mustn't believe every daft story you hear,' I told her.

'But Robert, Lizzie said ... '

'I told you I know Lizzie,' I put in. 'She claims to make the best bread in Larkhall but you and I know it's about as heavy as wet sod. Tastes like it too,' I added. I was pleased to see Ann smile at my little joke. 'Lizzie knows nothing about what happened to McNair in Glasgow. And I doubt if Alec knows much more. McNair, rest his soul, was unhinged. He made enemies all over the place. His murder was no more political than Lizzie's heavy bread.'

'Do you think so, Robert?' The glimmer of a smile.

'Think so? I know so, Ann.' Which wasn't exactly the whole truth, so help me, but there are times when a wee white lie, told with the best of intentions, does no harm. 'Besides,' I added, 'who would be daft enough to come after me with hundreds of Larkhall miners at my back? Can you see any political agent trying to get past Big Robbie or Jock the Shovel?' I laughed dismissively. 'Why, woman, they would be mad to even try.'

'I suppose you're right, Robert.' If she wasn't entirely convinced, she was at least happier now.

'Of course I'm right,' I told her. 'Now you finish your darning, I'll finish my pipe and we'll away to bed.'

It turned out that persuading Ann was more straightforward that running my campaign. Back then, Labour candidates were often despised by established politicians as being what they would call 'impertinent fellows' with no right whatsoever to enter politics and disturb the usual two-horse race of traditional election campaigns. The national newspapers dismissed us as irrelevant at best, trumped-up nuisances at worst. Not that the attitudes of our opponents or of the national press ever surprised any of us. We were well used through bitter experience to their partial view of the natural state of affairs. Indeed, the patronising and dismissive way in which we were received simply made us more determined, if that were possible. I suppose that we saw ourselves as pioneers, a breed often subjected to ridicule at best, so we tended to laugh at persecution and simply refuse to go away. We became pretty thick-skinned in the face of arrogant contempt. Given my experiences during that 1894 Mid-Lanark campaign, that was probably just as well.

With Ann now reasonably placated and limited funds secured, I set out to make my name and views known. Sometimes this meant venturing into unfriendly territory. I remember a meeting in Wishaw. It was a late-evening event and Wishaw was more than five miles away. Although my basic costs were covered by the kindness of the Larkhall Miners, my funds did not stretch to the hiring of any kind of vehicle. So it was Shanks's pony for me and a Labour Movement volunteer, a check-weighman by the name of John McAlleer. It was a damp night and the road seemed to be mainly made of long, steep hills and precious few down slopes. As a result, we arrived at the Victoria Hall, full of pit and engineering workers, feeling close to exhaustion. Our problems were just beginning.

'And where are you going?' demanded the plump, red-faced hall janitor as we made to enter by the side door.

'I have come to address this meeting of electors,' I told him. 'So, if you will just let me pass ... '

'You'll be that Labour candidate, I suppose,' he said, with a sneer on a face that looked ripe for hitting.

'I am,' I replied.

'Weel, ma mannie,' he said, grinning, 'the rent of the hall is thirty shillings and it's no' been paid for yet. My orders are no' to let ye on the platform till the money is paid. So there.' He seemed delighted to be able to impart this information.

Well, the news struck John and me pretty hard. I was a novice, you see, and had assumed in my naïveté that, for a public event like a campaign meeting, public venues would be available free of charge. From inside the hall, I could hear the hum of voices. We were past the due time for the start of the meeting and there were the clear sounds of impatience from the assembled gathering.

'How much money have ye got, Bob?' John asked, his hands deep in his pockets.

'Not all that much,' I replied, my hands searching the depths of mine. 'Let's see what we've got here.'

Between us we raised the thirty shillings. If you added what we had left over, it amounted to less than a shilling. The janitor seemed rather less than pleased that we had come up with the fee and, with scowling reluctance, showed us to the platform where John took the chair and I stood by a bare table which boasted two hard-used chairs. An odd thing about election meetings at that time was that when the Liberals and Conservatives were speaking many men were accompanied by their wives, but when a 'rough' Labour candidate was the main speaker those wives were left at home. Heaven knows why. Perhaps they thought that we were defilers of the fair sex! So that meeting in Wishaw was very much 'men only' and it was very clear from the first moment that, this being a Liberal stronghold, very few present had any sympathy with a Labour man. It wasn't long before I was regretting having exhausted all our money to pay the hall's rent fee.

I've heard it said that knocking knees are a good sign, that they indicate a presence of nervous energy which makes every speaker give of his best and draw an audience to his point of view. Well, I have to tell you that that theory was not validated by my experience in Wishaw that night. When I addressed that audience with my aforementioned knocking knees, I had almost every word thrown back at me. It was as if they dissented from every word I said, even before I had said it. It wasn't long before John had given up any attempt to chair the meeting. I could hardly blame him. It was less a meeting, more a verbal brawl.

It is no pleasure, I can tell you, to look into a sea of faces and see nothing but scowls. As I spoke, I felt that I hadn't a single friend in the house. At the end when question time came, it seemed as if they all got to their feet as one man to let me know exactly how they felt. Each time I tried to answer one of their increasingly hostile questions, I was peppered with boos, insults and all-round heckling. My trial only abated when my audience realised it was almost closing time in the local public houses and made a mad, en masse dash for the exit doors. There was no point in asking for the traditional vote of confidence in the candidate: there was nobody left to ask. Except for the hall janitor who was standing by the door, a bunch of keys jangling in one hand and the same stupid grin. I managed to resist the temptation to wipe it off his face and we left. John and I did not exchange a word until we reached the halfway point of our five-mile walk home.

'Man, but I thocht ye were a goner the nicht, Bob,' he said, bursting our laughing. 'If you could have seen your ain face when that big laddie with the muscles started waving his fist at ye.' He couldn't say any more, he was laughing so hard.

'Aye, John, all very well for you,' I replied, trying not to smile, 'but it was my ugly face that was in danger.' Then I too burst out laughing, probably a release of nervous energy. 'And what did you think of my speech then?'

'Think of it?' he gasped between laughs. 'Think of it? Man, I could hardly hear it with all the noise they were making.'

'Politics, eh?' I said.

'Aye, politics right enough,' he replied.

'And to think we paid thirty hard-earned shillings for the privilege,' I added.

The ridiculous nature of the evening had us laughing all the way home to Larkhall.

Of course, the local newspapers carried an account of the event. I don't remember the exact wording but one of them carried a headline to the effect that 'Smillie fails to carry the meeting', or words very much in that vein. That was one newspaper headline I could hardly disagree with! Oddly enough, Ann seemed not only amused but relieved. I had been into the 'lion's den' and come out with only dignity bruised. She seemed to feel that that was better than having my body bruised. I wasn't quite so sure.

Not all meetings were like that one in Wishaw, though there were others where I was less than generously received. On the other hand, at those closer to Larkhall I was supported very well. Then, closer to polling day, I received a very strange letter which I have kept to this day. It was from Mr John Wilson who was the MP for Falkirk Burghs. Not only was he a unionist, he was also a very significant coal master, owning a number of pits in the Mid-Lanark Division. On both counts, he could hardly be considered a travelling companion of mine. Yet in his letter he made an offer of £10 towards my election expenses. He stated his view that, as a mining constituency, Mid-Lanark ought to be represented by a man like myself instead of 'a man who would not know a "heading" or a "level" from a "dook", or a "plummer block" from a "bell crank",' as he put it. Not only that but, to ensure that I received what he called 'fair play', he offered to chair at any of my meetings. He concluded his letter by saying that, as soon as he received my acceptance of his offer, he would forward the £10 and that he had no objection to his letter being published.

Well, what was I to make of that? His offer was tempting, beyond question. My fighting fund was low and the £10 would come in very handy. Also, he was no doubt much more experienced than John McAlleer or any other of my friends when it came to chairing public meetings. But I hesitated. Why was he being so friendly? Between his Conservative leanings and my Socialist ones, there was no common ground at all. So why was he doing it? I did not then, any more than I do now, like to attribute base motives to anybody's intentions but, the more I thought about his offer, the more suspicious I became of them. I wrote back to him.

'While, personally, I might have no doubt of the honesty of your object in granting me assistance, there are many who would be only too glad to say that your object in giving aid was not so much for the purpose of getting me into the House of Commons as in keeping Mr James Cardwell, the Gladstonian Liberal, out.'

Wilson's preferred candidate for Mid-Lanark was the Unionist, Colonel Harrington Stuart, and Wilson probably realised that the Liberal Caldwell was the more likely winner of the two, hence his offer of help to me in an attempt to split the anti-Unionist vote. In spite of my reply to him, Wilson did not let the matter rest there. He sent out another letter to me. He admitted that I was probably right regarding the way in which his offers might be construed, but went on:

'I enclose five pounds in postal orders for yourself, as you have a good deal of expenses to bear, and nobody need know, unless you tell them yourself, where the money comes from. You do not need to give my name when lifting the five pounds. Simply send me a note saying you received it safely.'

Again I saw danger in accepting this apparent kindness which I still believed was designed to strengthen my campaign and draw more votes from Caldwell, to Stuart's advantage. So I returned the postal orders with thanks and best wishes. I did not see that I had any alternative. In the last days of my campaign, I met John Wilson several times. He did not seem in the least put out by my rejection of his offers and, in private, went so far as to say that I had done the right and proper thing. Our paths would cross often in the future and, I am pleased to say, that we dealt with one another in a very civil manner.

That incident introduced me to a subject which became quite a talking point in elections over the years. It was usually referred to as 'Tory Gold' and it was suggested that Tory money was spent on Labour candidates to increase their chances of reducing the Liberal vote. Such a method was called 'vote splitting'. From personal experience, I have to say that the so-called 'Tory Gold' was more rumour than fact. Apart from John Wilson's offer, I saw nothing of alleged purchase of advantage in any of the elections I fought, and neither did Keir Hardie. But the rumours persisted. You will have to work out for yourself who it was that kept the story boiling. I know that it certainly wasn't any of the Labour candidates and the Conservatives were hardly likely to perpetuate a rumour which discredited them. Which really only leave one source, does it not, but I have no evidence to offer so I will not draw the obvious conclusion.

Two days before that Mid-Lanark poll, I made the acquaintance of Michael

Davitt. He was in the Glasgow office of John Fergusson, at that time a well known advocate on behalf of Irish Nationalism. I was there on a fairly trivial matter while Davitt was a political opponent, a Liberal who had been fairly hard on me in his speeches on behalf of James Caldwell. To be frank, I had been somewhat surprised at the ferocity of his attacks. That day, in Fergusson's office, he explained why. Fergusson apparently had the pulse of the Irish electors in Mid-Lanark and had come to the view that I was likely to draw at least some of their votes away from Caldwell. So Davitt had been instructed to speak out as strongly as possible against me. To give him his due, that day he apologised to me and assured me that there was nothing personal in it. It was, he explained, 'just politics'.

'That may be so, Mr Davitt,' I told him, 'but your intervention has made it unlikely that I can win.'

'Frankly, Mr Smillie,' he replied, 'your chances of winning an election at the first time of asking were never better than slim in the extreme.' He smiled to rob the words of any offence. 'If it is any consolation to you them I can tell you in private that it is the opinion of both Mr Fergusson and myself that you are the best candidate. However, I'm sorry to say that the best candidates, particularly if they do not have a powerful party organisation behind them, do not necessarily win.'

He was right, of course. Caldwell and Stuart were experienced men of some reputation who enjoyed the support of their parties and influential men like Fergusson and Wilson. I enjoyed none of those advantages. But if our opponents thought we would be disheartened by our loss at Mid-Lanark in 1894, when I gained more votes than I had feared but less than I had hoped, then they were in for a big surprise. Naïve though we undoubtedly were, we had never really entertained any great hopes of winning. Rather, we were determined not to disgrace ourselves, which we did not do. It was clear to me that we had to regroup, make ourselves better organised, become better known to the electorate and, most difficult of all, raise more money to allow us to compete on more favourable terms with our opponents. We also had to be wiser about the manipulative activities of men like Fergusson who I thought of as the 'Glasgow wire-puller'.

I had no doubt that we would improve in all these ways and eventually enter elections with a realistic chance of winning. After all, Keir Hardie had done it once. Admittedly, he was the best orator of all of us, but we could learn, couldn't we? If I had had any doubts, they were quashed by Ann as we lay in bed together the night after the results. She put her arms around me and whispered, 'There'll be another time, Robert.' It was probably just as well that neither of us realised just how many more times there would be.

I do realise that, a little earlier, I said that these present words of mine would deal with the 1890's. Therefore, I apologise now for the fact that the other personal misadventures which I wish to relate concern my next attempt at becoming a parliamentarian, and that was in 1901. Not the 1890's I know but, so much of a piece with the 1894 election, that I felt that they should be kept together. You will judge the sense in that, or lack of it, for yourself.

For the 1901 election, I was the Labour and anti-war candidate for the constituency of Camlachie on the south side of Glasgow. For those of you who are not students of history, I should explain that the war I was opposed to was the Boer War which I regarded as a capitalist war and nothing to do with the defence of our country. This was not necessarily a popular stance to take at the time. As you probably know, wars have a horrible habit of being popular, especially among people who don't have to actually fight them. Let me point out, though, that I was in quite elevated company on this matter. No less a figure than Lloyd George had had the courage to oppose the war. The fact that he once had to escape from a pro-war meeting dressed in a police constable's uniform should tell you how unpopular our shared stance often was.

As was always the case when Britain was involved in an overseas war, the reporting of the campaign was partial in the extreme. Most of the war correspondents, men like Burleigh and Sackville, were very nationalistic and painted a picture of brilliant and heroic British soldiers fighting a treacherous foe. Letters home from troops often told a rather different story and just occasionally a more truthful account was published in a newspaper. For example, following a disaster at Spion Kop on January 25th, 1900, the condition of the British troops was reported in the *Morning Post*:

Men were staggering along alone, or supported by comrades, or crawling on hands and knees, or carried on stretchers. Corpses lay here and there. Many of the wounds were of a horrible nature. The splinters and fragments of the shell had torn and mutilated them in the most ghastly manner. I passed about two hundred while I was climbing up. There was, moreover, a small but steady leakage of unwounded men of all corps. Some of these cursed and swore. Others were utterly exhausted and fell on the hill-side in stupor. Others again seemed drunk, though they had had no liquor.

The correspondent who penned those words was Winston Churchill who I would have dealings with later in life. Churchill told the truth in that report. It should have been enough to sicken people of war but, by and large, it didn't. Of course, most of those people were men who were not going to be sent away to fight, so they could afford their long-distance bravery. Whatever, people like Lloyd George and I held a minority, anti-war view.

A few days before that 1901 poll, I was on my way to address a meeting when, remembering a pointed comment from Ann, I called into a barber's shop on the outskirts of Motherwell to have my hair cut and moustache trimmed. After waiting my turn, I took my place in the chair and found out that, like most barbers of my acquaintance, this one was a real blether. In short order, I found out that he wasn't keen on his wife, that his brother-in-law was 'over fond' of the bottle, and that he himself was a devoted Liberal. He finished trimming my hair, then hid my features behind a bonny lather and began stropping his shaving razor. All the while he talked non-stop.

'Well, isn't it just an awfy business that's going on the noo?' he asked, stropping away.

'What business?' I mumbled through the shaving soap.

'Well I just had the Liberal agent in,' he said, pushing back the tip of my nose with one hand, holding his razor in the other. 'He was telling me that the Liberal candidate is getting feart.'

'Feart? Feart of what?'

'Yon bluidy Labour candidate.' The razor was now poised above my upper lip. 'He's complicated the election an' spouting a lot o' bluidy nonsense aboot the war.'

'I see,' I replied, my eyes fixed on the keen blade hovering above me. 'Well, maybe the best thing to do would be to get rid of the Labour candidate.' I must have had an odd sense of humour in those days.

'Aye, I'd like nothing better,' he told me, razor hand descending. 'But how could ah dae that, eh?'

'Well, you could cut my throat here and now,' I told him.

'In the name o' the wee man!' he exclaimed, to my great relief withdrawing the razor. 'Are ye Bob Smillie himself?'

During the rest of the shaving, he could hardly stop apologising for any insult he had caused and, at the end and in spite of my protestations to the contrary, he would not accept his fee. Strange indeed are the ways of men! Though he rather spoiled the atmosphere of our new-found friendship when, after I'd left his premises and was some yards along the street, he shouted after me, 'Ye'll still get beat, mind.'

The Town Hall meeting that evening was like the one in Wishaw some years earlier but worse, much worse. They hooted and heckled at the sight of me and made it plain that I was to listen to them rather than the other way round. They shouted at me for a good twenty minutes until there was a lull. They were probably exhausted in the throat and unable to shout any longer. I took the opportunity to give them my views on a number of issues including land, housing and mining. I left the most awkward subject to last.

'Now, I told them, 'if you have bricks to throw, get them ready now. I am going to deal with the war.'

Almost to my surprise, no bricks were forthcoming so I was able to deliver my opinion that the Boer War was a futile affair engineered by capitalist and moneyed classes for their own advantage and, of course, at no risk to themselves. I concluded by offering my view that there would have been no war at all if there had been no gold in the Transvaal. Finishing, I prepared to duck at the first sign of a flying brick but, to my relief and no little amazement, I was greeted by a polite round of applause. Not a rapturous reception, you understand, but enough to make me believe that they held the same opinion as I did as far as the war was concerned, even if we agreed on little else. I left the Town Hall feeling rather happier than I had felt during the first part of the meeting.

It was during that 1901 election campaign that I first saw a candidate touring a constituency in a motor car. It was Cecil Harmsworth, the Liberal, who was quite popular in the area – excepting the local carriage-hirers who tended to see elections as rich harvests for their businesses. The idea of a candidate touring around in his own motor vehicle did not endear him to them. Their hostility towards Harmsworth provoked an incident in which I was directly involved.

One of the local carriage-hirers was a Labour man so, at very low cost, I had a little horse and trap put at my disposal as well as a capable and cautious driver by the name of Tom Scott. One day, we met the Liberal candidate's car as we were descending a long, steep hill on the approaches to Motherwell. Cars back then were neither as powerful nor as robust as they are now and it was obvious that Harmsworth's car was really struggling up the hill towards us.

'That's yon bugger Harmsworth with his fancy car,' Tom moaned. 'If there's more of the likes of him around, it's going to put a stop to our trade, damn the man!' At that point, with Harmsworth's spluttering car only ten yards from us, our horse began to get skittish and looked as if he wanted to dance on his hind legs. 'Hold on tight,' Tom warned.

I did as I was told which was just as well or I might have been thrown out of the trap. Tom held up his whip as a sign for Harmsworth to stop his car, which he did. Tom then proceeded to tell him that it was the rule of the road that a car driver had to pull up if he was close to a horse in a panic from the noise of the motor vehicle. Scowling, Harmsworth nodded and the rattling from his vehicle engine subsided. Calmer now, our horse was made to walk forward then break into its usual jog-trot. When we were perhaps thirty yards beyond Harmsworth, Tom looked back at him then turned to me, a huge grin plastered all over his face.

'Yon bugger'll have a deil o' a job starting up again on yon hill,' he remarked with some satisfaction.

'You're probably right, Tom,' I replied. As I watched our horse calmly jog-trotting along, I asked, 'Does your horse normally behave like that around motor vehicles?'

'Who, him? Old Blackie? Nah, not at all.'

'Then why did ... '

'Cause I made him, that's for why,' Tom growled. 'I telt ye that I didnae like them cars or their bluidy drivers.' He grinned slyly. 'So I just pulled Old Blackie onto his hind legs.'

'It was deliberate?' I gasped. Half of me wanted to laugh while the other half of me wanted to tell him off. In the circumstances, I compromised: I didn't do either.

That campaign had some very unpleasant moments, largely due to the fact that the war was high on the agenda. Many were for it and many against it, and feelings were running very high indeed. I have to confess that there were times when Ann's earlier fears for my personal safety seemed quite justified. However, among all the moments of bitterness, there were moments of humour which I can smile at now, even if they were at my expense.

There was a meeting in a small mission hall in a district where a large proportion of the voters were Irish Unionists whose general view was that the war was a noble venture. Needless to say, I wasn't expecting the best of receptions even though I knew quite a lot of the men in the crushed hall as a result of my trade-union activities. The silence when I took the platform was ominous and I noted that, after he made his introductory remarks of welcome, the chairman took good care to sit as far away from me as possible. Trying to keep calm, I spoke for about forty-five minutes and was received in total silence except for one man who, between long gulps at a bottle, shouted out the occasional 'Hear, hear!' usually when I was in mid-sentence. I quickly realised that my one supporter in the hall was the local drunk. When I had finished, again to an eerie silence, I asked if there were any questions. A tall, sour-looking man in the front now got to his feet.

'Mr Chairman,' he said in a deadly, soulful voice. 'Will the candidate tell us what he thinks about the Boer War?'

'I'll be delighted to,' I told him, realising that I knew him quite well. A retired miner by the name of Andrew Crichton, he had a long white beard which, allied to his miserable demeanour, had me thinking of John Knox. He'd been in my pit when I first started and we'd got on well enough. 'In my opinion ... ' I trotted out my usual anti-war statement.

'Well, well,' Crichton said to the assembly when I had finished, 'isn't that a nice candidate for you?' But he wasn't finished with me. 'And would the candidate tell us what his position is with regard to Irish Home Rule?'

'I've given the matter a lot of thought,' I replied. What I hadn't given a lot of thought to was addressing a hall full of Unionists, rabidly opposed to Home Rule. But there was no escape, so I told them how I felt. I finished by saying, 'I am in favour of the people of Ireland having a right to govern themselves if that is the wish of the majority.' The hall echoed to a chorus of booing, there being only one dissenter.

'Hear, hear!' my solitary supporter enthusiastically shouted, clutching his now empty bottle.

'Well, well, did you hear that?' Crichton was on his feet again, addressing the assembly as if he was the candidate. 'Mr Smillie is against the war and in favour of Fenian Home Rule. And he wants us to make him our representative in parliament. Can you credit it?' He smiled as his words provoked an outburst of hissing and booing. Then he turned to me. 'I tell ye what, Bob Smillie, as a union man ye're a' richt. But as a politician, ye're a damned fool! I don't know whether we should hang ye or drown ye!' That brought the first cheers of the night. 'But I can think of something more lawful. We'll just walk out an' leave ye.'

Which is exactly what he did. He made his way to the door and everybody else followed him. Except for the rather relieved chairman and my solitary supporter who, by then, was slumped over the seat in front of him. I don't think that in all my public life, I ever felt so humiliated or alone. Mind you, it could have been worse. If Crichton hadn't been worried about the law, I might have been hanged or drowned!

During that 1901 election, my most faithful companion was Sandy Haddow. A ridiculously powerful bull of a man, with a temper to match, he was our candidate in Govan which, being a county division, polled later than my constituency of Camlachie. This meant that, in the days running up to the poll, Sandy spent as much time in my constituency as his own. What a man that Sandy was! A staunch friend and a fearless fighter, he was as determined as I was to see the back of the Liberal, Samuel Chisholm who, in later years, went on to become Lord Provost of Glasgow.

Our Sandy's methods were sometimes a little less than conventional. At one of our open-air meetings in Camlachie, he came straight from his work at a forge still dressed in his working clothes, a muffler round his neck, and immediately took over presidency of the meeting. No sooner had he started to introduce me to the assembling crowd than a large man at the back of the crowd began to heckle him. 'I'll deal with you if you don't stop!' Sandy barked at him, but the heckling continued. Sandy marched through the crowd, raised his huge fists and, the next thing, the big heckler was on his back. At that moment a policeman arrived and Sandy proved he was quick-witted as well as handy with his fists. 'If this poor gentleman is not removed,' he told the policeman, 'he may well get hurt.' The heckler scrambled to his feet, looked dazedly around him, then made off. Calmly, Sandy resumed his introduction of me to the crowd.

It wasn't only in my constituency that Sandy could be intemperate. One day, I was resting after morning campaigning on his behalf in Govan when he came close to breaking down my lodging-room door, so hard did he bang at it. I let him in.

'What's the matter, Sandy?' I asked him.

'I'm away tae throw a fellow in the Clyde!'

'Throw someone in the Clyde?' I gasped. 'Whatever for?'

'Yon bluidy Tory's been tellin' a lot o' lies aboot me in a meetin' last night,' he explained. 'Get yoursel' ready an' come wi' me. Ah'm away doon his office tae see to him.'

He wouldn't listen to my attempts to persuade him to 'keep the heid' so I followed him along the river to an alleyway near the Jamaica Bridge. Up the alleyway was the Tory candidate's warehouse offices where Sandy almost knocked down another door before we were let in. I lost count of the number of people Sandy threatened while asking where 'yon bugger' was but he never did find him. Later, I was told that he'd been apprised of Sandy's approach and hidden in a dark corner of the warehouse. Just as well for him because, the mood Sandy was in, the candidate may well have ended up in the Clyde. Just as well for Sandy too, because he could have become a guest of the police rather than a political candidate.

Later in my career as aspirant politician, Sandy devoted a lot of his spare time to supporting me. He even sometimes took time off work and lost wages as a result in order to help me. Usually, he cycled around the area on an old solid-tyred bicycle, distributing Labour leaflets in support of my campaigns. One day, his old bicycle gave up the ghost, the front fork buckled and Sandy's sixteen stones went flying. He woke up in the Glasgow Infirmary with a broken jaw and cracked head. Visited by Keir Hardie two days after the poll, hardly able to speak, his first words were typical Sandy. 'Is Bob in?' Thinking of me, in spite of the agonies he was suffering. When Hardie told him that, once more, I had lost, he almost started crying. What a man! What a friend!

I have mentioned Sandy Haddow not only because he was a most loyal supporter but also because he was a good friend. But there were many more like him, mainly but not exclusively miners. Men who had next to nothing, worked long hours for very low wages, yet gave unstintingly of themselves for the cause. Without good men like Sandy around in the early years, the Labour Movement would never have got off the ground.

Back in that 1901 election, I awaited the result with a crowd of supporters in the Albion Hall near the court buildings where the votes were being counted. It may surprise you to note that I did not attend the count itself. In fact, I only did that once in the seven parliamentary contests which I took part in. That was in Paisley where the Liberal candidate, John McCallum, nervously paced the floor beside me. He was so tense that he refused to even acknowledge my presence. Election nights can produce some unpleasant atmospheres. So it was no bad thing that I spent that 1901 poll night away from the count and in the company of friends.

We talked, swapped stories, sang a few songs and enjoyed our pipes. Then a silence descended when a door was flung open and somebody rushed in. Every head turned to see who it was. It was John Brown, a prominent official of the iron moulders, who was my representative at the court. He made an excited rush over to us, waving in his hand a piece of paper bearing the official figures from the count. He was so excited that many people thought that I must have won. Briefly, and to my huge surprise, so did I. But when we managed to get everybody quiet so John could deliver his news with his usual stammer, reality dawned.

'Ch ... Ch ... Chisholm's oot!' he announced.

So the big news of the night was that the favourite had lost. The Tories had won the seat and I trailed in with a miserable 696 votes. It was no great consolation to me that, in the area, I had polled more votes than any other Labour Candidate. For the record, the figures were as follows:

Smith (Tradeston)	363
Wallacott (St Rollox)	405
Haddow (Govan)	430
Maxwell (Hutchesontown)	445
Watson (Bridgetown)	609
Smillie (Camlachie)	696

So neither my dear old Sandy nor I had got in and neither had any of the other local men. In fact, all six of us were beaten hollow, making a pretty lamentable show. You will be surprised to know that we, quite literally, laughed off our defeats. Our day would come, we were sure of that, and we tended to the view that he who laughs last lasts best. A little later, we were cheered by the news that, across the country, no fewer than twenty-six Labour candidates had won their seats. We would just have to wait a little longer to join them.

As I remarked earlier, my dearest memories of that period are of events in which people important to me were involved. But that is not to say that there were not other important matters which I remember, if not with the same sharpness of details. For example, in February 1900, I was part of a large group which met in the Memorial Hall in London and decided to form the Labour Representation Committee to organise Labour election campaigns. It was a meeting proposed by the Trades Union Congress and attended by a wide range of groups including the unions, the Social Democrat Federation, the Fabians and the Independent Labour Party. A rising star of the Labour Movement, James Ramsay MacDonald, was elected to the office of unpaid secretary. You should understand that the role of the committee was simply to represent working-class interest in parliament. At its inception, there was no great deal said about advancing the cause of Socialism. People like Tom Mann, John Burns, Keir Hardie and myself were rather disappointed by that but, nevertheless, we were satisfied that the formation of the committee would help to provide better organisation of our future election efforts.

Then there was the awful Taff Vale episode. Man, but that was a sore one to take and, for a while, dampened the euphoria felt after the formation of the Labour Representation Committee and winning 26 seats in the 1901 election. In South Wales, it all started innocuously enough. Well, by ordinary men's standards anyway. The Taff Vale Railway Company's workers wanted better working conditions and the right to join the Amalgamated Society of Railway Servants (ASRS). The company refused to negotiate on either issue and the men came out on strike. The society recognised the strike as official and industrial war broke out.

The company introduced blackleg labour which caused a lot of hostility in South Wales in the summer of 1900. Standing idle, no money coming in, the workers had no option but to return to work. That was in the August and they had to return on the same terms as they had suffered before. They had gained nothing through their sacrifice. Worse was to follow. The company decided to sue the ASRS for loss of profits incurred during the strike. After many months of heated argument, the House of Lords decided in favour of the company. Well, what a surprise that was! The ASRS was ordered to pay £23,000 in damages, plus costs, a total of £42,000. This was a disastrous decision not only for the ASRS but all unions. It meant that no union could call a strike – a legal weapon – without risking bankruptcy. That iniquitous decision was handed down by the House of Lords in early 1901.

'Man, we're in trouble with this,' I told Keir Hardie. We were in London for a Labour Representation Committee meeting when the news came through. 'It will destroy us.'

'Don't be in such a lather, Bob,' he said to me. 'It's not good news, there's no denying that. But the world has a habit of moving on. Things will change for the better, you'll see.' Was ever a man so eternally optimistic?

'Well, maybe you're right,' was all I could think of saying. 'But it will be damned hard work in the meantime.'

And damned hard work it was too. There was so much disillusionment around, so many men believing that the struggle was too uphill to be worthwhile, that trade-union activism slumped for a while. In fact, the position was so bad that the majority of trade unions were disinclined to show any interest in the Labour Representation Committee. But Hardie was right, as usual. Five years later, the new Liberal Government would pass the Trade Disputes Act which would make the kind of decision reached by the House of Lords in 1901 absolutely impossible. But it seemed a long, hard five years at the time.

The other event of note at that time which stays reasonably fresh in my memory was the death of Queen Victoria in January 1901. Having been monarch since 1837, we were all affected in some degree or other by her passing. I remember memorial services all up and down the country and certainly there was a dark mood about for some time after her death. She had been a fixture in our lives for so long that we all felt moved to mourn. However, I was not alone in wondering if her passing might not predict better times for ordinary people. In the poetic sense, I did feel diminished by her death, but, to be frank, no more so than if any one of my mining friends had perished at the coalface. After all, what had the Victorian Age, as it is now called, meant for us?

It had been a period of imperial expansion, the growth of great fortunes and government by men sometimes indifferent to the lot of ordinary people, and sometimes paternalistic; which some of us felt was even worse. Without question, Great Britain had been the dominant power of the century, but at what cost to her people? The lists of dead on war memorials had grown long, and Britain's undoubted strength had been won at the expense of the millions who toiled with poor reward in the factories and mines. In truth, ordinary men and women had no great cause to look back fondly on the Victorian era. Even those workers and their families who took pride in Britain's achievements could point to very little improvement in their own humble lives.

'She's dead then,' Ann said to me when we heard the news.

'Yes, God rest her soul,' I replied.

'And what do you thing of the new man, Edward the Seventh?' she asked.

'What do I think?' I laughed. 'The only thing I think is that his life will be rather easier than anybody here in Larkhall.'

'You have a real talent for stating the obvious, Robert Smillie,' she said, smiling the smile which every day endeared her to me.

By the time we entered the twentieth century, and in spite of the House of Lords' ruling in the Taff Vale Case, many of us felt we had at least made some progress. The Labour Movement had spawned the Trades Union Congress, the Independent Labour Party, the Labour Representation Committee and twenty-six Members of Parliament. It had been hard work, very hard work, and sometimes it seemed like two steps forwards, one step back. But at least there were tangible results for our efforts. We were now exercised by one thought. What would the twentieth century bring?

XI

Weathering the Storm

AS THE NEW century dawned, the Smillie family was living at 40, Miller Street in Larkhall. What with Ann and myself and the nine bairns, it was a crowded wee household. Did I say bairns? I'll be getting myself into trouble with Jeanie, Mary and John, who were twenty-two, twenty and seventeen years old respectively. Jeanie and Mary were courting, and there were always some lassies around looking out for John. William was always protesting that, at fourteen, he was a man. As he was learning his trade in the mines, I suppose he was in a way. James was eleven with a year to go in school, while Robert and Daniel, at ages nine and eight, were more like twins than brothers. Alexander, only four, was desperate to join his brothers in school and Joseph, hardly three years old, was the apple of his mother's eye.

Ann was wearing very well in spite of the hard grind of daily work and the size of her family. To my eyes, she was still as bonny at forty-two as she had been when I'd first clapped eyes on her a quarter of a century earlier. She was certainly wearing better than I was. My eyesight wasn't as good as it had been and, at the age of only forty-four, my hair and moustache were beginning to show signs of grey. I was inclined to put that down to hard work. Ann said it was due to all the pipes I smoked.

Having been thwarted twice in my attempts to become an MP, I was still very busy with my union work, both in Larkhall and Lanarkshire as a whole. There was still not a lot of spare time to be had so I used it as wisely as possible. I remember a wonderful Sunday in the summer of 1901 when the whole family travelled up to Glasgow by train to take in the sights of the International Exhibition at Kelvingrove Park. But such excursions were rare indeed and a more typical way of passing our limited time together was our evening reading sessions. Yes, after all these years, the book was still valued in the Smillie household. Only now it was Jeanie, Mary or John who did most of the reading while Ann, the rest of the bairns and I listened on. They were simple times with simple pleasures. In my old age, I think of them often.

My union work was very demanding. As I have already told you, after the Taff Vale case it was not a good time for any trade union. Morale was low, as was membership in many unions, and the role of union officials was very difficult. At many meetings, the atmosphere was despairing. Without being able to strike for fear of being sued, we felt powerless in the face of employers' demands. We officials did our best, of course, but it was not a happy period. Thankfully, now and again a character would pop up or an incident would take place and rouse us out of our despair. Such a man was Grant Munro, and such an event was an after-meeting conversation in Larkhall in 1902. We had talked for ages about demands we wished to make of our employers for better wages and conditions but had failed to come to a resolution because we recognised our weakness. Meeting over, an air of gloom pervading, Grant Munro piped up.

'Did ye hear the story aboot the Duke of Hamilton, Jock Simpson and Tam Smith?' he asked us.

Well none of us had and, pretty listless after an unproductive meeting, we gave Grant the nod to tell us his story. We were in such a dark mood that any form of brief entertainment was to be welcomed.

'Well, it was like this,' he began. 'Back in the 1820's ... ' and off he went.

It transpired that an earlier Duke of Hamilton owned several small collieries and took a strong interest in them. But however hard he and his miners worked, it was hard to make a profit. One obvious result of this was that wages were low and one day, at the pit gates, the men elected Jock Simpson and Tam Smith to visit the duke and ask for an increase in wages. Just as Jock and Tam were setting out, another man told them to also ask the duke for free oil and wicks for their lamps. Up until then, the miners had had to purchase themselves. 'Dinna forget aboot the oil an' the wick,' was his final reminder to them as they set out.

Reaching the 'big house', they had some trouble persuading the pompous butler to let them see the duke without an appointment. Luckily for them, he passed within earshot and invited them in. He took them to a nearby room and told them to sit down.

'Well, my men, what can I do for you?'

'My Duke, my Lord, my mannie ... eh,' Jock said, rising to his feet. 'We've baith been sent tae ask Yer Grace tae clap sixpence a day tae our wages an' we're tae tell ye that, if ye dinnae, we'll no work for ye ony mair.' He sat down, face flushed red.

'Well, I'm very sorry,' replied the duke, who was a kindly old man. 'I wish I could help but the colliery is running at a loss so it's quite impossible for me to increase your wages.'

'Ach, m'Lord, we've heard that tale often enough before,' Tam said.

'No doubt, but it happens to be true.' Then the duke smiled. 'I can tell you what I am prepared to do. If all you men can appoint a committee to take over the colliery and produce the coal, and sell it, I will hand over the colliery as a going concern. I will only ask for a small royalty of threepence or fourpence a ton.'

'Ye what!' Jock exclaimed. 'Ye'll give us the colliery tae oursels?'

'Yes,' the duke said. His words were greeted in silence as Jock and Tam struggled to come to terms with the enormity of his offer.

'So you will tell your colleagues?'

'Aye, we will so,' they both replied, rising to go. They had just reached the door when Tam remembered something.

'Och, yer Grace,' he said.

'Yes?'

'We'll no' be leaving until ye promise us free oil an' wicks for oor lamps.'

We all laughed merrily as the irony sank in. Tam demanding free oil and wicks from a man who had just made him part owner of a colliery! No doubt you will think this a trivial enough incident, and so it was. But it just goes to show how small events can raise the spirits and, in the tide of human affairs, that's anything but a small thing.

In the real world, there were some shafts of light in an otherwise gloomy picture. Back in 1900, my dear friend, Keir Hardie, had been re-elected to parliament, this time representing the constituency of Merthyr Tydfil in South Wales. I had been honoured to speak on his behalf on several occasions during his campaign there. Perhaps buoyed by that result, more unions affiliated themselves to the Labour Party. For example, the records showed that in that year, 168 unions had affiliated. They were still in the minority but at least it was a growing minority. My main regret at that time was that my own union, the Miners' Federation of Great Britain, in which I was becoming increasingly active, would not affiliate, many of its officials still being of the Liberal persuasion.

The general election of 1906 would change matters a great deal. Unfortunately, it did absolutely nothing to improve my status as an aspirant parliamentarian. You might be surprised to know that I fought not one but two seats that year, as I will describe. The first of those was Paisley which was not a mining community and I stood as the nominee of the National Independent Labour Party. It was a three-cornered fight in which, robbed of my customary mining constituency, I fared no better than I had in my previous two campaigns. If I had ever doubted it before, I was now discovering that this politics business was very much a school of hard knocks.

A little later in that same year, you would have found me crossing the border for my first, but not last, tilt at an English seat. My nomination was secured, oddly enough, by the influence of the Durham Miners' Association from way across the Pennines but with long-forged contacts among workers' groups in Cumberland. The seat in question was Cockermouth, a vacancy arising as a result of the death of Sir Wilfred Lawson, who had earned a reputation as one of the most popular men who ever enlivened the House of Commons with his wit and humour. My agent was Tom Richardson of the Durham Miners who later became the MP for Whitehaven. My opponents were Captain Guest, the Liberal candidate, and Alan Randalls, a local ironmaster, who was the Tory candidate.

I was to find that the men of Cockermouth took their politics very seriously, as a result of which there were very few dull moments during that campaign. I remember one day, when Tom and I were resting our weary bodies after a particularly stormy meeting in Maryport, enjoying a cup of tea in a workman's house, when the mother and father of all arguments broke out close by. We dashed out to see what was going on. We found an altercation reminiscent of David and Goliath.

'You're nothing but a foul-mouthed big bully!' Fists up, this was a local newspaper reporter by the name of Harry Henshaw. Watched by a crowd of about a hundred, he was addressing a giant of a young man. At maybe five-foot-five and nine stones, it looked as if wee Harry was taking his life in his hands. 'Come on, you!' he bawled. 'We all heard you and what you were saying about Bob Smillie was a pack of lies.' He passed his straw hat to a bystander. 'Put them up! I'm only half your size but I'll give you the damnedest thrashing you've ever had in your life.' By now he was dancing on the balls of his feet, clearly ready to take on the big fellow.

Well, big my slanderer may have been but he had no stomach for a fight, not even against a little fellow like Harry. Face red, he pushed through the jeering crowd and disappeared. At that point, Tom and I were joined by John Robertson, one of my Lanarkshire supporters and later an MP himself. Grinning broadly, he asked little Harry what he would have done if the big fellow had accepted his challenge.

'I don't rightly know,' Harry admitted as he put his jacket and straw hat back on, 'but I'm right glad he didn't!'

All of my meetings, whether in halls or in the open air, were packed out and I received a great deal of enthusiastic support. But when the poll was declared, there was my name at the bottom again. My supporters were astonished. They had assumed, from the popularity of my meetings that I was going to be elected. I, on the other hand, previously twice-bitten, understood the truth. That elections are won by the voting majority, and most of them never attend any meetings. Naturally disappointed myself, my friends took it worse.

'Bob, my heart is broken on your account,' said old Patrick Walls from Workington. 'And for your supporters too,' he added. 'They will be the sport of their workmates for weeks.' He couldn't prevent himself breaking down in tears as he spoke to me.

'Well, we can't have that,' I told him, desperately trying to think of a way to cheer up my Labour supporters. 'I tell you what Patrick, do you think you could get the Opera House in Workington for a meeting tomorrow night?' I had intended returning home that day but now felt that I could not leave without offering some comfort. 'If you can, get out some handbill advertisements and I'll address the meeting.'

'Do you mean it, Bob?' Patrick said, clasping my hands. 'I'll see what I can do.'

We got the hall. Patrick took the chair and I addressed a huge gathering that Sunday night. I spoke for over an hour. Gone were the days when my knees used to knock at the thought of public speaking. I spoke of many things, mainly Labour issues, then finished by telling them to go to their work the next day with their heads held high and their Labour rosettes pinned on. I later heard that they did exactly that and not a taunt was heard from their workmates who seemed to admire the fact that a defeated candidate stayed behind to cheer up his beaten supporters. My final statement to the meeting in Workington was a prophecy. I told the men that the time would come when a Labour candidate would be elected in Cockermouth. My audience cheered long and loud at that. In 1918, Tom Cape won the seat for Labour. Which was no great consolation back in 1906, of course. Once more I had failed to vault the parliamentary threshold.

But if I had failed, there were winners. The Tories were swept aside, the Liberals formed a government and there were twenty-nine Labour MPs, our best showing to date. Twenty-four of those Labour MPs were trade unionists which just went to show that, though there had been difficult times for the unions, we were not the spent force that our opponents alleged us to be. There were to be many acts passed through parliament, some of which I will deal with later, but one early one was of particular significance to us in the unions. This was the Trade Disputes Act of 1906.

You will remember how the Taff Vale strike concluded. Defeat for the railwaymen followed by an unholy judgement from the House of Lords which backed the company's legal action against the union and left them facing a bill of £42,000 which all but crippled them. And how, thereafter, no union could entertain the idea of a strike for fear of similar reprisals. Well, the Trade Disputes Act changed all that. This Act stated that unions could not be sued for damages. Further, it provided that peaceful picketing was legal. There were those who would commend this Act, saying that it liberated trade unions from unfair shackles and permitted them to represent their members in the way that they were set up to do. You will not be surprised to know that I strongly inclined towards that judgement. These were others, of course, mainly but not exclusively of a Tory persuasion who attacked the Act, claiming that it gave undue licence to agitators and represented a threat to Britain's industrial prowess. Certainly it is true that the Act enabled the use of strike action as a weapon, and that strikes became more commonplace as a result. But who did the opponents wish to have working in their industries, free men or slaves?

That election and the following Trade Union Disputes Act put more fire in the bellies of some trade union officials and, in the years following 1906, many more unions affiliated to the Labour Party. Still not a majority, but a healthily growing number. To my regret, the Miners' Federation of Great Britain had still not affiliated and I resolved to do everything in my power to make it do so. In the meantime, however, something else arose which commanded a great deal of my attention and time. It was time for another Royal Commission.

As befitted their reason for existence, the Miners' Federation of Great Britain had been a thorn in the side of the Home Office, always pointing out the need for greater safety in coal mines. No Home Secretary for fifteen years had escaped the constant reminders of the need for more and universal precautions. The change of government in 1906, and the increased number of Labour MPs, meant that the clamour grew from within parliament as well as from outside.

Thus it was that in June, 1906, the Royal Commission was set up. The Commissioners were:

Chairman: Baron Monkswell
Sir Lindsay Wood
Henry Cunynghame (Home Office)
William Abraham
Frederick Davis (South Wales Conciliation Board)
Enoch Edwards
Thomas Ellis (Mining Association of Great Britain)
Dr John Haldane (Fellow of the Royal Society)
Robert Smillie (President of the Lanarkshire Miners' Union)

Yes, that is my name on the list! The invitation arrived in a letter emblazoned with a royal seal. To say I was surprised is to put it mildly.

'Do you think somebody is playing a joke on me?' I asked Ann.

'Of course, Robert,' she relied, almost laughing. 'It'll be Billy Geddes on the second shift who's got hold of the royal seal.'

Before replying to the invitation, I contacted a number of senior men in the Federation and was amazed to find that my inclusion among our representatives had been unanimously supported. I must have felt a flush of pride at that, but I do not honestly recall. I signalled back my acceptance of the invitation then reflected on the matter. Why on earth had my name been put forward? I could only come to the conclusion that some of my colleagues had long memories and believed that I had performed well enough in similar circumstances some years earlier. Pipe in hand, feet warming by the fire, I found my mind drifting back over the years.

In consideration of the proposed special rules incorporated into the 1887 Mines Regulation Act, a Royal Commission had been set up under the chairmanship of Lord Mersey, Mr Justice Bigham before his ennoblement. A Mr Pope represented the Home Office with Sir Richard Redmayne, Chief Inspector of Mines, as his chief advisor. Sir Thomas Ratcliffe-Ellis represented the mine owners and

I appeared on behalf of the Miners' Federation. The fact that at that time I had spent only two years as Secretary of the Larkhall Miners' Association might suggest to you that the Federation had no great hopes of the Commission which opened with Lord Mersey having each of us state our qualifications to appear. He was rather curt with Pope, Ratcliffe-Ellis and Redmayne and, by the time it was my turn, I was feeling a little apprehensive.

'Who are you?'

'Robert Smillie.'

'Whom do you represent?'

'The Miners' Federation of Great Britain.'

'And who exactly are they?' At least he was honest enough to admit his ignorance.

'A Federation of all the mine workers' associations, representing not far short of a million men.'

'And what are you here for?' If he'd been any stiffer, he'd have broken.

'To provide information,' I replied, getting more than a little rattled by his Lordship's abrupt style. I decided to take my life into my hands. 'We feel that you cannot know very much about the subject, and we hope to some extent to help you, if possible.'

'Oh, that's alright,' Lord Mersey said, suddenly smiling. 'Excellent in fact.'

In the course of that pre-1887 enquiry, I had to oppose an owners' proposal which would have made it a criminal offence for a workman to be found asleep in charge of a safety lamp. I found myself in a difficult position because in such a case the workman could endanger the lives of his fellow workmen. I was unhappy at the thought of criminal charges being brought but could not, in all conscience, justify such a dereliction of responsibility.

However, I could reasonably argue that, in certain circumstances, it could indeed be very difficult to stay awake in the pit. Very often, the atmosphere underground was conducive to drowsiness. Certainly, I explained, I had known cases in which colliery officials, less used to the atmosphere than the miners, had fallen asleep after sitting down for only a few minutes. I also reported that an Inspector of Mines had once told me that he frequently experienced great difficulty staying awake underground in certain atmospheric conditions. As I was finishing my speech, I noticed that Lord Mersey was beginning to doze on the bench. I could not resist it.

'It has even been known,' I said more loudly, 'that the Chairman of the bench has been known to fall asleep during the hearing of an important case.'

At that, everybody laughed out loud and Lord Mersey raised his head, and asked me what I had said. Wriggling a little, I told him it was nothing important, but he insisted. So I had to tell him that, in the course of explaining how difficult it would be to stay awake in an underground atmosphere, I had illustrated my case by saying that the drowsy atmosphere of a court of enquiry could induce sleep. But he wasn't having any of that.

'Oh, but I was far from asleep, Mr Smillie,' he told me. 'I do assure you that I was following every word you were saying.' Which may have saved him from embarrassment but it gave the rest of us something to chuckle about. Personally, I was glad to escape without being charged with contempt of court.

For reasons I can't explain, Lord Mersey hit it off with me pretty well. Certainly, he was a lot less brusque with me than with a number of other members of the enquiry. I have fond memories of an afternoon session when I was not directly involved and wandered outside to enjoy a pipe. Inside, quite suddenly, Lord Mersey asked for me. I was told that his exact words were, 'Where is Mr Smillie, my guide, philosopher and friend?' Which was rare praise indeed, if you like. Anyway, I was sent for, went back inside, then answered his questions on some fairly technical points about the miners' job.

There's no doubt that, as a very young man, I was prejudiced strongly in favour of my own class and resented those whom I regarded as my oppressors. But I had mellowed over time, and Lord Mersey was part of that mellowing process. Given his lack of knowledge about mining, he was skilled at asking the right questions and adept at getting in touch with the subject. Throughout the enquiry, he was both firm and fair. Equally as important, he treated me as a human being from the same basic mould as himself. He proved to me, as powerfully as any man ever did, that a gentleman is a gentleman, whatever rank in life.

All those memories coursed through my mind as I sat at home waiting to set off for the 1906 Royal Commission. I did not know it then but that Commission would endure, with some interruptions, for five long years. It would spawn two Mines Acts and inform later legislation with significance across industry. Of course, my major concern was with safety in the mines and I was pleased enough by the wording of the Commission's Statement of Intent: 'Whereas we have deemed it expedient that a Commission should forthwith issue to inquire into and report on certain questions relating to the health and safety of miners, and the administration of the Mines Acts.'

The statement went on to specify particular areas of enquiry which included: compulsory watering of the roads in dry and dusty mines; the forms of safety lamps; the better prevention of accidents; the work of rescue; the present system of investigation and enquiry into accidents; a standard of ventilation; the disease known as *ankylostomiasis* (miners' worm); the adequacy of the administration of the Mines Acts; examination for Managers' and Under-Managers' Certificates of Competency and whether certificates granted by colonial governments should not be accepted in this country.

All of which was music to my ears, of course. It was a fair representation of what the Federation had been demanding for many years. Of course, I realised that the devil would be in the detail and in the outworkings. I believed it unlikely that everything would be resolved to our satisfaction, and so it turned out. However, much that eventually arose out of the work of that Commission was fair and good.

During my time as a member, I was both an informed witness and an interrogator. Baron Monkswell did not turn out to be another Lord Mersey. He certainly at no time referred to me as his 'guide, philosopher and friend'. However, he treated me as fairly as any of the other members. My most pointed jousts were with Thomas Ellis, representative of the owners. Sometimes, he fired questions at me. Just as often it was the other way round. Quite often, we became rather heated. Yet that heat never spilled over outside the sessions. I would go as far as to say that, off the battlefield, he and I got on rather well.

The work of the Commission dragged on and I will have more to say of its outworkings later. But at the same time as I was involved with that, I continued to work on behalf of the workers of Larkhall and Lanarkshire, as well as making my contribution to the work of the Miners' Federation of Great Britain which was taking an increasing amount of my time. And there were, of course, further tilts at a parliamentary seat which I will acquaint you with shortly.

All these commitments, particularly to the Commission and the Federation, meant more and more time spent away from home. This distressed me a great deal. I frequently felt dreadful when I caught the train to, say, London and, while away, I missed my family terribly. Coming home was always a double delight, of course, but my absences grew so frequent that I felt I had to discuss the situation with Ann.

'I could always give it up,' I told her one night.

'Give what up?'

'The Commission work, the Federation, the County, the branch, everything,' I said. 'Just return to the pit. At least I'd be at home all the time.'

'Tell me, Robert Smillie,' she replied, in that tone of hers which suggested a strong opinion surfacing. 'Who are you doing it for? Tell me that. Yourself?'

'No, not myself,' I replied honestly. 'For everybody.'

'Exactly!' she said, as if I'd just uttered the words of Solomon. 'It's for everybody, and everybody includes our children and myself. So you just keep on with your work and let's hear no more nonsense about giving it up.'

And that was that. Ann had spoken. The subject was forgotten for many years until there was no choice but to bring it up. But I am predicting myself. Suffice it to say that I undertook my duties with even greater determination following that exchange with Ann.

From some of the things that I have told you, you will assume that progress was being made in the cause of the working man. Indeed, to an extent, that was true. But in 1902 two events occurred shortly after one another which revealed most clearly the huge divisions which still existed in British Society. Divisions

which no cause, no movement or, for that matter, no legislation had done anything to alter. The first of these was the death of William, the 6th Earl
Fitzwilliam, one of the richest men in Britain.

I had got to know parts of Northern England quite well in my dealing with
the Durham and Yorkshire Miners, so I was well aware of the existence of the
Fitzwilliams, their Yorkshire estates of over 200,000 acres and their magnificent
home, Wentworth House, nine miles north of Sheffield. In the late eighteenth
century, huge reserves of coal had been discovered under the family's vast acreage
and, under the 6th Earl's reign, the family wealth had increased a thousand-fold.
I happened to be visiting the Yorkshire miners in February 1902, a particularly
bitter February, when the earl passed away. Inevitably, it was the talk of the town,
or should I say, the county.

I was in the company of Tom Richardson, the same Durham official who
would organise my election campaign in Cockermouth four years later. He
expressed an interest in seeing the earl's funeral and I was no less curious myself.
It was arranged that a horse and trap would take us out to Wentworth and bring
us back later to Sheffield from where I would catch the evening train home. Man,
but it was cold that February day! Foggy, too, so much so that several times our
driver suggested turning back, but we persuaded him to continue.

At Wentworth House, we could not get really close to the centre of events and
hung back with the general throng at a distance. There were still traces of fog
around, but less than there had been during our journey, so we had a reasonable
view of what was going on. And what a sight it was!

On the great lawns in front of the home stood a silent crowd numbering in
the thousands. Along the facade of the house a long row of about two hundred
servants, all in black, stood stiffly to attention, facing the crowd. The fingers of
fog drifting around seemed to rob the scene of any colour: everything looked grey-
black. In front of the pillared entrance stood a magnificent glass-sided hearse
drawn by four black horses which had ostrich feather plumes on their heads and
black-tasselled cloths across their backs. There was a number of those macabre figures they called mutes, really funeral attendants, their tall silk hats trailing veils
of black crepe. Bells tolled in the distance, the only sound to be heard.
Otherwise, all was silence. Then at midday, some three hours after the crowd had
begun to gather, the coffin was carried out of the great house, mounted on a silver bier. Following it was a long procession of the house servants carrying hundreds of wreaths of brilliant flowers, the first sign of colour in an otherwise bleak
scene. The oak coffin was handled into the hearse and the last journey of
William, 6th Earl of Fitzwilliam, slowly began.

Tom and I left just as the cortege began to move off. We had little time to
spare for me to catch my train home. As we raced back towards Sheffield, each
habitation we passed through seemed to have come to a standstill. All shops were

closed, there was no traffic, and any flag was at half-mast. On the sides of the roads, lines of people stood silently. They were waiting the passing of the funeral cortege, and had gathered to pay their last respects. It was as if the whole of Yorkshire had turned out in mourning. If so, they were to be disappointed. They never did catch a last sight of the noble lord. His cortege simply made the one-mile journey from Wentworth House to a local village church. The procession was led by a thousand miners from his pits and flanked by fifty soldiers from the Yorkshire Dragoons. I have no idea how many of those 1,050 men were volunteers. Neither at the time did I realise that the Fitzwilliam family would come to mean more to me in later years.

A few days after I got home and was lovingly reunited with my family, old Geordie Geddes passed away. Geordie had been quite old when I started in the pit and had been one of those kindly veterans who had shown me the ropes. Since his retirement, his wife had died and his children had left the area. Out of kindness, the Munro family had taken him in and he spent his declining years in the warmth of their company.

Geordie's funeral was as unlike William Fitzwilliam's as chalk is to cheese. Nobody dressed in finery, no mutes, no servants by the hundred, no expensive wreaths, no glass-sided hearse and no quartet of fine horses. His plain coffin was carried on little more than a cart pulled by four strong miners. After a brief service, he was interred in the public cemetery, his cold grave bedecked by bluebells and other wild flowers plucked from the nearby woodlands. His children, briefly returned from their homes out of the area, stood at the head of the grave, dressed in their best rough clothes, weeping silent tears into the grave where Geordie was laid beside his late wife. All around stood hundreds of folk, many of them miners on their way to their shifts, dressed in their work clothes. The whole funeral lasted less than forty minutes. It was as if Larkhall and Wentworth House were on different planets, inhabited by different species.

Immediately after Geordie's funeral, I had to make my way to Hamilton for a county meeting so it was late when I got home. Unusually for me, at that meeting my mind had often strayed from our business. Instead I could not help reflecting on Geordie and William. I knew that the sorrow expressed at Geordie's spartan funeral had been genuine and I wondered how true that was at William's. In Yorkshire, it had been impossible to see through the pageantry and determine how the mourners really felt, whereas at Geordie's funeral I knew everybody present and fully understood how they were feeling. Questions kept pouring into my mind. Can you judge a man's worth by the greatness of his funeral? Is a poor man less worthy because he is poor? Had William's funeral commanded so much attention out of love, or merely out of duty? Where did Geordie or, for that matter any one of us in Larkhall, rank as a human being in comparison with great men like William, 6th Earl of Fitzwilliam?

At home, Ann noticed that I was preoccupied by my thoughts and insisted that I share them with her. I told her the direction my musings had been taking me and confided in her that, from what I had seen over the past week or so, I was beginning to wonder if we would ever redress the balance between the owners and the owned, however hard we tried.

'Well, well, Robert Smillie, you are in a taking, aren't you?' Her words sounded rather grumpy but she was smiling at me as she said them. 'Remember your Robert Burns, man. How often did he write fine clothes were mere dressing and that the worth of the man lay underneath?' She tousled my hair as was her habit in an affectionate mood. 'Besides, old Geordie and that Fitzwilliam will never know how grand or sparse their funerals were. They were both beyond knowledge, God rest their souls.'

As ever, Ann had found wiser words than I could to get to the heart of the matter. I not only loved her: I admired her greatly.

XII

Wider Horizons

DURING THE FIRST decade of the twentieth century, I was becoming more and more active in the affairs of the Miners' Federation of Great Britain, little realising that my involvement would lead to great joy and, ultimately, deep despair. As I have already suggested, I played a role in exerting pressure on the Home Office over safety in mines and then represented the Federation at the Royal Commission set up in 1906. Also, on many occasions, I found myself speaking to meetings the length and breadth of Britain, describing the work of the Federation. Sometimes, those meetings were full of people sympathetic to our cause and such audiences were easy to speak to and usually a pleasure to be with.

There were other meetings where there was less pleasure to be gained. 'Preaching to the converted' is one thing. Entering the 'Lion's den' and trying to persuade people of contrary beliefs is quite another. I seemed destined to endure rather a lot of those kinds of meetings. The Federation took the view that our message had to be spread beyond the bounds of existing acceptance and that great efforts had to be make to make doubters and opponents alike aware of the strength of our arguments. So it was that I often found myself addressing extremely unsympathetic audiences such as the Mine Owners' Association, colliery management groups and, on several occasions, Home Office Select Committees. There were some I was able to enlighten but the majority were at best unreceptive, and not a few were downright hostile. In my earlier, less temperate days, I may well have reacted, even over-reacted but, as I approached my fifties, I generally managed to stay calm in the face of hostility and simply reiterate my arguments. My personal feelings did not enter into it. The message had to be conveyed, and the cause served.

Between 1906 and 1911, I served on the Royal Commission, which I have already told you about. The first piece of legislation which that Commission informed was the 1908 Mines Act. In one respect, it was a remarkable Act. You will remember how, years earlier, I had rather impudently informed Lord Mersey about the draining nature of long shifts underground in certain atmospheric conditions. In addition to pressurising the Home Office over basic safety precautions, we in the miners' federations had argued strongly for years for shorter shifts. After all, even in a well ventilated shaft, there are still noxious fumes around and, the longer a miner has to tolerate those at a stretch, the more likely he is to become drowsy or perhaps fall ill, thereby endangering himself and his workmates.

Therefore, it was with great enthusiasm that we greeted the main provision of the 1908 Mines Act. It stipulated that the maximum working day for miners would henceforth be eight hours. This was the first time that a British government had intervened to regulate the working hours of adult males. You will not be surprised to know that the mine owners were less enthused than we were and, in time to come, some got involved in some very unscrupulous practices in order to circumvent the Act. But we were delighted, of course. Suddenly, it seemed that all the years of banging our heads against what had seemed like brick walls, the endless campaigning, the eternal provision of evidence to enquiries and commissions, had been worth it after all. It still left a lot of unfinished business, of course, but we felt that it might be a harbinger of better things to come.

There were several lengthy breaks in the work of the Royal Commission to allow the chairman to draw together all the evidence, of which there was a mountain, and to decide on the shape of future sessions. It was during one of those lulls in 1908 that I received an invitation to which I was delighted to signal my acceptance. The Miners' International Conference was to be held in Paris and I was asked to attend on behalf of the British Federation. I asked Ann's opinion about whether I should go or not because it would mean another absence from home and I did not strictly have to attend. Somebody else could have taken my place. She did not hesitate for a moment, told me that I had been overworking and looked tired, and that a rest would do me good. Well, my trip to Paris, my first abroad, was certainly a change, but I am not sure I would have described it as a rest!

I came across many new men on my visit, a number of whom impressed me greatly. Among others, there were Jean Jaurès, a great French Socialist, and Jean Longuet, grandson of Karl Marx, and a man with whom I forged a strong friendship. Following a lengthy session in which Longuet and I had spoken a great deal about the future for Socialism, I suggested to him that I would like to visit the Chamber of Deputies, the French equivalent of our House of Commons. Longuet was only too happy to oblige, he told me in excellent English, which was fortunate as I had no French, and said that if Jaurès, whom he knew I greatly admired, was there then he would introduce me to him.

When we reached the chamber, larger and more magnificent that our House of Commons, Longuet sent a message to Jaurès who appeared a few minutes later. I had shared a platform with him on two occasions but never before had the chance to speak to him personally. He was most cordial with me and, sitting on a bench in the passageway we talked for some time. I do not remember a great deal of our conversation, which no doubt was centred on Socialist affairs, but I clearly remember him giving me advice on public speaking. He quoted

Demosthenes' view that there were three rules for orators: Action, Action, Action! He was a great example of that himself, like a number of other French speakers I heard at that conference. His Gallic expressiveness and extravagant gestures absolutely commanded your attention. Even the German delegates responded animatedly to him, and that was a trick I never managed.

To my delighted surprise, Jaurès invited Longuet and myself to view the inside of the chamber. For a moment, the attendant was unwilling to let us enter because it had just risen and the rule was that no stranger should be admitted until half-an-hour after any sitting. But such was Jaurès' reputation and the respect in which he was held, that the attendant relented and let us pass inside.

As we studied the interior, which was quite splendid, Jaurès pointed out to us the places at which the great men of French politics usually sat and then told me a particular arrangement which differed greatly from the House of Commons. In our house, our parliamentarians address one another directly from their places on opposite sides of the 'floor'. Not so in the Chamber of Deputies. Jaurès adhered to his country's old proverb which says, 'we do these things better in France' and explained how the Deputies delivered their addresses from the Tribune, a sort of pulpit set above the seats. I was not sure if this was in fact any better than our way of doing things, but it was certainly different.

To my amazement and initial embarrassment, Jaurès persuaded me to go up into the Tribune and say a few words to see what it felt like. Of course, the place was empty but, even so, I found standing 'in the Gods' rather daunting. Jaurès and Longuet standing way beneath me, I was suddenly stuck for something to say. Then the idea came, and for two or three minutes I spoke of my love for Ann, our children and the town of Larkhall. When I had finished, I gave a short bow. Jaurès, who spoke no English and had communicated with me through Longuet, gave a loud cheer and the three of us left, laughing. 'Wee boys never grow up,' as the saying goes.

After a visit to the Chamber's library, where Jaurès pointed out the finely-painted ceiling showing Demosthenes on the seashore addressing the waves, we retired to the refreshments room. Over glasses of refreshing lager beer, we talked for ages. You will know by now that almost my entire interest lay in mining matters and domestic affairs and that, while I was aware of the events in the wider world, I had no great knowledge of them. That hour, perhaps two, rather changed that. I discovered that my European colleagues were a lot more worldly-wise than I was or, for that matter, most folk back home were.

They seemed to know about every international alliance, real or impending. They discussed the Anglo-Japanese Alliance, the Entente Cordiale between Britain and France, the Anglo-Russian Agreement and predicted the emergence of two great power blocs opposing one another. They saw Britain, France and Russia on one side and Germany, Austria and Italy on the other. Perhaps I misunderstood some of the nuances of what they said because I was following it through Longuet's translation, but that's as I remember it.

They also talked at length about the Moroccan Crises and the then current crisis in Bosnia. They concluded by discussing what they called 'The Arms Race', countries stockpiling armaments in preparation for whatever cause. They knew more about Britain's *Dreadnought* programme than I did. Only later did I realise that they were predicting the dreadful events which would envelop the world only six years later. Throughout, I sat listening, like a student learning from two venerable professors. Only at the end did I feel bold enough to venture anything.

'All that is going on,' I said to Longuet. 'These alliances, crises, and building up of weaponry. What is it all for? Please ask Mr Jaurès on my behalf.' I waited while Longuet translated, then Jaurès spoke briefly.

'Monsieur Jaurès says it is simple,' Longuet told me. 'It is what it is always for. Power, land and national glory.'

There were two footnotes to that illuminating time I spent with Jaurès and Longuet, one pleasant, one not so. First, many years later, I received a letter from a gentleman in Canada. As far as I knew, I had never met him. However, he remembered me. Many years earlier, as a teenager, he had been an interested visitor to our Miners' International and had heard me speak on a number of occasions. More strangely, one day he had visited the Chamber of Deputies and had sat down in the equivalent of our Strangers' Gallery. Sitting there, he had listened to me speaking from the Tribune, proclaiming my love for my family and Larkhall. How very odd this thing called coincidence is.

Second, there was a far less pleasant footnote. While we talked that day in the Chamber or, rather, the two Jeans talked and I listened, I think we all realised that tensions were rising across Europe and, indeed, further afield. But I doubt if any of us actually believed that, within a few short years, the nations we represented at the conference would be at one another's throats. For one of us in particular it was as well that an iron curtain blocks our view of the future. I was to meet Jean Jaurès several more times before the outbreak of the Great War and, on those occasions, we resumed our conversation with the aid of an interpreter. I came to admire him greatly. But only six years after that first meeting in Paris, Jean Jaurès would die cruelly at the hands of an assassin.

During 1908, on several occasions, I tried to persuade the Miners' Federation to affiliate to the Labour Party, but met some stubborn resistance to the idea. This was particularly true of some of the representatives from certain areas of Northern England. While there was support for my proposal from Scotland and South Wales, our English colleagues were less convinced. Some of them were Liberals, which they had every right to be of course, while others simply did not like the idea of affiliating to any political party. Naturally I was disappointed, convinced as I was that progress would be better achieved by all representatives of the

Labour Movement joining together. However, I consoled myself with the thought that most of those who opposed the proposal were among the oldest of us and, that in the regular elections for officers of the Federation, younger men with a greater attachment to Socialism would come forward.

In those early years of the twentieth century, a particular word began to circulate more and more frequently in union circles. That word was 'Blackleg'. According to the old dictionary I kept at home in Larkhall, a blackleg was 'a low, gambling fellow'. However, from experience, I began to regard that definition as considerably out-of-date. I tended to think of a blackleg as the kind of rogue who would steal a sick man's grapes, or a penny from a blind man's tin. In short, an unprincipled scoundrel.

Blacklegs have always been a curse to the striking miners. I remember a particularly unusual episode connected with the strike in 1909, when a general British stoppage was ordered to assist the Scottish miners in their demand for six shillings a day. I was in London, working on behalf of the Federation. One day a porter at the Westminster Palace Hotel, where I was staying for a few days, handed a registered letter to me. I was surprised to receive it because it was addressed to the 'Conference of the Mine-Owners of Great Britain, Westminster Palace Hotel.'

'You've got the wrong man,' I told the porter. I almost laughed as I added, 'I'm not an owner. You had better take it away.'

'But it must be for you,' he insisted. 'I know you're not one of the owners, but as it is obviously connected with mining it has to be for your people. The mine owners never have letters addressed to them at this hotel.'

I wasn't convinced but, to save the fellow any further agitation, I signed for the letter then found a seat in a quiet area of the lobby to have a look at it. The first thing that surprised me was that I noticed on the flap of the envelope that the letter had come from Austria. I assumed that it had been sent by the Austrian miners who knew that our headquarters were at the Westminster Palace Hotel. However, on opening the envelope and withdrawing the letter, I got my second surprise, an even greater one. The letter was not from our Austrian colleagues to us. Rather, it was from an Austrian organisation I had never heard of and it was intended for the mine owners, as the title on the envelope suggested. I resealed the envelope without reading the letter and, next day, called on Thomas Ratcliffe-Ellis, Secretary of the Mining Association of Great Britain. After some early skirmishes with him on the on-going Royal Commission, he and I had become quite friendly. Quickly, I told him about the letter, sent to me by mistake.

'And do you know what the letter says, Mr Smillie?' he asked.

'I assure you that I have not read it in its entirety,' I told him, 'but I could not help but notice that it seemed to be an offer to you.'

'An offer to us?' He laughed gently. 'What on earth could a letter from Austria offer us?'

'Something to do with Austrian and Polish workmen, I believe.' Some words had jumped off the page at me even though my glance had been extremely brief.

'Not again,' he said, shaking his head. 'Mr Smillie, I have to tell you that I don't want to see the communication, far less have anything to do with it.'

'But it really is your business, Mr Ellis,' I protested, 'and nothing at all to do with me.'

'I'm sorry,' he insisted, 'but I don't want it.'

'But what am I supposed to do with it?'

'Frankly, Mr Smillie,' he replied, grinning, 'you can start a fire with it for all I care.'

Back at the hotel, I reopened the envelope and, this time, read it carefully. To say I was appalled by what I read would be an understatement. I reproduce the letter here in full.

Gentlemen,

From reports in the national Press we notice that one of the most important subjects of discussion at this year's conference of the mining companies of Great Britain will be to ameliorate the present labour conditions, and, if possible, avoid any unjust encroachments of organised labour tyranny.

Permit us, therefore, to offer you a way. If acceptable to this conference, or to any other individual mining company, it will eventually no doubt prove to be the one possible way to repel the attacks of the Unions. The undersigned is a representative of a consortium exporting agricultural and industrial labourers to Germany, France and Scandinavia.

Wherever he goes the Polish labourer is welcome as a hard-working, obedient, and frugal man. The coal-mines of Germany, and especially the United States of America, are run chiefly and most satisfactorily by Polish labour. The chief virtue of the Pole is that he counts not the hours of labour, works willingly from ten to twelve hours a day; adapts himself to any kind of circumstances and conditions.

We are capable of supplying the mines of Great Britain with an unlimited number of men. No responsibility rests upon the employers. We house, feed, and transport the men at our own risk. All that is required of the employers is a definite wage scale per day, or per hour, and the employment of an agreed-upon number of men throughout the entire year.

We are ready to enter into communication with the companies individually or with the honoured conference as a body, and should a satisfactory understanding be possible I and two representatives of the company will immediately leave for London to attend to this matter in person. Trusting that the honoured conference will give this their due consideration, and awaiting the honour of a reply

I am, yours respectfully
ISAAC WACHTELL,
Rzeszow, Galicia,
Austria, Malykostrasse 14.
June 10th, 1909

Perhaps I should not have been as shocked as I was by the contents of the letter. However, as somebody who always tried to see the best in men, I was horrified by the duplicity of the author. Not that I was unused to Polish miners. In Lanarkshire, as elsewhere, they had been used to just the purpose suggested in the letter. But, since the passing of the 1908 Mines Act, I had assumed, perhaps rather naïvely, that a new spirit was prevailing. Not only that, but I was aware of the previous pattern when Polish labourers had been imported. They tended to be followed by other Polish miners, who brought their families with them. At that time there were almost two thousand Polish miners in Ayrshire and Lanarkshire alone. I had nothing against them as people, or as miners for that matter, but I was concerned about what their presence would mean in terms of employment opportunities for local men.

Given their lack of English, the Polish workers had often been exploited by the owners who tended to pay them lower wages than Scottish miners for the same class of work. To start with, we had also found difficulty in organising the Poles, again because of the language barriers, but also because they were conditioned in their homeland to tolerate conditions which would be unacceptable to our own. However, over time, as they learned the language and became used to our ways, we had eventually organised them and they became excellent trade unionists, as anxious as we were to improve our working and living standards.

But hundreds, perhaps thousands of men, more of them, arriving as strikebreakers, abhorred blacklegs? In 1909? It seemed out of the question, beyond the pale, to me. Not to mention the fact that the Austrian intermediary seemed to regard them as mere cattle, easily exported from one place to another. I read the letter to our executive committee, who empowered me to respond to it as I saw fit. Unusually for me, I adopted a tone of sarcasm with which to convey my contempt. Again, I reproduce the letter in full.

LONDON,
June 30th, 1909

DEAR COMRADE,

The enclosed letter has been delivered to us, but on perusal we have come to the conclusion that it has not yet reached its proper destination. We have no doubt that you were actuated by the highest and most unselfish ideals in making this kind offer, but we sincerely hope that it will not be necessary to come to you for an unlimited number of competent, practical, and hard-working fellow creatures who count not the hours of labour.

Might we suggest that arrangements for the transport, feeding and housing of the men sent here would not be sufficient.

It might be necessary to make provision for hospital accommodation and funeral arrangements.

We take it that it is the condition of the Scottish and Welsh miners that you are desirous of ameliorating.

But might we point out to you that the atmosphere in these parts is not at all healthy, and, besides, the present inhabitants of Wales and Scotland, who are descended from a wild and warlike race, have not yet reached a very high state of civilisation, and do not regard as particularly sacred the lives of foreign invaders.

We hope, dear comrade, that you at least will keep out of harm's way in any future negotiations, and we feel honoured in subscribing ourselves with hearty 'gouck auf' (good luck).

Yours fraternally
Robert Smillie

I doubt if you will be surprised to know that I never received a reply to that letter. Perhaps I got the tone about right.

Still on the subject of blacklegs, some three years later I received a telegram during the National Miners' Strike. Again, I was in London at the time and once more I was astounded at the lack of accuracy of the people who sent that telegram, particularly given the fact that it did not come from a foreign country but from much closer to home. The words of the short message was as follows:

The Strike Emergency Committee, London – Will the services of seventy mining students be any use to you? - Cane, School of Mines, Camborne.

Again, we had received a message clearly intended for the mine owners. It did make me seriously question the intelligence of some of our allegedly better-educated adversaries. Given that the sender had thoughtfully prepaid a reply, I felt it was our duty to reply. I returned the following message:

Cane, School of Mines, Camborne – Thanks for the wire offering assistance. Getting on nicely. Hoping to pull through – Mines Emergency Committee.

We heard no more of the matter from Camborne than we had of the one from Austria. Those messages gave us cause for laughter at the time, but there was a serious, almost malign, side to them as well. They were clear evidence of unscrupulous efforts to undermine legitimate industrial action. There was more bitterness felt about the offer from the School of Mines. The mine workers of this country did not easily forget that that offer to supply blackleg labour came, not from a foreign country, but from British sources. That was a bitter pill to swallow.

At last in 1909 the blinkers were removed from the eyes of the Miners' Federation. It was in that year, with a few new faces round the committee table, that I helped to finally persuade the Federation to affiliate to the Labour Party. I think that the Federation's conversion was due in part to the role that Labour MPs in parliament played in securing the Trade Disputes Act which was seen as a real milestone in union history. Not only that but, for several years, there had been a steady decline in real wages and an increasing number of disputes with employers many of whom were well known Liberals. So, within the Federation, the reputation of the Liberals was at a low ebb. Most of the officials now viewed the Labour Party as the party of their future, and so finally the Federation allied itself with the Labour Party.

The newspapers made much of the news. Other unions also affiliated that year but we were seen as the biggest catch of all for Labour. Several articles I read pointed out that if, in future, all miners voted for the Labour Party, that would swing as many as sixty parliamentary seats in its favour. In spite of the fact that these were still difficult times for working men, including those of us in the mining industry, there was a real sense of excitement in the Federation at that time. In truth, I may have been the most excited of all!

By this time, we had fewer feet running round our small household. Jeanie, Mary and John were all married and away, though not far from us. William was close to doing the same thing – James had a steady lassie, while Robert and Daniel were 'chasing the field' as the saying goes. Alexander and Joseph, at thirteen and twelve respectively, were growing up fast. Ann and I had been blessed with our children and fortunate that they were growing up as decent people, which was probably more due to her influence than mine, with me being away from home so often. It remained the case that the joy of returning home was often tempered by the thought of leaving again. It is at difficult times that a man most needs his family round him. Take 1910 for example.

Politically, 1910 was a busy year, there being two elections. In both of those, I again let my name go forward as Labour candidate for the Mid-Lanark constituency. On both occasions, I failed to get elected. I will never be sure but I suspected at the time that, in addition to residual Liberalism in the area, the fact that I was away so much counted against me. I was spending so much time away on Federation business, at the Commission, speaking at rallies across the country and all the rest of it, that people outside dear old Larkhall might well have been asking themselves – 'Bob who?' Anyway, those were the last occasions on which I contested Mid-Lanark and I was sorely in need of the love and sympathy given to me by Ann and the children still at home.

Those election defeats of 1910 set me well on my way to an election record which no parliamentarian would wish to admit to. I can claim to be the champion parliamentary defeated candidate in all of Britain. Another Labour man, Pete Curran, was a dangerous rival for this dubious title with his five defeats, and

Frank Smith, of Salvation Army renown, ran me even closer with seven losses. In total, I suffered seven-and-a-half of them. 'Hang-on Bob,' I hear you thinking, 'how do you arrive at a figure like that?' Well, a little later I will tell you about the one remaining major campaign I fought but, for now, I will content myself with letting you know about the half.

You see, I toured South Ayrshire as a prospective Labour candidate for the seat held by Sir William Arrol. As a matter of record, I eventually decided that I was unsuitable for that constituency and let another man take my place. But I did enough campaigning to justify me calling it a half-campaign. Well, that's my opinion, and my record, anyway.

During my tours of North Ayrshire, before I rescinded my candidacy, I came across a remarkable woman, Mary MacArthur, who later married a good friend of mine, William Anderson. She was the daughter of a successful businessman in Ayr, and worked in her father's drapery. He was a strong Liberal and, though he tolerated her activities in her trade union, he absolutely forbade her taking part in Labour politics. But that did not sit easily with Mary MacArthur.

'Mr Smillie,' she told me one day, 'I love my father but I find it impossible to obey his political wishes. I intend to go out and speak on your behalf.'

'But, Mary,' I told her, 'that will only cause trouble between you and your father, and I would hate to be the cause of that.'

She would not listen to me. She had made up her mind. In part, it was due to her support for Labour. Also, she felt it her duty to follow her conscience and demonstrate to women everywhere that she had a mind of her own. She spoke at a number of my meetings. Sadly, as I had warned her, this caused huge tension between her and her father. This led to Mary leaving Ayr and moving to London where she began on the great work of her life, trying to ensure the better treatment of women in the labouring workforce. Happily, she and her father became reconciled and he took great pride in the work she was doing. Mary died young, far too young, and her death was a great loss not only to her father, but also to the working women of Britain.

Although I failed in my election attempts in 1910, the Labour Party improved its position by winning forty-two seats. The situation in parliament was unusually interesting. The Liberals had had relatively poor elections and were left with only 272 seats compared with the 400 they had won in 1906. The Conservatives also won 272 seats, while the Irish Nationalists had eighty-four and ourselves forty-two. This left Campbell-Bannerman in something of a quandary as he would have to rely on the Irish and Labour to maintain a Liberal majority. Although the Irish were more numerous than we were, we presented his second quandary. He was keenly aware of the fact that, as far as mainstream politics was concerned, we were the coming party. The Irish Nationalists, if not quite a 'one-issue' group, were not going to threaten the future of the Liberal Party on the mainland. However, he saw that one day we might and so, in spite of the difficulty of the arithmetic, he continued with the Liberals' reforms, in part at least to 'out-Labour' Labour, as you might say.

Although Campbell-Bannerman was the prime minister, Lloyd George and Churchill were the big names of the day. I did not realise at that time that I would have many dealings with them in the future. They were both ambitious men, determined to establish their reputations. I believe that they both wanted to help the poor, particularly Lloyd George, but in so doing they also wanted to further their own careers. Later, I would find out from both men how 'political' politicians can be. Lloyd George was always keen to be involved in really big matters which would attract public attention, not only to the matter in hand but also to himself. And I remember an article in a newspaper at that time – I do not recollect the exact source – which said of Churchill, 'He is out for adventure: he follows politics as he would follow the hounds. I wonder whether he has any driving motive save ambition.' All of which might well have been, indeed probably was, true. However, in spite of their own ambitions, both men did some good for the Labour Movement. They did harm too, of course. I will tell you more about both in a little while.

If I was enjoying little personal success on the electoral front, in 1911 I secured an honour which, in all frankness, meant even more to me. By now, you will have realised that I was a mining man through and through. My sole reason for venturing into politics was from my belief that the miners, and other workers, would be best served by having as many parliamentary representatives as possible. But, apart from the actual election campaigns, I did not work at becoming a parliamentarian as so many did. That may well explain my continuing lack of success in my attempts to become one. My time and efforts were always far more devoted to the union side of the Labour Movement. My work as branch secretary, then county secretary and, again, as a member of the Federation, had always been more important to me than seeking public office.

In these circumstances, perhaps you can imagine my delight when, in 1911, I was elected Vice-President of the Miners' Federation of Great Britain. When I got home with the news, Ann told me she hadn't seen me so excitedly happy about anything, apart from the births of our children. I think my excitement can be easily explained. You see, there are those offices to which a person can be appointed on the basis of the right qualifications, a good speaking voice and, perhaps, a pleasant personality. I would not seek to denigrate those things, but my election as Vice-President of the Federation was not based on those sorts of factors. Those who elected me know me well. I had worked with them for years. I was one of them. They knew exactly what I could and could not do. They knew me with an intimacy which no elector knew about a prospective MP. I had been elevated to a position of influence by my peers, and that meant a great deal to me.

One thing that intrigued me was this. They all knew that I was a Socialist, which numbers of them were not. They would have realised that I would push for a more Socialist approach in our work, and yet they still elected me. What, I wondered, did that suggest about the future? I was not daunted by the prospect: instead, I felt a deep well of excitement.

In that year, I also had the pleasure of renewing my acquaintance with Jean Jaurès when he was visiting London. He was speaking at a Socialist conference but sought me out at my hotel. Jean Longuet was not with him this time but he was in the company of a fellow delegate who spoke excellent English. We settled into the hotel lounge and, remembering his hospitality in Paris years earlier, I provided large glasses of lager beer. Not bothering with his interpreter, Jean addressed me directly.

'Bonjour, Monsieur le President,' he said smiling and raising his glass.

'Not quite right' I told him, laughing. 'I am merely the Vice-President.'

We blethered for some time and, as it had in Paris, our conversation turned to foreign affairs outside my immediate field, and I felt rather less the stupid pupil that I had done the first time we had talked. Nevertheless, I was still amazed at his grasp of things and his detailed knowledge.

'Your man Fisher,' he asked me through his colleague, 'does he get his four Dreadnoughts a year?' referring to Jackie Fisher's efforts at the Admiralty to maintain Britain's naval lead over Germany. 'Or are the rumours correct?'

'Which rumours may those be?' I asked him.

'That your Government cannot afford four, so is laying down the keels of only three capital ships each year.'

'I believe you are right,' I replied. Indeed, I knew he was. 'Mind you, that's still a lot of naval tonnage.'

'It is indeed, Bob. Indeed it is.' A sad smile. 'And for London, read Paris, Berlin, Rome and St Petersburg. All the nations engaged in the same old race.'

'Scotland isn't,' I said, laughing.

'Vive l'Ecosse!' he cried, after having my words translated.

'You think it is becoming really serious, then?' I asked him.

'Deadly serious, I am afraid, old friend.' Then he slapped me on the knee. 'But don't worry, Bob. The lights are still on!'

A few years later, I would remember those last words of Jean, whom I never saw again. A statesman who would talk about lights on the eve of the greatest horror the world has ever known.

XIII

Reform and Reversal

FROM MY YOUNGER days, by which I mean the time when I began to give any serious thought to the world and its works, I suppose that I had been generally liberal in my outlook. By that, I do not mean that I was a Liberal, just liberal in my views. There is a difference between those two things. However, once I had worked in the mines for a few years and saw the reality for working men at first hand, my views strengthened and, as you know, I embraced Socialism. Mine was not a socialism born of theories such as those of Marx. Rather, it was Socialism born of experience and supported by my conviction that working men had to represent themselves in what are known as the corridors of power. So, by the time that the twentieth century was well under way, I was no great political friend of the Liberals. True, I found them in the round to be more sympathetic towards the lot of ordinary people than the Conservatives generally were, but you must understand that I was no supporter of the Liberal Party. I emphasise that point because I feel the need now to pay tribute to the Liberal Party, for its efforts on behalf of working men, women and families during the early years of this century. I wished you to be clear that I will pay this tribute from without rather than within.

The Liberal Government which took office in 1905, won two elections, then governed until 1915, and was the first British government not to be dominated by wealthy landowners and aristocrats. There were some of those but, in the main, they were lawyers, writers, journalists, educated men who knew the world. The prime minister, Mr Henry Campbell-Bannerman was a businessman and, by Liberal standards anyway, a radical, as were many members of his cabinet. The early stars of that government were Asquith, as Chancellor, and Lloyd George at the Board of Trade. Over time, I would get to know both of them. When Asquith became prime minister in 1908, Lloyd George became Chancellor and Churchill went to the Board of Trade. These two would be the engineers of many of the Liberals' reforms.

I will not bore you with too many details of those reforms. This is not, after all, a history book. However, a number of them touched our people so keenly that they are worthy of mention. I have already mentioned the Trade Disputes Act and its beneficial effects. There was a further Trade Union Act in 1913 which also helped us by remedying the Osborne Judgement of 1909 which declared it illegal for unions to demand a political levy of its members. The 1913 Act helped to stabilise Labour Party funds which had already been eased somewhat by the introduction in 1911 of an annual salary of £400 for MPs.

A number of measures were introduced to help children. Local education authorities were empowered to provide free meals for needy children, special juvenile courts were set up for child offenders and a 'free place' system was put into secondary schools which had to reserve 25% of their places for children from elementary schools.

Alongside the Poor Law, a system of old age pensions was introduced, and the Compensation Act allowed workers to claim compensation for injury or ill health caused by industrial conditions as well as for injuries caused by accidents. A Merchant Shipping Act regulated standards of food and accommodation on British-registered ships, and an Act of 1912 attempted to establish in practice the principal of a minimum working wage. Labour Exchanges were introduced and proved useful at a time of high unemployment.

New ground was broken by The Trades Board Act of 1909, introduced by Churchill. Eventually, some 400,000 of the lowest-paid workers, mainly women, received a degree of protection they had not enjoyed before. The Shops Act provided a statutory half-day holiday each week though some employers got round this provision by making employees work extra hours on other days to make up for it.

Perhaps the most important piece of legislation was the National Insurance Act of 1911. Very much Lloyd George's initiative, it was a compulsory scheme in two parts. The scheme was a contributory one into which workers themselves had to pay. We in the Labour Movement believed it should be non-contributory but Lloyd George believed that, with the added burden of old age pensions, The Treasury could not afford a non-contributory scheme. The reason for the introduction of health insurance was in part a desire for a greater national efficiency, though Lloyd George himself was genuinely shocked at the annual death toll from tuberculosis, estimated at 75,000 souls. Unemployment insurance was to a large extent a response to pressure from us, the Labour Party and the trade unions. Without question, great reformer though he was, Lloyd George's work often had the objective of heading off Socialism.

There were other reforms too, but it was the National Insurance Act which caused the greatest furore. To hear the Conservatives whine about it, you would have thought that it was an edict from Karl Marx himself. They managed to bring together a range of dissenting voices in support of their negativism. They turned some workers against the Act by persuading them to believe that no government had the right to force people to pay directly into the scheme from their wages. They had many doctors on their side of the argument too. Medical men argued that, under the new system, they would lose their independence. Also, some Friendly Societies and insurance companies argued that they might lose business as a result of the changes.

On our side too, there was opposition. Labour moderates by and large accepted the changes as representing an advance. However, the stronger Socialists, like my good friend Keir Hardie, spoke out against the Act. They were totally against the contributory principle and demanded higher taxes on the wealthy so that the scheme would become a genuinely collectivist solution to the problem of poverty. He also argued that, given how small the State contribution would be, workers were effectively being forced to finance their own sickness benefit. I was never an economist and, from time to time, I found my head buzzing with the complexities of the argument. A fact I candidly admitted to Keir one day in London.

'You don't seriously mean to say that you support Lloyd George on this, do you?' Disbelief was etched on his face.

'Well, you have to admit it is an advance,' I suggested.

'An advance! Did you say an advance?' He was more astonished than angry. 'It's my opinion that an advance from nought per cent to ten per cent, when you could go all the way to a hundred per cent, is no advance at all.'

'But the cost, Keir,' I said to him, only vaguely sure of my facts. 'Lloyd George says the treasury can't afford a non-contributory scheme. How could we afford one?'

'I'll tell you how, Bob,' he replied, in a more volatile tone than he normally used. 'Less money on bloody Dreadnoughts and more money on people. That's how!'

He and I never quite saw eye to eye on this issue. In an ideal world, I would have shared his view. But maybe I had been down the pits, and working for miners, for so long that I realised, perhaps better than he did, that the real world was not an ideal place. That it was somewhere in which progress might have to be achieved in small measures. In the main, I simply asked myself if my mining workmates would benefit from the provision of the Act. On the whole, I believed that they would, so I tended to be in favour of it. At the same time, I hoped that Keir Hardie's ideal world would not be too long in the coming and that then we could do even better.

From what I have written, you may think that I have been describing the start of a golden age for ordinary people and that I was an unqualified admirer of everything that the Liberals did. In that case, you would be mistaken. I am happy to pay tribute to much of their work during that period, but I will also tell you that there were many weaknesses in their legislation, some of those weaknesses being very serious indeed. Taken together, the Liberals' reforms took some of the sharpest edges off poverty but they could, and should, have gone further.

There were some things that were hardly touched by legislation. Hardly any of the recommendations of the Poor Law Commission Reports were carried out, other than establishing Labour Exchanges. Nothing was done for agricultural workers, who were the lowest-paid of all. Aspects of some reforms were voluntary and therefore, in practice, quite useless. Disturbingly, by 1914 the percentage of army volunteers rejected as physically unfit was as high as it had been in 1900. Also, there was no attempt whatsoever to create a fairer society by equalising opportunity and reward. The reforms, though often welcome and beneficial, fell some considerable way short of changing the lives of the vast majority in a way significant enough to make them believe that they were equal in life with the favoured minority.

But should we be surprised by that? I certainly wasn't then and am no more so now as I look back. You see, although not a party of the great landowners and aristocracy, the Liberals at that time were still a class apart from the majority. Oh, you will hear people say that their reforms did not go any further because of the strong opposition of the Conservatives and, indeed, from the non-radical wing of their own party. But the real truth goes deeper than that. The Liberal cabinet, to a man, came from a background of at least relative comfort, good education and self-certainty. Land-owning aristocrats they may not have been, but they were clear that they were not something else too. They were not working men in the sense that I, and many millions of others, would have understood that to mean. Though they were very often sympathetic towards us, as shown by many of their reforms – and I salute them for that – they were not of us. Neither, in my experience, did they wish to be of us. They did not view us with the contempt which the great landowners and their followers generally did, but they still did not quite see us as being the same as them. It was as if we were children to be looked after, perhaps even loved, but never to be treated as equals. It was, rather as I suggested before, a case of 'grannie giving sweeties to the bairns', which was tolerable to a degree, but far from the situation those of us immersed in the Labour Movement wished for our future.

Clear evidence of the massive inequality in British life was easy to find in the summer of 1911, five years after the Liberals' programme of reforms began. I spent a lot of time in London that summer, to the extent that I dreadfully missed my family and home in Larkhall. Not only was I attending the final sessions of the Royal Commission, I was also heavily engaged on behalf of the Miners' Federation, discussing with Labour MPs ideas such as the continuing poor safety conditions in the mines. There were gaps in my schedule of course. Sadly, not long enough that I could very often make the long journey home to see Ann. Instead I did a lot of walking around London. I always found that walking was good for clearing my head and giving me time to think. June, July and mid-August were particularly hot that year, there were plenty of people out and about, and I saw much to think about.

Over the bank holiday weekend of August 5-7th, for example, it seemed like the whole population of London was on the move. After so many weeks of heat, people were determined to enjoy the fresh air. Those with money travelled by car or taxi to the coast. Those with less money used the excellent railway service. Towns like Ramsgate and Margate quickly filled with Londoners anxious to enjoy the delights of the seaside.

It seemed that the city itself was only populated by two groups of people. On the one hand, there were the wealthy. No doubt their numbers were reduced by those undertaking their annual foreign tours but, in the better parts of town, there were still plenty of them to be seen. These were the people who, almost literally, owned the country. At that time, it was estimated that fewer than seven hundred families owned almost a third of Great Britain. I cannot vouch for that. As I have told you, I was never a master of economics, but I can vouch for the fact that, during that long hot summer, the few seemed to own the centre of London.

The royal family visited Cowes for the regatta, Henley was as popular as ever, and debutantes were wildly keen to be photographed in their finery. Society weddings drew all the best people and the best hotels were doing a fine trade. Occasionally, I would rest during one of my lengthy walks, across the road from one of the hotels in the Savoy group, which included Simpson's, Claridge's and the Berkeley as well as the Savoy itself. I heard that the Savoy's reputation had soared after Edward VII had persuaded the great French chef, Escoffier, to leave Paris and work in London. I wish I could tell you how fine the food was at the Savoy but, alas, I was never invited to dine there.

I would stand and watch the hotel guests come and go. By then, very few arrived in horse-drawn carriages, though there was the occasional quite brilliant one emblazoned with crests. But most guests came and went by motor vehicle. I used to think that, outside those great hotels, I would see more vehicles in one hour than were in the whole of Lanarkshire and Ayrshire put together. The expensively dressed guests would be met and dispatched by doormen and concierges dressed in the most ornate uniforms. Those hotel employees would bow deeply in order to ingratiate themselves with the wealthy customers. I tried to imagine myself doing that, but found the idea sticking in my throat. On the other hand, I knew quite well why they did it. Their wages were so low that they needed the occasional sixpenny tip from hotel guests to allow them to, as we said in Scotland, put food on the table.

Those guests and hotel workers were, by and large, of the same nationality. All born from their mothers' wombs, they shared a common language and the same biology. In effect, they were of the same people. Yet their lives were so different. The guests had wealth and, no doubt, power and influence. The hotel workers had none of these things. The former were pampered, waited on hand and foot. the latter had to fend for themselves and behave ingratiatingly merely to survive. The tableaux I witnessed at the portals of those great hotels reminded me more clearly than most things of Burns' 'sair divided' world.

The great parks were perhaps quieter than usual. With so many of the city's inhabitants away at the seaside, the pathways and drives were mainly populated by people I described to myself as 'strollers.' Well dressed men, wearing top hats and carrying silver-topped canes, walking slowly and discussing the affairs of the day. Exquisitely dressed ladies, mainly in long white dresses and frothy hats to withstand the heat of the sun. Well fed children skipping along, rolling hoops or spinning tops. An idyllic scene, you might say. And you would be right. But in addition to the seaside-bound thousands, and the strollers in the parks and hotels, there was another side to London, a side that no tourist would find pleasing to the eye. It was where you saw the other kind of people.

Among the families who owned Britain, there was total ignorance of the lives of the poor. A renowned trade unionist by the name of Ben Tillett showed me round the areas of the East End of London, in particular near the docks, where his people lived their lives in appalling squalor. You would not have known it from the air of rich gaiety in the centre of London, but Ben was then leading a strike of dockworkers. Their poor pay and lack of job security forced them into this. If a man was lucky enough to find work, he would be paid sixpence an hour. If he obtained work for the whole week, he might earn 25/- and that would do little more than pay his weekly rent for a single room to house his whole family. And that man might even be the lucky one. Too often, men would wait all day for work but, if there was not enough movement on the Thames, there might be no work at all and they would have to go home empty-handed. This had gone on too long and a tidal wave of frustration and rage born of desperation broke out. So, the dockers went on strike.

When I visited the London docks with Ben Tillett, the area was deathly still. Where there was usually frantic activity, with men sweating over their labours, there was only inertia. The huge black doors at the entrance to the docks were shut and the towering cranes stood still, like accusing fingers. There was only one sign of life there, and a cruel sight it was too. Above the London Wharf stood the largest mechanical sign in Europe. Electrically wired to make it stand out, it was a huge caricature of a Scotsman, wearing a grotesque kilt, brimming glass held in one hand. It was the famous advertisement for Dewar's whisky. It seemed a particularly cruel location for this unseemly giant, poised high above thousands of men who, even if they had been able to afford whisky, had little in their lives worth celebrating.

The sights of the living quarters of the dockers and their families was offensive to my eyes. So many souls squashed into so few rooms in such densely-packed streets. Years earlier, I had thought Glasgow to be a crowded city, and when I first went to Larkhall I found some of the older colliery rows far too over-crowded. But what I saw close to the docks in London was worse again. It was heart-breaking. I left imbued with some of the same rage as Ben Tillett must have felt, and I had only been there a few short hours. Anybody who might have felt that the Liberal

reforms were over-generous and heralded some kind of golden age wholly unde-
served by its alleged beneficiaries should have spent some time there with me.
Mind you, the way some people view the world, it probably would not have made
a whit of difference.

London at that time was a mirror to our whole society. There, the extremes
were evident on a daily basis. The privileged minority thoroughly enjoyed their
lives, very often in ignorance of the despairing poor living so close to them, and
yet in a dark world entirely of their own. Between those two extremes, there existed a growing number who were neither wealthy nor poor. They were educated,
worked in the professions, or some other safe occupation, lived in comfortable
homes and viewed themselves as successes. Many, no doubt, aspired to be as
wealthy as those in the class above them. None would have wished to be as poor
as those in the classes beneath. Those generally satisfied and purposeful people
were the middle class. They were also the Liberals.

During those years of political hubbub, I was rather more than a detached
observer. For reasons which I have already somewhat embarrassedly explained to
you, I was hardly at the centre of things. I was not a parliamentarian. However,
as Vice-President of the Miners' Federation, I had regular contact with Labour
politicians with whom I had many meetings. Usually, these were to discuss strategies by which Labour MPs and the trade unions could maintain pressure for
reform on an occasionally wavering government. With the blessing of Enoch
Edwards, our retiring President, I quite often found myself in London leading
our delegation in talks with our parliamentary colleagues. I have to assume that
I made a reasonable success of presenting our views because, in 1912, a signal
honour befell me. One which, given certain circumstances which I will now
describe, I could hardly have anticipated.

It may or may not come as a surprise to you that all organisations suffer from
the devil known as 'internal politics.' However united a front it may present to
the outside world, any organisation will have its arguments among its members.
Often enough, these arguments will be positive in their outcomes, based on principle and centring on policy and strategy. All organisations need such arguments;
they are developmental and healthy. However, there are other kinds of arguments
which are more negative in nature, and consist of members' personal views of
other members. These arguments can be very destructive and hinder progress.
Men can become too interested in attacking one another for personal reasons
rather than proposing or countering serious arguments. I would never go so far
as to say that the Miners' Federation ever suffered from that level of interperson-
al difficulties but there were issues which occasionally weakened our cohesion.

Men are different to one another. I do not mean by social class, important
though that can be. Rather, I mean they come from difference strains, products
of differing geographies, cultures and beliefs. I was always very aware of the fact

that that was the case with the Miners' Federation. Our membership was drawn from across Britain, and the members brought with them the traditions of those areas. Believe it or not, one of the issues which tended to separate us, rather than bring us together, was religion. Or, should I say, our varying practices in, and views of, religion.

Given the respective sizes of the countries involved, the Church of England was the majority church among our members. However, there was also a significant number of Methodists among us. Most of the Welsh, to start with. That number, of course, included the great Mabon, greatly sought after not only as an orator, but also as a singer and preacher. The same could be said of Enoch Edwards, our president from 1911-12. Brought up on the outskirts of Stoke, he had inherited the Methodist tradition of people like Hugh Bourne and William Clowes. Throughout the time I knew him, Enoch preached every Sunday he was at home in his home town of Burslem. Meantime, those of us from Scotland brought two traditions to this religious feast. Alas, those of us who were Presbyterians regarded the Church of England as prelatical, while our Roman Catholics regarded it as heretical. You may think it odd these days that such difference could cause any tension, but our members often took their religions as seriously as their union activities.

Do not think that our religious differences caused great animosity, for that would be an exaggeration. However, it would be accurate to say that many members quite naturally looked more kindly towards people of their own cultures than on others. Which was why I was rather surprised to be elected Vice-President of the Federation in 1911. It had been mooted before, but dear old Sam Woods, of the majority culture, was regularly elected instead. I did hear that Sam, who had been ailing for some time, was the one who had worked behind the scenes to get me elected as Vice-President, but I was never entirely certain about that.

In retrospect, I believe that a more sensitive soul than me might have seen what was coming his way by the autumn of 1912. After all, Enoch Edwards himself had frequently delegated me to lead at major events, most particularly in London, in his stead. However, I do not believe that I was ever much of a fortune teller. So, when we gathered in Swansea for the twenty-fourth Annual Conference of the Federation between October 1st and 4th, I was simply looking forward to lively debates on the recent Coal Mines Act. That was more or less what we got, and I was leading speaker in a number of sessions.

Then it was time for the election of officials to the representative committee. I could hardly believe the result: I was voted in unanimously as president! I quite candidly admit that I was close to tears when I made my presidential address. There were so many people to thank and, sadly, a rather long list that year of friends who had passed away. I offered thanks and dedications to each in turn and concluded by promising to continue to work hard on behalf of the Federation, clarify our positions on the important issues, and work even more closely with our brothers in parliament. The round of applause at the end of my address provided me with one of the most emotional moments of my life.

As I was catching my train at Swansea Station the next morning, big Mabon came panting along the platform, thrust a newspaper into my hand and told me, 'You've got a lot to live up to, Bob Smillie.' He was still laughing at me as the train pulled out. I didn't have time to study the newspaper at length to find out what he meant, for there was my face smiling out at me on page one. It was a report of my election and my address to the conference. Well, it was a very long journey back to Larkhall, so I had all the time in the world to read the report. I believe my face and neck flushed red with embarrassment as I read the words written in such a glowing tone. Was it really me who the un-named reporter was writing about? Apparently, I was one of the 'great pioneer Socialists' of whom the report claimed 'his qualities were gaining him an ascendancy over the other leaders and among all the miners of the United Kingdom'. I hope I don't suffer from undue vanity but I have to admit that I felt a thrill of pride when I read that article. 'No' bad,' I told myself, 'for a poor miner from Larkhall.'

Grateful to be at home for a few days, I asked Ann what she thought of the newspaper report. 'Pleased to have a famous husband?' I asked her.

'Well, they got your name right,' she replied, 'but I'm not too sure about the rest of it.' Smiling, she leaned over my chair and kissed me gently. 'But I'm right proud of you, Bob Smillie. I really am.'

Those few words meant even more to me than my election or the round of applause which greeted my presidential address. As for the newspaper report, I believe it was used to light the fire the next morning.

I have deliberately left to the last in this piece an event which was momentous and, perhaps less importantly, almost got me involved in a scandal. The event was the Miners' National Strike in the spring of 1912 during which a million miners came out in dispute against grievances which no negotiations had been able to remedy. I had been involved in those negotiations while still Vice-President of the Federation so you can see that it pre-dates my election to the presidency. However, it is such an important event in itself that I have decided to deal with it on its own so that the details do not become confused with other events.

The Liberals' Minimum Wage Act was a reaction to our strike, a wholly use-less one as it turned out. We had been campaigning for what became known as the 'fives and twos' – a minimum wage of five shillings per man per shift, and two shillings for a boy. As I said, the negotiations failed and there was a nationwide agreement to strike. This was the first time in Britain that such a thing had hap-pened. The closest parallel was perhaps the Russian General Strike of 1905. Unsurprisingly, in certain quarters our action was greeted by howls of outrage.

The strike was described by Lord Cecil as 'part of a great conspiracy ... an attempt to gain powers over the industries of this country by a small band of revolutionaries.' His attitude reflected the outspoken views of many other Conservatives, some Liberals, and many newspapers.

But nothing could have been further from the truth. Our aims were much more basic than that. Our living standards which, as you know, had never been high, had actually suffered since the turn of the century in spite of all the Liberals' reforms. For example, the price of bread, a staple part of any mining family's diet, had risen by 25% over a decade. Our wages had not, so we were actually worse off than we had been. This was true of other commodities as well. Hunger in mining areas was commonplace. No doubt Lord Cecil and his like simply hadn't noticed that! While there may have been some among our numbers who were full of revolutionary fervour, as a body the miners were striking to make sure that their families could eat.

Within days of the start of the strike, industries began to slow down, then close down, due to lack of coal. Asquith's cabinet was in a lather of indecision. The prime minister and the king exchanged letters, both worried about the situation, and a royal tour to Europe was postponed. Meanwhile, negotiations resumed and the Foreign Office was often used as a base for meetings between the Mine Owners' Association and our Federation. During one session, a rather odd thing happened. I had to leave a meeting to take a phone call from Jim Gallacher, one of our local officials in Hamilton. He was in an excited mood.

'Boab, this bluidy telegram ye sent ... '

'Telegram?' What telegram?'

'The one tellin' us tae gae back to work,' he shouted down the echoing line. 'Ye've settled wi' the owners.'

'Take no notice of it, Jim,' I told him. 'There's no telegram from me.' Then I added grimly, 'and no settlement either.'

It turned out that such a telegram had indeed been sent, bearing my name. It had been dispatched from Parliament Street in London, just after that morning's joint conference had broken up. Clearly, it was sent by somebody anxious to disrupt the Federation's work, get the Lanarkshire men back to work, and suggest to the outside world that there was a lack of solidarity in our strike. I had my suspicions as to who the perpetrator was, but never got enough proof to accuse him. It was an unwholesome affair which reminded me of the earlier anti-union actions from Austria and the Mines School.

After only a week of our strike, the prime minister was in a state of near panic. Around him, industries were grinding to a halt and the clamour for action was resounding from the Conservatives in the Commons and the Lords as well as the national press. Asquith took it badly and aged visibly. I was sorry about that. I had met him and his wife Margot on a number of informal occasions and they had both behaved most affably towards me. Privately, I believed her to be the stronger of the two, and certainly more sympathetic to my points of view. It was generally held that she exerted considerable influence on him though, for obvious reasons. I cannot vouch for that. What I can tell you is that, to my great amazement, I received a letter from her, delivered to my hotel. We had talked briefly only the day before at a lunch hosted by Sir George Asquith and had talked for a little while, but why on earth would she be writing to me of all people?

In later memoirs and reports, it was claimed that I had agreed that I would meet Margot Asquith, an agreement alleged to have been reached at the lunch I have referred to. I came to no such agreement with her. Why on earth would I have done so? Yet her letter to me suggested that, for no reason I have ever understood, I had agreed to meet her to discuss the strike, the miners' motives, what we needed and wanted, and all the rest of it. I was totally dumbfounded by it all. I was already involved in negotiations with the mine owners and involved in tripartite talks in which the Government was represented. What more could I have told her and what difference would it have made anyway? I put her letter down to stress on her part. Her words made it clear that, in addition to her concern for the country, she was also in some fear for her husband who was coming under almost intolerable pressure to resolve the strike.

I felt sorry for the good lady, but what was I supposed to do? Our Federation had set procedures for negotiations and they did not include the involvement of third parties, even it the third party was the PM's wife. In her letter, she advised me to 'keep your blood warm. Don't let it get cold'. In all truth, I felt that her blood was running over-warm in her anxiety. My decision was perhaps ungallant. I did not write back to her to confirm or reject our alleged meeting. I did not do this out of any coldness of heart. In the same way as her husband had, I had a major strike on my hands and had to concentrate all my energies on negotiations. I had no time to meet her, however well intentioned she might have been, had no desire to encourage her to believe that I might, and felt that any return message from me might have compromised my position and, by association, that of the Federation.

To my increased amazement, she wrote again. This time, she said she did not want to discuss the strike at all. Given the tone of her first letter, this made me wonder about the balance of her mind. She claimed that I interested her and that she wanted to discuss what she called 'abstract ideas' with me. She suggested a meeting place, the house of Sir Edward Grey of all people. Again, she virtually begged my presence. My quandary returned. Again, I was not certain what to do. I had no wish to insult or hurt the lady, but I wanted no part of any private discussions with her. In the real world, political heat was being turned up over the strike so, again, I neither answered her letter nor kept the suggested appointment.

I cannot leave the subject of Margot Asquith without saying that I admired her support of her husband and her clear interest in the mining community. However, if she had wanted, as she claimed in her first letter to me, a better understanding of the aims of the strike, she might have done better to enlist the conversational attitudes of John Cairns, a miner from Northumberland. In a famous article, he explained our position quite clearly. 'Our men have been under the thumb of the masters from at least 1870 until now and our men are more refined that they were forty years ago. They desire better homes, better food, better clothing, better conditions.' As I remarked earlier, that National Miners' Strike had little if anything to do with insurgency or now revolution. Rather, it had to do with life.

By March 27th, the strike in its fourth week, Asquith decided to act. In a parliamentary session which began at 10.30 at night, he introduced the third reading of a Minimum Wage Bill. According to witnesses, including the Labour MPs in the house, he was in a highly emotional state. To an extent he was addressing not only the house, but us as well, pleading with the unions to 'stay the havoc' as he put it. Normally a calm and lucid speaker, in tears he begged the House to pass the Bill which would set up local district boards to provide locally agreed minimum wages. Yes, he really did cry because he felt humiliated. It could be argued that this was the first time since the Civil War that the sanctity of parliament had been breached, forced into legislation by what most of the newspapers referred to as 'an unelected body', that is to say those of us in the mining community. I do not believe he was ever the same man again.

Well, he got his vote and the Bill was passed. This left us in a very difficult position. That new piece of legislation was a concession of sorts. However, it fell well short of the guarantee we had been seeking. Effectively, the Government had delegated responsibility to local boards and who could tell at what levels they would set the minimum wages? Many on our committee felt that they would be unlikely to be at the level of the 'fives and twos' we had been demanding. For this reason, opinion among committee members was split. In spite of the fact that I was reputed to be among the most Socialist of our officials, I spoke in favour of ending the strike. There were several reasons for that. First, the provisions of the new Act would at least take decisions about our wages out of the sole grip of the mine owners and that had to be a good thing. Second, I believed that the new provision was likely to be the best outcome we were likely to achieve. If the strike had carried on much longer, the Government might even have fallen and powers might have passed back to the Conservatives who would most likely have immediately repealed the Act. Third, the strike was causing hardship to fellow workers in other industries which had fallen idle. Fourth, our men were being tested to the limit. With little money coming in, if any at all, absolute hunger was a real possibility. As ever in a strike, it was the strikers themselves who were worst hit. These arguments carried the day and the strike was called off. It was no great victory, I have to add. The Government had been badly embarrassed and we had not achieved what we really wanted. On the other hand, the strike had sent out a clear message. That miners were strong and organised, and would never again quietly suffer the oppression which had been our lot for so long.

I cannot leave this subject without commenting on the oft-stated views that we were 'an unelected body intent on revolution'. As pieces of crass stupidity go, that view had to rank pretty highly. The Federation had always been a democratic group, its officials elected by its members. Major proposals were always put to the men at pithead ballots. We had the will of the vast majority of our members behind that strike. True, we were not parliamentarians elected by the voting public, but are parliamentarians not supposed to represent the wishes of that public? That being the case, the wishes of our section of the public were not being represented at all. Further, who ever elected a mine owner? Nobody, as far as I know. Throughout industrial history, they have been 'an unelected body' and few people in positions of influence ever query their right to undertake actions injurious to others.

As far as the idea that we were revolutionaries is concerned, that was an absurdity put about to frighten the public. As a body, the Federation was a long way short of being militantly Socialist. I was considered to be among the most left-leaning among us, and I never entertained the idea of starting a revolution. Change, yes. Better opportunities for working people, of course. A redistribution of the power bases in industry: yes, I was in favour of that too. But a revolution to bring down parliamentary structures, remove the monarchy, and destroy the nation? That was never in my thoughts. All that mattered to me at that time was finding ways of ensuring fairer play for the people in the mining community..

The best example of our desire to improve the lot of the miner can be found in the words of George Barker, one of our officials in South Wales. When presenting the case for a minimum wage, he commented:

> Let us now look at the family budget, which will work out at something like this for a family of six persons. Rent, six shillings per week, coal one shilling and six pence, fuel one shilling, clothing and footwear five shillings, club doctor and Federation one shilling, making a total of fourteen shillings and six pence. This leaves ten shillings and three pence a week to feed six persons. Allowing a bare three meals a day, eighteen meals a week – 126 meals in total – with 123 pence to pay for them, or less than a penny per meal per head.
>
> Have we overstated our case? No, if anything it is understated. There are thousands in this movement that are existing for less than one pence per meal per head.

These figures would have suggested living conditions way beyond the experience of any mine owner, the likes of Lord Cecil, or Mr Asquith. If trying to secure better wages for our members in order to improve such awful living conditions made us revolutionaries of some sort, then I am content to be called one. But the reality was that few people outside the mining communities, and other groups of working people, knew what it was really like to suffer such hardship and indignity on a daily basis. If a revolution was indeed necessary, then it would have to be a revolution in the minds of men.

XIV

Places and Policies

I RECOGNISE THE fact that different organisations work in different ways. Their structures may be unique to them and the ways in which officials are deployed may vary a lot. However, I have never understood why any organisation would wish to have at its head a president but expect that role to be merely honorary or symbolic. Any dictionary will tell you that a president is ... 'one who presides: the chief officer of a society'. It is clear to me from that sort of definition that a president must be a leader. If his role is to mean anything at all. From the day of my election to the presidency, I was determined that I would lead. Otherwise, what would have been the point in accepting the honour in the first place?

Of course, there are different styles of leadership and it is not for me to say which one is best. To a great extent, those different styles are based on personality rather than belief. For example, had the great Mabon ever been President of the Federation, I am sure he would have conducted his presidency in a style very different to mine, even though our views were generally similar. I can imagine that he would have been an inspiring leader, his great soaring oratory lifting our aspirations. I smile to imagine him even singing to us, given that he rarely missed an opportunity to do so. As you may guess, my style was very different. I actually enjoyed debate. I believed that every man's view, however different to mine, was worth hearing. And when there was a conflict of opinion, which was not unusual during meetings on important issues, it was my role to state my own position as clearly as possible and try to draw different factions together. As far as I can recollect, I never shouted, never thumped any tubs, and never banged any drums. Instead, I concentrated on the details of any argument and, by sticking to the facts, did my best to reconcile differences. In honesty, my style never made me an exciting president, but I believe that it made me reliable and credible.

I doubt if it is common knowledge, but one normal requirement of the presidency almost caused me to give it up only weeks after taking it on. It was expected that the president should devote all his time to the interests of the Federation. In itself, that was entirely what I would have expected and it presented no problem whatsoever to me. However, a corollary did. Our headquarters were in London and I lived in Larkhall, some few hundred miles away. There was a clear expectation that I should live in London, the hub of the universe as far as major

issues were concerned. I was unhappy at the thought of living there on a permanent basis, so far from home, but I went through the motions of house-hunting
in the neighbourhood of our central offices in Russell Square. I found nowhere
suitable, though I suspect that that failure was more to do with my black mood
rather than the choice of housing. Much troubled, I returned to Larkhall to discuss the matter with Ann.

'I think I will have to resign the presidency,' I told her.

'But, Robert,' she said, 'You can't do that. You have only just been elected,
and I know you have such great plans for the Federation.'

'But I will not live in London,' I replied. 'Spending a lot of time there is one
thing, but living there, so far from my home in Larkhall, is out of the question.
Unless ... '

'Unless what, Robert?'

'Unless you and the little ones come to London with me.' I watched her face
carefully. In spite of her efforts, I could see a gloom settling there. 'Not that you
have to, of course,' I added.

'I'll do whatever you think best,' she said, trying to smile but failing miserably.
That told me everything I needed to know.

On the train journey back to London, I made up my mind. I was not prepared
to uproot Ann and the bairns from Larkhall and their friends and relatives.
Neither was I prepared to live in London on my own. I reported my feelings to
the executive committee as soon as I reached Russell Square and suggested to
them that they should seek a president who would be happy to live near his place
of work. To my amazement and delight, they told me that they wanted me to continue as president and that I could continue to live in Larkhall.

So began a period, which turned out to be much longer than I would have predicted, when I made innumerable journeys to London. On my first journeys years
earlier, I had travelled during the day, keeping my nose pressed against the window to take in all the sights as we moved along. But by now, a seasoned traveller,
I generally travelled overnight. I made the compartment into a bedroom and,
before trying to snatch a few hours of sleep, I would pour over whatever papers
were relevant to coming meetings. I normally arrived in time to join the trek of
workers heading for their places of employment, but I doubted if any of them had
travelled as far as I had. My arrangements were perhaps not ideal for the president of a large organisation but, over a period of many years, I hardly missed a
meeting in London. Most precious of all to me, I never had to give up my home
in Larkhall and, though I was away from there too often, my family was always
there to welcome me when I returned.

I would think it likely that if I hadn't so often expressed my admiration for
the place, many of you would never have heard of Larkhall. 'Hands up,' as the
primary school teacher might say. 'How many of you had heard of Larkhall before

reading Bob's memoirs?' I would imagine that most of your hands would have stayed down. Not that Larkhall is famous: it isn't. Not that it is a particularly handsome town: it isn't. Not that it's a place of finery: no, it's far from being that. But it was my place, you see. My place and my family's, and that was my main reason for loving it so dearly. But I didn't just love that wee town: I was proud of it. Let me explain why.

Although Larkhall was not even mentioned in the atlas in common use in the local schools, it did have its features of interest. For example, it is a little-known fact that the first building society was formed there. Following Britain's famous victory at the battle of Waterloo in 1815, a number of the victorious army returned home to Larkhall. Those ex-servicemen formed themselves with other local residents into what they termed a building society. Each member contributed a few shillings weekly into their joint fund which then had enough equity to allow them to borrow more. With that larger sum, they began construction of new workmen's houses. Back then, each house had a shed for the weaving of silk which was Larkhall's earlier industry before coal mining overtook it. Those building society houses were better built then the average and were still among the best available to working people when I moved to Larkhall in the 1870's.

That building society tradition was handed down to the following generation and still survived when I first lived in the town. In comparison with many pit villages and towns across Britain, Larkhall had a higher than average percentage of workers living in their own homes, particularly in the old centre of the town. There was a considerable number of cottages tied to the colliery by then, of course, but a surprisingly high number of workman-owned houses as well. Those homes normally boasted a garden plot at the rear. And maybe there would be some flowers growing in them. But, by and large, those garden plots were given over to the growing of vegetables. One of the main reasons for that was that, for a man used to spending much of his life underground, tending a vegetable garden was a pleasant release in the fresh air. Also, of course, carefully-planned, a vegetable garden can provide fresh produce to enrich a family's basic diet. For the truly gifted gardener, there might be the added bonus of making a few shillings from any surplus. Other pit towns and villages learned the lesson of Larkhall's building society tradition and developed their own schemes. Truly, it was a case of where Larkhall led, others followed.

I have already told you how I served on the Larkhall School Board for a number of years and how we were in the vanguard of the provision of free school books. Years later, I was delighted when my daughter, Jeannie, followed in my footsteps and became a Labour representative on the same board. In terms of Labour management of local matters, Larkhall became a standard-bearer for others to follow. Local Labour members not only were a majority on the School Board but also on the Parish Council. We were well represented on the district council, and eventually returned a Labour member to parliament. He was Duncan Graham, Secretary of the Lanarkshire Miners' Association. Clearly, he was more persuasive with the local electors that I ever was! But from this perhaps you can see how Larkhall was a hot-bed of the Labour Movement, yet another reason why I admired the place.

That it was a forward-looking community is illustrated by the fact that Larkhall was among the first small towns to be lighted by gas. No big thing, you may think, if you are one of those unfortunates, a city dweller. But if you lived in a wee place like Larkhall, being lit by gas was very much a thing to boast about. It makes me smile now to remember that when gas lighting was first introduced there it was decided, with typical Scottish economy – which the unenlightened mistake for mean parsimony – that the street lamps should not be lit during the summer. Just to make sure that there really was no waste of such a precious fuel, it was further decreed that when the moon was shining brightly no lamps would be lit. This caused the lamp-lighters a difficulty. How would they know beyond a doubt that the moon would shine on any given night? They were informed that they would have to rely on the calendar. So if the calendar said 'moonlight,' then moonlight it would be, and bad luck if there were any clouds around.

I remember arriving back late one night on the train from Glasgow. Leaving our small station, I found the streets in total darkness. I knew the streets well, of course, but still found myself groping for familiar landmarks. It must have been really dark because I bumped full tilt into a man coming from the opposite direction. It was Tam Findlay, one of the gasworks directors.

'It's awfully dark the night, Tam,' I remarked, once I'd established who it was. 'Why are the lamps not lit?'

'It's the calendar,' he replied a little testily. 'According tae that, the moon ought tae be shining the night.'

'Aye, well, maybe,' I said. 'But see for yourself, Tam, the town's as dark as the pit.'

'Nothing we can dae aboot that,' he snapped. 'If ye want tae blame anybody, blame the Almighty. It's his fault, nae oors. Good night tae ye.' And he made his way off, banging into his own lampposts, his curves softly disappearing into the darkness of the night.

So, you see, Larkhall was always a special place to me, not only for family reasons but also because, in its small way, it was an active, forward-looking wee town. Of course, most of us feel that way about our own small piece of God's earth. Most of the Larkhall folk I knew were certainly proud of their area. I only ever knew one other group of citizens who were quite as fierce in their loyalty as the people of Larkhall. They were the citizens of Leadhills, another small town about twenty-five miles south of Larkhall. I visited it a few times on family excursions, but got to know it better when out campaigning and running meetings there. In its own way, Leadhills too was a special place.

The library in Leadhalls is one of the most wonderful I have ever seen. I visited it often when I was in the town, at first as a place to relax between campaign meetings but later simply as a very special place to be. It has a direct connection with one of the great periods in Scottish Literature, having been opened by the renowned poet Allan Ramsay way back in 1740. The Leadhills area, as the name would suggest, is an area surrounded by lead mines and, for many decades, the lead miners and their families made up virtually the entire population of the town. The miners were all members of the Library and were rightly very proud of it.

Outside the Highlands, Leadhills is one of the most elevated habitations in Scotland, perched some 1,500 feet above sea level. My first serious visit there was when I went to help the lead miners organise themselves into a union. As was often the case in our industrial history, they were having wage restrictions imposed by the mine owners and were not sufficiently well organised to offer any coherent resistance. I was more than happy to offer my help, informed as I was by my experience at Larkhall.

You will remember how I said that, in the coalfields of Lanarkshire and Ayrshire, there had been an influx of Polish workers. In one or two pits in particular it was said that there were more 'owskis' than 'macs.' Well, there was a strong foreign influence in Leadhills as well, but there it was from a different source. Back in the sixteenth century German miners were brought across to Leadhills by one of the Stuart kings. From the first day I visited the town, I was very aware of the numbers of German names in the area. The German miners were not originally wanted for their lead-mining skills. Instead, they were imported as gold-miners.

Some gold reefs had been discovered in the Leadhills area and there were no men in that area with experience of gold-mining, which was why the Germans were brought across. The gold was never found in huge quantities – there was certainly no California-style gold rush – but there was enough to make it a profitable venture. Even to this day small quantities of gold are still found in the streams there. My dear wife Ann still wears a ring made of Leadhills gold. It was presented to her by local men after a prolonged strike there which I played some part in bringing to a successful conclusion. The gold for that ring was secured by careful washing of the sand from a local stream. Then they measured my wife's finger before sending the precious metal to Glasgow, where it was made into a ring for her. She wears it every day and reminds us of our affection for the place.

There are some oddities of life in Leadhills. For example, there is one quaint old custom observed every day. Standing on a trident there is a little bell. Every single night, a watchman goes to it and pulls a rope attached to the clapper of the bell, thereby sounding the nightly curfew. Then there is the local water supply. Bear in mind that Leadhills stands at a great elevation, and that water does not naturally lie at such heights. The miners formed a committee among themselves, then designed and built a dam on a river which had the effect of creating a reservoir high in the hills. That reservoir provided the local water supply. Men of real resource, those Leadhill miners!

They have always enjoyed a curious privilege, that of grazing animals on the hills around the town. Which explains why, a rarity for workmen, quite a number of mining families there own a cow and it is common practice for families to join together in the ownership of some sheep. When the men first joined the Lanarkshire Miners' Union, it was not unknown for some of them to sell a beast in order to raise money for their subscription fees. The main reason for that was when I first came across them their wages were scandalously low. If I remember correctly, skilled miners were paid 3/- a day while boys got 1/-. The first strike ever held in Leadhills had the aim of ensuring a weekly wage of £1 for a skilled miner.

That strike failed and the owners even refused to recognise the union. It took a very long time, and not a few stoppages, before better wages were finally paid and union recognition achieved. It was the old, sad story of intransigent high-handedness on the part of the employers who felt that they could do what they liked with the men. I am proud to say that the work of the union went a long way towards righting that situation.

On several occasions, I accompanied the miners to see what their working conditions were like. I have to tell you that I did not envy them one little bit! The workings in the deepest parts of the mines are virtually at sea level, depth almost beyond imagination when you remember the great elevation of the area. When I first visited, there was no shaft to raise and lower the men and so they had to descent and ascend by a long series of ladders. Just getting to and from the workplace was exhausting in itself. And still the employers baulked at the idea of paying a man £1 a week. Man, man, profit ledgers have an awful lot to answer for.

Earlier, I mentioned Leadhills Library. Let me now briefly return to it. It was rather more than a library even if that was its main attraction for me. There was a wide collection of good books, neatly arranged along shelves on the walls. Many of those books had been presented to the library by former residents who had moved to other districts or, indeed, to other countries. With good reason to remember the pleasant hours they had spent in the library, they made book donations to it and many even maintained their subscription to the library long after they left the area. Perhaps they also fondly remembered the other facilities which the library had to offer. On my visits, I saw men playing carpet bowls, draughts and chess. The concentration of the chess players always impressed me as did the quiet, gentlemanly behaviour of all the other men. I sometimes think that if Heaven has a library, I hope that it is modelled on that wonderful one in Leadhills.

I wasn't the only person to be impressed by that library: far from it. Whenever visitors from other areas visited Lanarkshire on mining matters, I always arranged for a tour of the hilly districts of the southern parts of the county, which invariably ended up with a visit to Leadhills Library. I remember one particular occasion – I can't be sure of the year – when I was showing round the area a Mr John Walker from Illinois, on a visit to this country representing the American mine workers. John wasn't actually an American. He was born near Stirling and had worked in the pits there before he emigrated. He had been there long enough to sound completely American but he was interested in his Scots ancestry. Believing that his ancestors had originated in South Lanarkshire, he was particularly keen to visit Leadhills.

It would be no great exaggeration to say that he fell in love with the library. What was intended as a very short visit ended up being virtually a day-long one. He seemed to want to go through the whole stock of books, showing a particular interest in anything to do with mining. He quoted regularly from pages containing statements of contracts and prices paid for the cutting of rocks. He seemed delighted to read pieces which told him that Leadhills was renowned for the production of beautiful specimens of quartz of different kinds. I had rarely seen a man so engrossed in reading matter.

But that day ended up highlighting some cultural differences between the Old World and the New World. In spite of his Scots roots, John showed himself to be very much a New World man. The local union secretary, who had proudly taken us round the library, revealed that he was a very keen collector of rare specimens of quartz and showed us his fine collection of it. As we were leaving, John noticed a little square tin box hanging from the wall near the door. He asked me what it was for.

'Oh, it's just a collection box,' I told him. 'The proceeds go towards the upkeep of the library. Visitors usually drop a few coppers into it.' I took a coin from my pocket. 'Here, I'll be putting in this sixpence myself. You can do the same yourself, if you like.'

'A sixpence? Is that all?' John boomed, suddenly becoming very American. 'I don't think that's much of a donation for somebody like me to make. This is probably the only time I'll ever be here. Tell you what, Bob, I'll put this in.' He was holding a sovereign which he dropped into the box.

'I just hope you don't give somebody a heart attack when he comes across that sort of money,' I said.

The secretary hadn't seen John's donation. He popped out for a minute but was waiting for us when we got outside. He was holding a small parcel in his hand. 'Mr Walker,' he said, 'would you like to take back to America with you a few of my mineral specimens? I have brought three from my collection and I would be delighted if you would accept them as a wee gift.' Lovingly, he opened the parcel to reveal three specimens, each wrapped in a piece of silk paper.

'I shall be delighted to accept them,' John said, beaming with delight. 'I will be happy to tell all my friends in America of this day's visit and your great generosity.' Then he turned to me and whispered, 'Bob, can I give this man a tip?'

'For pity's sake no, John!' I replied. 'These people are of a very proud and independent nature. You will just insult him.'

Whether I hadn't made myself clear, or whether it was just New World culture, I couldn't really say. Whatever, John pulled some silver coins from his pocket and offered them to the secretary. By that fine man's reaction, you would have thought that John had hit him. He stepped back a few paces with a look of deep regret on his face. Then he collected himself. Smiling as well as he could, he simply said, 'No thank you, Mr Walker. We are not out for tips here.'

As we left, John was almost inconsolable and couldn't work out what he had done wrong. Tipping was a way of life in America and, even Britain: from the dockers in Liverpool to the railway men he'd come across during his train journey, workers had been happy enough to accept tips. But not in Leadhills, apparently. This made a very deep impression on him. Some time later, I heard an amusing sequel to all of this. When the collection box was opened by the library committee, there were gasps of astonishment at the site of John's sovereign. They spent weeks going round Leadhills, trying to find out who was short of money because he had put the wrong coin in the box. That was a mystery they never solved.

You may well wonder why I have spent so much time reminiscing about Larkhall and Leadhills. In fact, I did think of telling you some stories about the village of Moscow – yes, Moscow! – in Ayrshire, but I'll leave the telling of those to someone else. I just wanted you to be clear about the life I was leading. I have told you so much, with more to come, about union work, politics and other serious matters, that you must be beginning to imagine that those things totally consumed Robert Smillie. I cannot deny that they were, indeed, hugely important, but there was another Robert Smillie as well. A man who loved his wife and family and, almost as much, the area which he always called home. I very much hope that you now realise that.

If my presidency of the Federation was to mean much, I was going to have to get my feet under the table, as the saying goes, and show clear leadership as quickly as possible. That is exactly what I set out to do. As I saw it at the time, there were three issues I wanted to be heavily involved with. Two were very specific: the five-day week and nationalisation of the mines. The other was more general, but related to the other two: moving the Federation towards a more Socialist outlook. Let me first deal with the last of those.

Although the election of officials of 1912 brought in some new men, most of the committee were still 'the 90's men' as they were often referred to. Not because they were in their ninth decade of life, I hasten to add, but because they had served the committee since the 1890's. Indeed, I had served for some time myself but had always been among the more Socialist-leaning members, whereas many of the others had been more Liberal in their persuasion. You might remember how difficult it had been to persuade the committee that we should even go so far as to affiliate to the Labour Party.

To give you an idea of how our Federation was viewed by real Socialists, let me quote to you the words of Bernard Shaw, the great writer and eminent Fabian, who viewed our affiliation to the Labour Party with something less than enthusiasm:

'I had said repeatedly, when the Miners' Federation joined the Labour Party, and put money and an overwhelming card vote into it, Socialism would have to take a back place in the Party, and the term Socialist would come to mean no more than the term Christian after the Edict of Constantine.'

These words hardly paint the picture of us as 'Socialist agitators', the kind of picture which our opponents liked to depict. But, to an extent at least, Shaw was right. Like many other unions, our ranks contained many men who were Liberal rather than Socialist in their outlook. During my early years in the Federation, I had had many a brush with people like Pickard, Edwards and Woods who, though good men all of them, were nowhere near as passionate in their advocacy as I would have wished.

However, in another sense, Bernard Shaw was wrong. Things were changing. By 1912, within unions everywhere and certainly within the mining unions, there was a drift away from Liberalism, particularly among younger men. At first, that drift was not particularly dramatic, but it was real enough. In my heart of hearts, I felt that it was inexorable.

I think that I had one particular strength when it came to my efforts to turn the Federation towards a more overtly Socialist direction. That strength lay in the depth and breadth of my experience. In particular, my five years of work on the Royal Commission on Mines had given me a detailed knowledge of British and continental operations in all kinds of coalfields. A wise man – I do not recollect who – once observed that 'knowledge was power'. I found that to be the case in my early days as president of the Federation, particularly when involved in debate with the more Liberal members of our committee. I do not believe that there was a single major issue on which any of them knew as much as I did. I do not say that boastfully, rather as a reflection of fact, given how fortunate I was in the range of my experiences. For this reason, I won more and more arguments without ever having to resort to 'tub-thumping' or 'drum-banging', but by resort to facts and details. I believed that we were on the point of being able to pursue a more Socialist programme.

The issues of the five-day week and mines nationalisation became closely linked. I will do my best to separate them out though the matters are very complex. I can trace my advocacy of nationalisation back to the Trades Union Congress of 1892 when, with William Small, I obtained unanimous acceptance of two proposals, one for State ownership of minerals, the other for the nationalisation of all mines. As a matter of fact, that demand for the nationalisation of mines was frequently supported by opponents of Socialism: they simply differed from us in terms of how and by whom nationalised mines would be controlled. However, it wasn't until the Federation's meeting in October, 1911, during my vice-presidency, that the miners' representatives decided that it was time to come to a view on nationalisation. That was because so many of the successive officials of the Federation had not been Socialists.

By the time that the 1912 Conference and my election to the presidency came round, the five-day week had become the main issue. For three months a proposal to have the five-day week as part of Federation policy had been with the various districts who were asked to sound out their men on the subject. Accordingly, at the conference in October the matter was fully discussed and it was decided:

'That the Miners' Federation of Great Britain adopt a five days working week for all miners in the country.'

At the conference, seventy delegates voted in favour and fifty against. I asked for a card vote. There were 306,000 votes in favour and 283,000 against. I suggested to conference that, in view of the relative closeness of the vote, a ballot of all miners should be held to determine the matter. When that was held, in early 1913, there was a majority in favour, but not an overwhelming majority. Following that, I had a major decision to make. By the normal, simple rules of democracy, the proposal had been carried, but I had my doubts. I remember a conversation to that effect. I was talking to Alan Wright who was not a committee member but one of our most willing activists and an ardent Socialist.

'You've got the vote then, Bob,' he said, smiling happily.

'Well, maybe,' I replied quietly.

'Maybe? What do you mean, maybe?'

'It's only fifty-five per cent to forty-five per cent,' I told him.

'Well, what of it?' he asked. 'A simple majority vote of one, supplied as usual by a half-asleep octogenarian, is enough for a majority in the House of Commons, no matter how serious the issue.'

'There you go, insulting the Torys again,' I said, laughing at him. 'But real democracy is not as simple as that, Alan.'

'In what way?' He sounded almost indignant.

'Look at it this way, Alan,' I told him. 'On the figures, it means that for every eleven men who supported the proposal, nine men are against it. Agreed?'

'I'll take your word for it. Arithmetic was never my best subject.'

'So what do we do? Announce that the proposal has been carried and make nine out of twenty men unhappy? It's sensitive, Alan. It could cause bitter arguments.'

'It would be even worse,' he pointed out, 'if we were to say that the proposal had been defeated.'

'Of course it would,' I agreed. 'It would also be a lie.'

'So what are you going to do then, Bob?'

'I'm not quite sure yet,' I replied, tapping my pipe against my chin. 'I'm still considering the matter.'

Once I had finished my consideration, I made the only decision possible. I made my report to the committee and recommended that all miners should not only be informed of the final figures, but that they should also be told that this was but one stage in a longer process and that we would return to the issue in the near future. With one exception, the committee agreed with me and there the matter lay, for the time being.

Our deliberations on mines' nationalisation followed a similar pattern. Some years of debate had taken place to very little purpose. I had taken part in many and felt only a deep sense of frustration at the lack of progress. It was by an ironic twist of fate that a piece of Liberal legislation paved the way for the development of the Socialist agenda. I have already told you about the Miners' National Strike and Asquith's anguished enactment of the Minimum Wage Act. I also hinted at our view that that Act had a limited chance of doing very much to achieve a genuine minimum wage. So it proved, and very quickly.

Of course, that Act had been an emergency measure forced through parliament to end the coal strike. Even allowing for that, you might have imagined that better thought would have been given to its provisions. Local boards were set up to fix minimum wages in each district. Who elected the members of these boards? Nobody did, as a matter of fact. They were appointees. No doubt some of them were well meaning. A few many even have been competent, though competence to judge proper wages was a skill given only to those experienced in mining matters, and very few of them were. The result was nothing much less than chaos. Like the tattered pieces of a patchwork quilt, those boards spread across the country and the deliberation and judgements of one board bore little semblance to the work of another. Different wage standards were set from board to board for no other reason than the decisions made by unversed boards.

It was against this background that I felt able to approach our committee, point to the shambles caused by the Minimum Wage Act, and ask their agreement for the drafting of a Coal Mines' Nationalisation Bill. Their agreement was quickly obtained and we moved to securing that policy as part of the Federation's programme.

Let me offer a few final thoughts about our work at that time. It concerns democracy. I have already indicated that I deemed it unwise to push ahead with our demand for the five-day week in 1912 because, although we had a majority in favour of it, it was not an overwhelming majority. Perhaps we should reflect now and again on the ancient Greeks' original concept of democracy. To take their view of things, democracy does not describe a count, it describes a process. It is not the counting of votes which is true democracy, though that can be part of it. Rather it is the process of argument and persuasion in which all people's views are treated equally. In the Federation, we tried very hard to honour that process.

Clearly, with a million men in our ranks, it simply was not possible to have one mass meeting at which all views would be heard. However, as with the proposal for the five-day week, we went to extraordinary lengths to ensure that any decision ever made by the committee or at a conference was as representative of all views as possible. All the facts and ideas which the committee had were disseminated to the men through their district and county representatives. Meetings were held at all collieries so that the men knew the facts and heard the ideas. These were then discussed at meetings at local level. Following that, their representative took their views back to conference. Only then was a decision readied. Often enough, as in the five-day week case, the matter did not rest there. Instead of relying on a card vote, all miners were balloted before a final decision was reached. In my opinion, more than just a counting on hands or votes, the way in which we went about things demonstrated democracy in process.

We demonstrated the fact that we wanted to enhance the democratic process when we officially rejected the idea of a simple majority in a unanimously-carried conference proposal which said that, in the case of a national strike, no action would be undertaken without a ballot of all miners in which at least two-thirds of them voted in favour of striking. The same provision would apply if, in the course of a strike, there was a proposal to continue the action.

I defy you to name a political party which conducted its business in such a spirit of democracy as we miners did. Or any other large organisation for that matter. The aristocrats, mine owners and newspaper editors who regularly preached against us, using words and phrases such as 'agitators', 'revolutionaries', 'demagogues', 'unelected bodies' and, to my disbelief 'destroyers of democracy', were all considerably less democratic in their activities than we ever were. When did an aristocrat ever ask his colliers to vote in favour of his reduction in his wages? When did a newspaper editor ever consult his readers before writing his editorial? The answer to each of those questions is never, never, never!

I was proud of the way in which we took our decisions, proud of the men who participated so fully in our democratic process. As a believer in Socialism, I took the view that it could never be enforced. It could only be achieved through persuasion based on informed debate. As President of the Miners' Federation, I was determined to maintain and enhance that proud tradition and ignore the insults from our less democratic opponents.

XV

Excitement and Tragedy

ON APRIL 15th 1912, the whole of Britain was shaken by the news of the sinking of RMS *Titanic*. The ship, on its maiden voyage, had been speeding through an ice field, hoping to win the Blue Riband for the fastest transatlantic voyage. It hit an iceberg, was holed along much of the length of its hull, and sank within hours. Of the 2,340 passengers and crew, more than 1,500 were lost. It was the worst-ever disaster at sea.

I remind you of this horrible event not only to stir your memory and remember the dead, but also because in that same year I undertook the same voyage as those unfortunate 1,500 who set out never to return. It hardly seems credible to me now as I look back that, with everything else that went on in 1912, I had the time to undertake any voyage longer than a rowing-boat trip on a park lake.

1912 was a full year by anybody's standards. I have already told you about some of the main events. Proving myself as Vice-President of the Federation, then taking up the reins of the presidency and trying to develop a Socialist policy programme. All the work involved in the National Miners' Strike, my intense work and negotiating with owners and political opponents. Reacting to the Minimum Wage Act, organising national ballots, and all the rest of it. You would not have thought that all these in combination would have left much time over for anything else, particularly something of considerable duration. But there was something else, a major event in my life. With John Seddon, I was invited to represent the British Trades Union Congress on a Fraternal visit to the American Federation of Labour Annual Conference. At the time, I was still Vice-President rather than President of our Federation, and I was very honoured to be asked to go.

My first visit to America was made all the more enjoyable by James Seddon's presence. As dedicated a Socialist as I was, and even more of a talker, we had much in common. Before leaving, we did not dwell on the fate of the *Titanic* and, as we moved out into the Atlantic our early conversations were dominated by sport, of all things. On that subject, there existed the only major point of difference between us. As you know, my main sporting love was cricket and it didn't take long to find out that James hardly knew the difference between a wicket-keeper and a batsman, though he tried hard to mollify me on the subject. I was as weak on his first love, which was football. I think he was a supporter of the Bradford football team, though my memory may be playing me a trick on that.

What I do remember is that he was a walking encyclopaedia where football was concerned and seemed to know the name of every player who had ever played the game. I professed a mild interest in the Rangers from Glasgow but, as I knew little more about them than the name of their ground, our sporting conversation petered out pretty quickly. Naturally enough, we gravitated towards a subject we both knew something about – politics!

James and I shared a double cabin on the SS *Carmania*. As representatives of the Trades Union Congress, you may take my word for it that it was not a first-class cabin. We were in steerage, the cabin was below the waterline so there was no porthole. To our relief, the outward passage was a calm one. The weather was delightful and, when we weren't discussing Socialism, we played a lot of deck quoits. Several times during those games, we had noticed a passenger looking hard at James who began to return the other man's stares. After a few days of this, he finally came up to us.

'Excuse me,' he said to James, 'but I believe you are Mr James Seddon and that I once dined with you in the British House of Commons.'

'I thought I recognised you,' James replied, 'but I couldn't quite place you. Wait a minute, it's Mr Williams, is it not?'

'That is indeed my name,' the man said, smiling and offering James a firm handshake.

He turned out to be Jack Williams, engineer of the Cape-to-Cairo railway, an old friend of that eccentric pioneer, Cecil Rhodes, with whom Williams had travelled all over Africa. On the *Carmania*, he was keeping in close touch by wireless with all the engineering work going on in Africa in connection with that vast railway adventure. As miners, we showed an interest in the technical details, and over the remainder of the voyage to America the two of us spent a lot of time with Jack Williams. He was an interesting companion and he gave us impressive details of track-laying work, the problems encountered, the progress of operations, even down to a likely finishing date for the whole project.

Apparently, one of the greatest problems they had faced was securing land rights for laying track in the Congo. Through a third party, he managed to get a letter of introduction to King Leopold of Belgium, that country having dominion over the Congo. The king made a big impression on Jack Williams.

'I've known a considerable number of what the world calls great men,' he told us, 'politicians, diplomats, chieftains and all the rest. I would have said that Cecil Rhodes was the sharpest of all of them, but I have never met a man with such all-round ability as Leopold. He was as keen as a razor when we discussed business projects. As the American saying goes, he never missed a trick. I finally got what we wanted, a large track of land through the Congo. But you can take my word for it, King Leopold was not a loser by that transaction. He would have made a very fine company president.' And he chuckled at the memory of it.

Thanks to deck quoits, lengthy discussions about Socialism, and Jack Williams' stories, our outward voyage passed quickly and pleasantly. Sadly, I never met Jack Williams again. I could have happily tolerated more of his wonderful stories. There again, I was just glad to have met him. Man, man but I've met some interesting people in my life.

When we disembarked, we were met by Samuel Gompers, President of the American Federation of Labor. We stayed with him for several days at his home in Washington where we were received with the utmost kindness. Gompers himself was a rather peculiar mixture. Perhaps he was just typically New World, a real American, but there were two extremes to his personality. In his home, and around Washington, he was cordiality itself. He could not do enough for us. He showed us all the great buildings of State and the magnificent monuments of Washington. Nothing was too much trouble for him. But when it came to the main reasons for us being there, my address to the Labor Annual Conference, we saw another side to him.

Knowing my views as you do, you'll not be surprised to know that, in my address to their conference, I was as clear as I could be about my adherence to Socialism. I discussed the role of the State in managing industry for the benefit of all the people, and the greater fairness that that would bring. As I spoke, I was aware that Gompers, who was presiding over the conference, was wriggling in his seat and making some groaning noises. As I finished, I realised that he was just waiting his chance.

Before the applause for my address had died down, he was on his feet. Face flushed red, mouth twisted, he angrily denounced a number of the things I had said, particularly about the potential role of the State. When he sat down, to rather less applause than I had received, I demanded the right of reply. After all, I had not been told that I was taking part in a debate. Generous host to a fault, Gompers agreed. So I spent for another thirty minutes or so replying to the objections he had raised. I took care to be as calm as possible, never once showing a shred of temper. I had always believed that you would come out of a debate better if you showed yourself to be in calm control of your argument.

When I had finished, I received a quite rapturous round of applause. I could not quite understand that. I believed that I had spoken well under pressure from Gompers, but not that well. At the reception which followed immediately afterwards, I discovered the reason for the warmth of the reception. Yes, they had enjoyed my address, and my courage in replying to Gompers' outburst. No, they had not agreed with everything I had said. What had moved them to respond to my address so heartily was the fact that they had been embarrassed by Gompers' intervention, seeing it as an act of rudeness towards a fraternal delegate. In truth, if my experiences there were anything to go by, the American people had little to learn in the art of entertaining strangers.

Over the years, I had become quite used to dealings with the press. Often enough, I felt that the miners were unfairly treated in our newspapers and had written various letters of complaint to various editors, very few of which were ever published. However, by 1912 I felt that at least I knew who and what I was dealing with when it came to the British press. I found their American colleagues rather different. We had moved on to New York before we first encountered at length an American reporter. Or, should I say, he encountered us.

I could sum up our experience of the American press by saying that there was more danger in saying a little than in saying a lot. Man, but they loved windbags over there! If only they had shown the same regard for facts. For reasons I never understood, that first reporter, from the *New York Times* if I remember correctly, attributed to James and myself status and influence which no king has ever enjoyed. He seemed to think that we were great men, that we 'bossed' – as he put it – all the British unions between us, that we autocratically dictated terms to all British workers, and that we only had to crook our little fingers to have the prime minister or government give into our every whim.

His reporting style amazed us. We fondly imagined that he would ask some questions and we would do our best to answer them. Instead, he embarked on a long monologue about our power and influence and hardly asked a question at all. The upshot was that, apart from protesting about some of his so-called 'facts' about us, James and I said very little at all. In spite of which, two days later there was a long article in his paper giving a mass of fictitious details about how Robert Smillie and James Seddon were running Great Britain. From this, we concluded that American reporters were rather different to their British counterparts. They actually preferred it when their interviewees had little to say. This then allowed them to imagine what the interviewee would have said, if he had chosen to say it. I almost envied them their powers of imagination. While I frequently despair of what a British pressman will write, on balance I prefer ours to theirs.

It was while we were speaking in New York, in what was turning out to be something of a lecture tour, that we got the only real chance to do some proper sightseeing during our visit. Our hosts had added some new speaking dates to our already busy schedule and, perhaps realising that they were taxing us too much, arranged for us to spend two nights in the town of Buffalo at the eastern limit of Lake Erie. Our hosts were a family by the name of Anderson, who had moved to America from Ayrshire some fifteen years earlier. As all our hosts in America had, they treated us wonderfully well.

The highlight of our short break there was a visit to the Niagara Falls at the junction of Lake Erie with Lake Ontario. They were awe-inspiring and we were suitably impressed. On the way back to Buffalo, Willie Anderson asked me what I had thought of them.

'Quite wonderful, Willie,' I told him. 'Well worth the trip.'

'I'll bet you've never seen anything like that before,' an American friend of Willie's said to me. He was one of those very friendly types who, nevertheless, can't believe that anything in his country can be bettered elsewhere.

'Well, you may be right,' I replied, then winked at Willie. 'But there's that huge waterfall in Ayrshire, isn't there, Willie?'

'Oh aye,' he replied, catching on quickly, 'you'll be talking about the one on the River Ayr.'

'No, no, Willie,' I said. 'The bigger one, the one on Lugar Water.'

'Aye, you're right, Bob.' He whistled. 'Man, but that's a monster, that one.'

'True enough.' I turned to our American friend. 'That Niagara Falls of yours is but a child by comparison, but maybe it'll grow up some day.'

We laughed all the way back to Buffalo, and eventually let our American friend in on the joke. He didn't mind at all and joined in our laughter. He was yet another of the many warm-hearted Americans I met.

James and I continued our speaking tour. Often enough, we were much too Socialist in our views for our audiences but the debates which followed our speeches were always invigorating. However, in Chicago we talked to two meetings of very different complexions which revealed to us just how multi-layered American opinion was. At the first of those, we discovered that we were talking to a group of extreme Socialists, many of recent European extraction, and they considered our address too tame. It seemed to us that the Chicago Socialists wanted everything for the asking: Heaven today and no waiting. But at the second of those meetings, with the city's Trades Council, we found just the opposite. They were staggered, horrified even, when we described the influence of British trade unions and the growth of the Labour party. We felt like evangelists without a Christian in the room.

When we returned to New York, it was time for the declaration of the presidential election which had been in progress during our four weeks stay. We were amazed and impressed by the American's use of technology. In Times Square, the results were declared on illuminated screens to a host of wildly excited people. It was so different to the way in which major election results were dealt with in Britain. James and I were there, looking on, in the company of John Mitchell who had been the President of the American Mine Workers' Union. As the results were flashed up, he explained their significance to us but I have to admit that I have never quite come to terms with their electoral college system which seemed unnecessarily complex to James and myself. Among the huge crowds there was what I can only describe as a carnival spirit. I had never been among such people before, and haven't since. Their unbridled good humour was most refreshing. They let themselves go without the first semblance of restraint. Very un-British but, after all, this was the New World.

We must have made some kind of impression on our American hosts, for we both received later invitations to return. Perhaps we had sowed some seeds of British Socialism after all. For example, I was later invited to go to Chicago to address a demonstration. That invitation came from the Secretary of the Chicago Trades and Labor Council. It would not be a speaking tour. I would only be expected to make one address and there was no indication in the letter of invitation as to what they wanted me to talk about. I declined the invitation to attend. Apart from any bewilderment I may have felt about the purpose of my presence in Chicago, I was not feeling in the best of health. I sometimes consider what kind of reception I would have got if I had gone.

Then, during yet another presidential campaign, I received a cablegram asking if I would go out to America and address no fewer than eight meetings in support of Mr Christiansteene, the Labor candidate for the presidency of the United States. The invitation was accompanied by an offer which was amazingly generous. In return for my eight speeches, my first-class travel and accommodation would be paid for and I would receive a fee of $1,000. It all seemed too good to be true. But I would never have been tempted to go anyway. There were too many internal politics going on for my liking. For example, Mr Christiansteene's rival for nomination, a Socialist by the name of Mr Debs, was actually in jail and there was talk of breaking him out to allow him to continue his campaign. It was all rather messy and certainly not very attractive so, once again, I politely declined.

There was another attempt to attract me to go to America on a speaking engagement. Once again it came from Chicago. The text of the letter was as follows:

Dear Sir,

The Chicago Federation of Labor is arranging a Labor Day demonstration for Monday, September 5, in this city. We are more than anxious to have you with us, that we may hear from your lips the story of the present political and economic conditions of your country.

Our newspapers and press dispatches are so much under the control of the enemies of the masses, that we should feel more sure of our position (if we prepared for a future conflict) if we could hear the story from one who has seen and is actually engaged and as widely trusted as you are.

Any expense incurred will be gladly borne by this organisation. Hoping to hear from you in time to arrange our programme.

The Chicago Federation of Labor.

Well, it was flattering of course and it may indeed have been interesting. But once again I was disinclined to travel. I was not sure that my health was robust enough to tolerate the experience and, besides, I had plenty on my plate at home. Accordingly, I wrote back to them:

Dear Sirs,

I beg to thank you for your letter of the 7th ultimo, written on behalf of the Chicago Federation of Labour, in which you are kind enough to invite me to visit Chicago and address a demonstration on September 5.

I deeply regret to say that it is impossible for me to accept this invitation. I am not in very good health at the present time and, in addition to this, the industrial situation in this country is such as makes it necessary that those who are looked to by the workers for guidance should remain here until matters reach a more satisfactory state.

Yours very truly,
Robert Smillie.

Those kind invitations and my rejections of them were some way in the future as James Seddon and I picked up the SS *Carmania* once more for our journey back to Britain. The weather was not as kind as it had been on our outward voyage, which meant that there were fewer games of deck quoits but plenty of time for conversations in which we exchanged views of our experiences in America. We tried hard not to make direct comparisons between the American Labor Movement and our own but, of course, it is difficult to entirely resist that. It is in human nature to compare the new with what you know best.

Unsurprisingly, we both agreed that American people were among the kindest and most considerate we had ever met. Each of us had on occasion been rather less warmly received in parts of Britain where we should have been among friends. However, as far as the development of a Labour Movement was concerned, we felt that America was considerably less organised than Britain or, indeed, any of the major European countries. As far as Labour politics was concerned, we felt that America was barely at the stage Britain had been during the 1880's. From that period, we had emerged with growing and stronger trade unions, and the formation of the Labour Party. We had more or less rid ourselves of the older political alliances and unified the trade union movement into an effective organisation. More or less, all arms of the Labour Movement were pulling in the same direction. But where, we wondered, was America headed?

We fancied that the Labour Movement in America had to forge a path through the same sea of troubles as we had. However, we felt that the outcomes of that difficult journey on the other side of the Atlantic would be rather different to the outcome in Britain. From what we had seen, we believed that the forces of capital in America were liable to prove even more brutal and soulless that their British counterparts. We had found organised capital in America to be particularly cosmopolitan and it seemed clear to us that the major stakeholders in American capital controlled politics to an even greater degree than was the case in Britain. Their big financiers not only controlled industry with a very powerful grip, but also had a direct influence on the selection of political candidates who, once in office, were obliged to repay favours given. Those financiers seemed only interested in expanding their industrial power, beyond which they seemed to possess little in the way of idealism and tended to regard their employees as little more than beasts of burden. James and I shared the view that, if capital and labor were brought face to face in some great industrial struggle, capital held all the winning cards. In the years which followed that visit to America, events have borne out that pessimistic view.

We reflected on our several visits to collieries and other industries, where we had been anxious to see at first-hand the actual conditions in which workmen were employed. The time we spent at a colliery in Gillespie, Illinois, had been particularly interesting. The manager showed us round everywhere and brought is to one particular area where I saw a most heartening sight. This was the 'washing and drying' set of rooms, where the men, having returned to the surface, would have a hot bath and change from wet and dirty clothes into their ordinary day wear. When they left, each man's newly cleaned working clothes were hung up in an assigned place in an area so heated that they could not be anything other than warm and dry when the man returned for his next shift.

Later, I would find that this boon to the working conditions of miners was universal in Germany too. It was also widely provided in France. On our voyage home, James and I contrasted the provision in America with the situation in Britain. Back home in Britain, in spite of frequent demands made by our Federation, miners were much less well provided for in this respect. Little wonder that, in the public perception, the miner is a dirty workman, as black as any chimney-sweep covered in coal dust and grime.

The return of a British miner from his shift presents a pitiable scene. Imagine it if you will. He has walked home, wet and filthy from head to toe. Avoided by strangers as if he was bearing a disease. At the door of his house, he pauses and tries to knock from his clothes as much clinging dirt as possible. He strips off as soon as he enters the house and goes to the tin bath which is filled with hot water which has taken his wife ages to prepare in pans on the fire. While he tries to wash the daily grime from his body, she is trying to wash it from his clothes. Unless it is mid-winter and the clothes have frozen in which case she will first bang the clothes against a doorpost to shake the ice out of them. Once washed, the clothes are set to dry in front of the fire as the miner towels himself dry in front of the same fire. All of this happening day after day in small rooms which, in the case of the poorest families, serves as sitting-room, kitchen and bedroom.

While delighted for the American miners with their 'washing and drying' areas, I was suffused with rage on behalf of the British miner. For years, before and during my membership of the Federation Committee, I had fought for baths and drying-rooms at the pitheads so that miners should not be forced to walk home in their wet and filthy clothes; so that they could feel the dignity of simply being human. In my naïveté, I had originally thought that simply advertising this affront to human dignity would be enough to bring about a remedy. Years later, I was still fighting for the same thing!

The women members of the Labour Movement were stirred into action. They were shocked at the way in which their menfolk were treated, husbands and big sons housed in such a way that they had to wash together, practically nude, in the sculleries and even in the backyards of their tiny houses in the Colliers' Rows. Whatever the weather! One particularly formidable member, Mrs Bruce Glaiser, made quite a name for herself and drew considerable attention to the issue by touring round the country lecturing on the subject and distributing pamphlets illustrating the enormous benefits of pithead washing facilities. She was a real fighter, that Mrs Glaiser.

Eventually, when we were all just about hoarse with shouting, there came along an Act of Parliament which was about as worthwhile as several other useless ones of my acquaintance. In it there was about as duplicitous a clause as you could ever wish to read. It recommended the installation of pithead baths and drying facilities which, on the surface, seemed reasonable. But it went on to say if it could be proved by an employer – and since when has an employer not been able to prove anything he wished to – that the cost of erecting and maintaining such facilities exceeded 6d per man per week – half of which the men were expected to pay anyway – then the employer would not be required to provide them. And you probably still wonder why I was a cynic where the work of government, whether Tory or Liberal, was concerned.

I think I mentioned that the journey home from America was not as smooth as the journey out. Well, that was an understatement if you like. We ran into a storm mid-Atlantic. James and I tried to talk through the rolling of the *Carmania*, as much to play down our fears as anything else, for we were a long way from being seasoned voyagers. But it was no use. Our throats went dry, no doubt due to terror, and we decided to try to sleep out the storm. James went over to switch off the light but, before he could do so, he realised that he was walking in water. Our cabin was flooding!

'Bob,' he said to me, his face a grim mask. 'It's all over! We're going down.'

'It looks damned like it, Jimmy,' I replied, surprised at my own calmness. I began concentrating on Ann and the bairns, and our wee home in Larkhall.

Our light went out and, as we sat there dripping wet, we heard shuffling noises from the passageway outside our cabin. Seconds later, our door was pushed open and two seamen entered, lighted lamps in their hands. Looking at us sitting on our beds, James' hands clasped in prayer, me with a faraway look as I dreamed of Ann, they started grinning. I found their grins a little impudent but, at the same time, rather reassuring. They explained that the sudden lack of light was caused by storm-tossed waves battering the lighting apparatus which had permitted a slight ingress of water. So we weren't marked down for a watery grave, after all. Sad to relate, as we were not first-class passengers, we were not offered a fresh, dry cabin as a replacement for our sodden one. A few days later, James and I both stepped back onto British soil for the first time in a month. We were both suffering from heavy colds!

When I returned to Larkhall with the promise of a week off before I returned to Federation work, I was full of joy to be reunited with my family. The old saying is very true: absence does make the heart grow fonder. By now, only Daniel, Alexander and Joseph were still at home, even if they seemed to spend little enough times in it. By day, they were at their work. In the evenings, they were out courting. Well, it's the way of the world, isn't it? We've all been through it. The bonus was that Ann and I had more time on our own; time to make up for lost time, you might say. Like most long-married couples, we talked about everything and nothing.

'So, what was America like, Robert?' she would ask me.

'Well, there were a lot of Americans there for a start,' I would tell her laughing. That was the most pleasant week's break I'd enjoyed in my life.

I cannot leave this period without talking about a particularly dreadful event, much though it pains me to recall it. It goes perhaps a year beyond these memories at that stage, but it was very much a part of that particular period. During my vice-presidency of the Federation, the 1911 Coal Mines Act had seemed to promise so much. It contained four major parts and nearly a hundred sections and was generally acknowledged as providing the most forward-thinking piece of mining legislation in the civilised world. However, events were to show that it is one thing to secure the passage of an Act of Parliament, and it is quite another to ensure its full implementation and proper administration. The tragic events which overtook a small village near Caerphilly in South Wales horribly proved that truism.

It was well known that the coal seams at Senghenydd Pit were prone to emitting gas. In 1901, there was an explosion causing considerable loss of life when 82 men lost their lives. Then, in 1910, there had been an outburst of gas which was not brought under control for four days and had caused the withdrawal of all the men from the pit. So, all the signs were there. In spite of this, the owners, or their agent who was also the manager, had taken no special precautions. Indeed, the minimum precautions prescribed by the 1911 Act had been ignored. The result was a disaster waiting to happen.

That disaster duly occurred on October 4th, 1913. It was the worst explosion in the history of coal mining in Britain. Again, it was a build-up of gas which caused it, replicating what had happened in 1901 and what had been threatened in 1910. The problem was well known and nothing had been done about it. The result was carnage. 439 bodies, including eight 14-year-old boys, many of them mutilated beyond recognition, were pulled out of that pit. So much for legislation with enforcement!

I was one of those men appointed to conduct an enquiry into the disaster. The others were R.A.S. Redmayne, Chief Inspector of Mines, and Evan Williams, Chairman of the South Wales and Monmouth Coal Owners' Association. Due to the, in one opinion, somewhat partial view expressed by Williams, we were unable to submit a unanimous verdict in respect of the specific cause of the explosion, though it seemed clear enough to Redmayne and myself. Even so, we were able to present our collective opinion that the provisions of the 1911 Act had not been carried out in a number of important respects, as well as pointing out a number of lesser matters. In his 1915 publication *The British Coal Trade*, no less a figure than HS Jerous summarised our report very fairly: 'The report of the Enquiry bristles with evidence of infractions of the Act.'

Our main findings were as follows:

i)   The failure to provide apparatus by which direction of the currents of air throughout the mine could be immediately reversed was probably responsible for a large number of the deaths;

ii)   Means of extracting coal dust which gives rise to gas had never been dealt with;

iii)   A circular from the Home Office on the dangers of unprotected signalling equipment had been ignored; and

iv)   On several occasions and in a number of respects, recommendations from visiting inspectors had been ignored.

In his addendum to our report, Mr Redmayne referred to what he called 'a disquieting laxity in the management of the mine'. I was strongly inclined to add some rather more severe words of my own.

The whole question of responsibility went to law. The Divisional Mines' Inspector for Wales prosecuted the owners and the manager for breaches of the 1911 Act. The company, effectively the owners, faced few charges. The three magistrates in charge quickly dropped the charges against the owners who argued that the manager was responsible for the running of the mine, which was true, and that they therefore bore no responsibility, which I found considerably less true. The manager was employed by the owners to run the business in their names. He was responsible to them. It was surely their responsibility to make sure that he carried out his work in accordance with their wishes and standards. So, how could they not share in the responsibility for what happened? The only emotion I did not feel at that decision was one of surprise. I had long known that establishment figures had ways of looking after one another.

There were seventeen charges against the manager, seven of which were dropped, including the charge that he had failed to clear coal dust from the seams. Redmayne was enraged by that decision, but could do nothing about it. On a number of charges, particularly those relating to ventilation and supervision, the manager was found guilty. He was fined for each infringement the fines ranging from £2 to £10. The total of his fine was in the region of £35. And 439 men had died. Little wonder that the local Labour newspaper headed its report 'Miners lives at 1/1d each'.

Following the trial, there was widespread indignation bordering on fury, and not only within the mining community either. People in general were appalled to find out that the tragedy could have been avoided if precautions had been taken, and also horrified at the levity of the sentences handed down. I was gratified to note that even those newspapers which could hardly be called our friends felt that the judicial decisions had been as partial as anything seen in the worst trials of the early nineteenth century. As a result of public fury, an attempt was made to re-prosecute but it came to very little.

Through a large section of the population there ran a strong feeling that the colliery owners and manager should have been brought to trial charged with manslaughter. There was a precedent for that, the Home Secretary some twenty years earlier warning the directors of railway companies that, if their race to establish lines northwards to Scotland resulted in fatal injuries, they would be prosecuted for manslaughter. Again though, nothing came of that public demand. The owners escaped Scot-free while the soil on top of the graves in Senghenydd cemetery slowly subsided.

Naturally, that disaster provoked in the Miners' Federation a determination to ensure more rigorous administration of the provisions of the 1911 Act. Over time, our pressure on the Home Office brought some success. The total inspectorate was raised bit by bit. Eventually, the number of inspectors was four times greater than it had been in 1911, about fifty in all. It was an improvement, but bear in mind that that small number of men was not only responsible for some 3,000 coal mines but also thousands of metalliferous mines and quarries. At the Federation, all we could do was keep the pressure on.

I remember returning home from a series of dedications held in Senghenydd to commemorate the lost souls. I had rarely felt so depressed. When Ann greeted me at the door of our wee house, I confess that I burst into tears. But at least Ann had her husband coming home to her in one piece, which was a lot more than hundreds of widows in Senghenydd could ever look forward to again.

XVI

Into The Darkness

FROM EVERYTHING I have told you, you will understand that the Federation was extremely busy in 1913. Not that there was anything new in that. With a million members to represent, we were eternally busy. Perhaps it was the mood following Senghenydd which made our work seem even heavier than usual. As well as making arrangements to support all those bereaved families after the disaster, we had to keep our eyes on the upcoming Regulation Bill which the Government was introducing following Senghenydd. However, I would not like you to run away with the idea that, although stricken by the tragedy and buried in work, we were the perpetually dull and grey men that the newspaper cartoonists portrayed. When those cartoons first appeared, at the time when the Federation was growing, I cannot deny that we were offended by the way in which we were presented. No man likes to have it suggested that he has the demeanour and personality of a mouse, and we were no different to the next man in our indignation at it. Of course, it was all part of the right wing's attempt to mark us down as insignificant people but, as Keir Hardie pointed out to us, it was better to be lampooned than to be ignored.

Even at times of great seriousness, events can arise which raise you from your sadness and make you laugh. Such was the case with Sandy Brown's report. I had a few days back in Larkhall and attended a Lanarkshire Miners' Meeting purely in the capacity of a guest. Seven or eight collieries were claiming an increase of sixpence a day in wages and the afore-mentioned Sandy and his pal Jock had been delegated to present the miners' demand to one of the managers, a Mr Thompson. It was the first time Sandy and Jock had ever undertaken such a mission, so it was also the first time they had ever to report back to a meeting. Neither man was known for great powers of good speaking. The chairman, a man by the name of Nesbit, duly asked for their report.

'Jock will gie it tae ye,' Sandy announced, rising from his seat in the hall.

'No, I'll no',' Jock replied, also standing. 'You make the report, Sandy. You're a better speaker than me.' He promptly sat down again.

'Aye, alright,' Sandy muttered. 'But if I make any mistakes, you'll hae to put me right.'

'Get on please, Mr Brown,' Nesbitt told him. He was a stickler for procedure and known to be lacking in patience. 'We are all anxious to hear your report.'

'Fair enough,' Sandy said, sniffing wetly. 'Well it was like this, you see. After the last meeting, Jock and myself agreed tae meet next day at the toon cross after work. We didnae see the sense in losing a day's pay, did we? Anyway, I got there first, because Jock had ripped his breeks and had to go home and put on another pair. Am I right, Jock?'

'Aye, right enough, Sandy.'

'I didnae mind waiting though, for it was a bonny night. In fact, I was fair enjoying the fresh air. I started singing a song. I think it was "Loch Lomond". Oh, wait a minute, I tell a lie. It was ... '

'Mr Brown,' Nesbitt put in. 'We are not really interested in your performance as a soloist. We want to hear how you got on with Mr Thompson.'

'Aye, alright,' Sandy said, a little huffily. 'I was just saying ... ' He caught Nesbitt's glare. 'Oh, alright then. Jock finally arrived and we walked along to Thompson's hoose. We knocked on the back door three times.' He paused and looked over at his pal. 'Or was it four times, Jock?'

'It was four times, Sandy.'

'Aye, that'll be right, Jock. Four times it was then.' By now he was standing at the slouch, hands in pockets, as if he was settling in for a long shift. 'We waited for ages and then, at last, the door was opened tae us by the wee servant lassie, yon Jeannie McPherson. She's a daughter of auld Tam who lives in the Gorbals. Like as not maybe many of you will know her. I know the lassie fine and we had a bit of a blether about her father. You'll maybe remember that he finished work on account of the rheumatics.' By this stage Nesbitt was fidgeting in his seat, looking as if he was about to explode, but Sandy ignored him. 'Anyway, Jeannie said her father was getting on fine and sending his regards tae all of ye.' His massive brow furrowed. 'Now, where the hell was I?'

'On the road to nowhere, Mr Brown!' Nesbitt suddenly bellowed. 'You're supposed to be giving a report, man. Kindly get on with it.' By this time we were all grinning, in part at Sandy's rambling story-telling technique, in part at the sight of Nesbitt losing his temper.

'Is it you or me that's giving this damned report?' Sandy asked indignantly. 'As it's me, ah'll go aboot it in my ain way.' He shot Nesbitt a withering look, then carried on. 'We asked the lassie if Mr Thompson was in, but she said he'd gone back tae the pit again. So we went ower tae the pit, didn't we, Jock?'

'Aye, that's right,' his pal replied. 'So we did, Sandy.'

'Get a move on, Mr Brown!' Nesbitt said, as many of us were beginning to find it difficult not to laugh.

'Aye well,' Sandy sniffed, 'no need to be rude, Mr Chairman. So, we asked the engine-man where Mr Thompson was. My but it was hot in yon engine room, wasn't it, Jock?'

'Aye, real hot, Sandy.' Not noticing that Nesbitt was now slouched over the table, clenching and unclenching his fists.

'But Thompson wasn't there, was he?' Sandy continued. 'He'd gone away hame for his dinner. So, we went back to his hoose and Jock and I hatched a plan, didn't we, Jock?'

'Aye, that we did,' Jock agreed, apparently oblivious to Nesbitt's groan of despair.

'Jock went to the back door and I went to the front so Thompson couldn't slip past it. Anyway, he came to the front door and I let him have it, both barrels. Told him we were demanding the extra sixpence like we all agreed last week.' A dreamy smile came to Sandy's face. 'Aye, I gave him a right talking to, I can tell ye.'

'And what did Mr Thompson say?' Nesbitt asked, finally seeing the light at the end of a very long tunnel.

'Well, tae cut a long story short,' Sandy replied, to the sounds of stifled laughter, 'he said – "No sixpence, bugger off!"' The whole meeting dissolved into help-less laughter in spite of the reported rejection of their demand. It is said that some people take you round the whole town and back again.

I told that wee story now and again in front of various audiences, just to break the ice as you might say, and it always went down well. But there was no great opportunity for levity as 1913 grew older. It seemed to be bad news all round. There was the war in the Balkans when Bulgaria, wanting to annexe Macedonia, attacked Serbia. Then Greece, Romania and Turkey rallied to support Serbia. Bulgaria was defeated and it all ended in the Treaty of Bucharest. Our Foreign Secretary, Sir Edward Grey, seemed reasonably pleased with the outcome. Many of us were less pleased. We believed that the Serbians, strengthened by the treaty, were likely to foment trouble with the Austrian Empire. And, of course, Austria was an ally of Germany. We foresaw trouble, but who would listen to us? After all, we were only grey, ignorant trade unionists.

Like everybody else we were also aware of the fact that, across Europe, coun-tries were building up their military ordnance. Several years earlier, Jean Jaurès had warned me of this. Now, through newspaper reports and photographs, the evidence was all around us. Large-scale troop manoeuvres, reviews of fleets, some impassioned nationalistic speech-making: things were moving quickly. Our col-leagues in the Labour Party seemed to lack a common voice over this. Some urged restraint, some talked of the need for national defence, while others said very lit-tle. I do not believe that that reflected the Labour Movement's finest hour. Within our Federation's committee, there was more unanimity of opinion, even if it wasn't total. I was appalled by what I saw as an inevitable build up for war. I resolved to take every opportunity to speak out in favour of peace and, in spite of the opposition which I attracted, I began doing so later in the year.

Then there was the awful tragedy at that year's Derby horse race in June, when Emily Davison was fatally injured as she threw herself in front of the king's horse.

It was an incident which appalled the nation. What a pity that they had paid so little attention to Emily Davison's cause in the years before her death. Perhaps that might have saved a young woman's life. Campaigners to give women the same rights as men were not new. You could point to the Campaign for Women's Education which stretched back to the 1850s, the demands for recognition following the magnificent work of Florence Nightingale and many other things. But, outside the trade unions, which had many women members, recognition for women was slow in coming.

While the trade unions, the Labour Party and a number of Liberal MPs advocated suffrage for women, the collective might of the House of Lords, the Conservative Party, the judiciary and the professions fiercely opposed it. Out of such opposition, the Women's Social and Political Union was formed by the remarkable Pankhurst family in 1903. I had the privilege of speaking at a number of their rallies. But, again, their voices were ignored. Little wonder that a number of them resolved to what they called direct action.

I cannot say that I entirely approved of those ladies' tactics, but I understood the rage and frustration which led to them. We miners had often enough felt that we were banging our heads against a brick wall when dealing with owners' associations and governments, and now the suffragettes, as they were known, were enduring the same experience. At the Miners' Federation, we passed a number of resolutions in support of their demand for the franchise, and they enjoyed a good deal of public sympathy, but still the powers would not yield. The fuse which lit the bonfire of their exasperation was a botched-up Government Bill. The Plural Voting Bill was already before parliament when Asquith, by then more or less convinced of the principle of women's suffrage, made a late addition which would have given the vote to certain categories of women. However, in January 1913, the speaker ruled that the addition could not be allowed, since it changed the nature of the Bill.

That decision drove the suffragettes to desperate, and I have to admit, illegal and often dangerous measures. They resorted to the burning of pillar boxes, churches and railway stations. They smashed windows and chained themselves to railings. There were even physical attacks on government ministers, particularly Asquith. While golfing at Lossiemouth, he was attacked by a number of extremists, who tried to strip him of his clothes while others beat him about the head with whips. His colleague, Lloyd George, did not escape either. His new house in Surrey, which was thankfully vacant at the time, was badly damaged by a bomb that had been planted by Emily Davison. Mrs Pankhurst was found guilty of being implicated in that and sentenced to three years' imprisonment, though she only served six weeks. Then, to cap it all, Davison's death four days after she was struck by the king's horse was a most heroic but wasteful attempt to draw attention to the suffragettes' cause.

My heart went out to them, but I felt that their tactics were wrong. Really, they had already won the argument. Their outrages, as the press liked to call them, were really counter-productive. The Liberal Government was minded to give at least some women the vote as the botch with the Plural Voting Bill had demonstrated. But now, according to our members in the House, Asquith was making it known that he had no intention of giving in to violence. Meanwhile, the suffragettes began to fight among themselves, no doubt in part due to their continuing frustration, but also because of the direct action tactic selected by some. I felt heart-sore for them and, in meetings with one or other group, tried to persuade them to stay together. But the cracks were already too wide for that. The moderates led by Millicent Fawcett, an admirable woman of high principle whom I had the pleasure of meeting on a number of occasions, were disgusted by the direct action tactics and distanced themselves from it. Even within the Women's Social and Political Union, there was discord, Emmeline Pankhurst even expelling half of the membership, including her daughter Sylvia. It was a right mess and no mistake. On a visit home to Larkhall, I asked Ann what she thought of it all.

'Perhaps they should take a leaf out of the miners' book,' she told me, as we took our Sunday walk.

'And what book would that be,' I asked her, pausing to stop a wrestling match between a young boy and a wee lassie.

'Stick to principles and, above all, stick together,' Ann replied. She laughed when, as soon as I had split up the wrestlers, the wee lassie slapped the boy around the head and he ran off. 'Take that as an example, Robert Smillie,' she said, laughing. 'Women are every bit as good as men.' Then she added, 'as long as they don't fight each other.' I could hardly disagree.

In fact, the less moderate suffragettes would carry on their campaign of violence into the next year, only ceasing when a dreadful period of even greater violence enveloped the world. It would be another five years before their dreams would be realised, in part at least. If they could only have followed more reasonable tactics and held together, I am certain that they would have achieved their goals much earlier and at much less cost, including the life of that poor lassie, Emily Davison.

On the trade-union front, I found myself very busy on behalf of the Federation as 1913 slipped into 1914. In general, the trade unions had grown in number and had shown themselves less and less prepared to accept authoritarianism on the part of employers. The period between 1910 and 1914 has been described as the 'Great Unrest' because of the number of strikes that took place. You will remember that we had been the first major union to call a National Strike of our members following a ballot in 1911. Yet it became clear to us during that period that no single union, however large and united, was likely to ever achieve the influence over the employers which they had always exercised over us. I had thought for some little while that it would only be by combining our union strength that we would ever be able to achieve anything more than a temporary and meagre improvement in pay and conditions. On its own, no union would expect anything more than that, as the events of 1911 had proved.

I was pleased to be one of the leading voices which began a new strategy at our annual conference in October 1913, when I was a year into my presidency of the Federation. It was moved that ' ... the Executive Committee of the Miners' Federation be requested to approach the Executive Committees of other big Trade Unions with a view to co-operative action and the support of each other's demands.' For the time being, it was decided to make informal approaches to other unions, to test the water so to speak. As president, I became heavily involved in those talks.

At first, we decided to enter into talks with representatives of just two other trade unions, comparable in many ways to our own. I felt that, if we could engage with only two to begin with, then approaches to other unions could follow. In terms of size, organisation and industrial influence, the railway and transport unions were most similar to ourselves, so we started talking to them. Among us we had over one-and-a-half million members, so if we could form an understanding we believed that we could deal with employers more effectively. We hoped that the simple fact of our joint power would be enough to intimidate employers because we had no good reason to want to resort to major strikes. In a strike, as I have said before, it is always the strikers who suffer most. When men are idle, they only have union funds to draw on, and those funds are not substantial. Also, action by one union can impact on another union. For example, during our strike in 1911 which slowed down many industries, the railwaymen alone lost £94,000. There was every good reason, therefore, for joint action which would so intimidate the employers that strike action would not be necessary.

Following several months of informal talks, the three Executives finally met in April, 1914. As I wrote in the *Labour Year Book* of 1915, we met to ' ... consider ways and means of working in common and so avoiding the evils of disjointed action'. The meeting over several days was very positive and I had no difficulty in persuading the executives of the railwaymen and transport workers that a common approach was worthwhile in any number of ways. We were clear that we were not going to become a single Federation because the main work of each executive would still focus on its own membership. Neither did we wish that our alliance would be as a rival of, or detrimental to, any other union or unions. As I further wrote, 'The predominant idea of the alliance is that each of these great fighting organisations, before embarking on any big movement, whether defensive or aggressive, should formulate its programme, submit it to the others, and that upon joint proposals joint action should then be taken.'

I was absolutely clear from the outset that this combining of unions, which I hoped would spread, was a step on the ladder to the achieving of Socialism. I was certain in my view that capital, in all its forms, from owners through the judiciary to significant parts of the parliamentary system, was very well organised against us. It had generations of experience, wealth, the legal system and the corridors of power on its side. Not only was capital well placed to defend itself against trade unionism, it was powerful enough to attack it as well. This was why we had to combine, so that each of us could render sympathetic action, deliberately thought about and agreed upon, to any of the others. I believe that these opinions were received sympathetically by the other Executives, though I was fully aware of the fact that some of their members were less Socialist in their outlook than I was.

Naturally, news of our meeting spread quickly enough. Among owners and their creatures in the national press, there was almost a sense of panic, expressed as outrage in the newspapers. Apparently, we were going to bully the owners and the natural order of things into submission, or, failing that, simply bring the country to its knees. Naturally and as ever they completely missed the point which was that we were simply aligning ourselves in a more organised way to defend the interests of our members against the all-too-common rapaciousness of their employers. Had I owned a newspaper, I would have pointed back to Senghenydd and made the point that, had the unions been combined in power and influence back then, the owners would never have been allowed to ignore the need for advanced safety precautions, and the disaster would never have happened. Unsurprisingly, no newspaper reported that point of view.

Among trade unionists in all industries across the country, the emergence of what became known as the Triple Industrial Alliance created a dawn of renewed hope. A belief that we would become stronger and at last be able to negotiate with owners on a relatively equal footing. But, for the moment at least, events caught up with us and the formal creation of the Alliance would have to wait. Across Europe, the clouds were darkening and all minds were turned to events elsewhere.

The signing of the Treaty of Bucharest which followed the Second Balkan war in 1913, did nothing to solve Europe's tensions. In fact, that war was just the most recent in a series of confrontations which had raised the temperature across the continent and further afield. It was as if mankind was spoiling for a fight. We had seen the Moroccan Crisis, the Bosnia Crisis, the Agadir Crisis, and following each one nations aligned themselves with other nations in reaction against the latest emergency, By the time the world crawled wearily into 1914 there were, in effect, two groups of nations, each facing each other with less and less trust and more and more hostility. One group, the Triple Alliance, was made up of Germany, the Austro-Hungarian Empire and Italy. The other, The Triple Entente, was composed of Britain, France and Russia. Through their alignments, they had created two powerful blocs. For some time, I had been convinced that there could be only one outcome to this. Frankly, I was in despair.

Almost all of the Labour MP's in the House of Commons were totally against the idea of war. Keir Hardie was particularly outspoken. I shared a number of platforms with him in the summer of 1914, and we preached against the iniquities of warfare. Within the Miners' Federation, I was less outspoken. Everybody knew my views, of course, but I took good care not to preach. You may wonder why, given the strengths of my opinions. Well, it was quite simple. No miner, or his union, was preparing for, or willing to undertake, war. Neither was any other union member or his union. If it was to come, it would not be at the instigation of the working man. So, what could be achieved by preaching my anti-war views at people who had no influence in the matter? Nothing, absolutely nothing.

No, the mounting feeling in favour of war was strongest in other echelons of society and rested in the hearts of the decision-makers and the profit-takers. Mark my words, many men have made fortunes out of wars and the sufferings of other human beings. It was to people like that that I took my crusade, for a crusade it was, sometimes in the company of Keir Hardie or other Socialists, sometimes on my own. I used public halls when the authorities would permit me to do so, open spaces when they wouldn't. I addressed dozens of meetings in front of audiences who were sometimes sympathetic but more often hostile. I was not at all surprised at, or disheartened by, the reception I often had to endure. Arguments, catcalls, booing and hissing were the least I had to put up with. I was lucky in one sense at least in that I was never physically attacked, but some of the reactions to my views were more horrible that mere physical force.

I lost count of how many letters and postcards I received, many of them sent anonymously. For every one that praised my anti-war stance, there were maybe a dozen which were abusive. The word 'traitor' was regularly used, as well as defamations of myself and my family. Many letters threatened me with injury, death, maiming, extermination and all sorts of unpleasantness. Frequently, they were illustrated with crude drawings of graves, coffins, skulls, knives or revolvers, and the manner in which they would be used against me was described in some detail.

These messages were sent to me at Federation Central Offices in Russell Square, London, and at my home in Larkhall. At first, I derived a sort of macabre interest from reading them but then found it tedious and a waste of time. They generally ended up as kindling for starting fires. It was impossible to stop them, of course, because they were just part of the incoming mail and, until opened, looked no different to any other letter. They were not all vicious in their nature. Some were simply rebuttals of my views, written by people with genuinely patriotic feelings. I could understand their points of view, even if I did not agree with them. I believe it would be true to say that there was an intense feeling of patriotism in the country at that time. Millions of people were seized by nothing more than a deep love of the country. Well, I loved my country too. That was one of the reasons I held such strong opinions against war.

I saw what was coming then as a capitalist war. Nothing I have learned since has changed my mind about that. It was never going to be a war sparked by the words or deeds of ordinary men. What war ever is? No labourer, no trade unionist in any of the European countries was seeking conflict. When conflict came, as by now it surely would, it would be politicians and generals who lit the fuse, not ordinary men and women. The war would be fought, as wars always have been, over territory and glory, not over jobs and food. Neither would it be fought for the security of Britain and the safety of its people. Not even the most militant of the speakers I heard at the time suggested that Britain was about to be invaded. So defence of the realm was not the issue. In Britain, as in other countries, the issues were territorial possessions and national pride, no bases upon which to risk the lives of men. People like Keir Hardie and Bertrand Russell kept trying to make the point that it was yet another capitalist struggle of little significance to most people. But nobody was listening. Nobody was thinking. In the distance, the martial music was playing more loudly.

Europe was like a tinderbox back then. All it needed was somebody to light the fuse. That was provided in far-off Sarajevo when a man called Gavrilo Princip assassinated the Austrian Archduke Franz Ferdinand. Not only was the heir to the Austrian Empire killed, so was his wife. The world trembled at the thought of the repercussions. I was convinced that it was the beginning of a tragedy, and so it proved. Though moved to declare war on Serbia, the Austrians were at first reluctant because they felt that their armies were unprepared for war. However their German Allies offered them encouragement and support and on July 28th, 1914, Austria declared war on Serbia. The Russians were determined to support the Serbs and mobilised their troops on July 29th. On the 31st, Germany demanded that Russia should stand down her troops, but the Russians refused. On August 1st, Germany declared war on Russia, then on August 3rd declared war on Russia's ally, France. German troops marched into Belgium on their way to attack France. Back in 1839, Britain had guaranteed Belgian neutrality and now demanded that the Germans withdraw. When the Germans ignored that demand, Britain declared war on Germany on August 4th. On August 6th, Austria-Hungary declared war on Russia. Within the space of thirty-nine days, Europe had lurched into what would become known as The Great War.

Back in Russell Square, the telegrams arrived so quickly that it was hard to keep track of them. Each day seemed to bring a new ultimatum, fresh threats, and final declarations of intent. For peace-lovers like myself, it was a miserable time. Then Sir Edward Grey made his famous comment about the lights going out all over Europe, and wondered when, if ever, they would be lit again. Some words catch your mood more than others and those certainly caught mine. I thought of Jean Jaurès predictions and felt distraught at the knowledge that good trade unionists from across Europe, used to meeting in the spirit of fellowship and fraternity, would soon quite literally be at one another's throats. I advised my colleagues in the Federation that they should spend time with their families, then caught a train north back to Scotland.

On the Sunday following Britain's declaration of war, Ann and I attended the morning service at one of our local kirks. I do not remember which one, nor the name of the minister. But I do remember the tone of his sermon. He preached against the senseless slaughter of war and talked warmly about his belief in the ultimate brotherhood of men and nations. It was as if Robert Burns had returned and was standing in the pulpit. It was music to my ears. I said as much to Ann when we got home and shut the door, and the world, behind us.

'It was a beautiful service, Robert,' she agreed. There was a catch to her voice.

'Whatever's the matter, Ann?' I asked, putting my arms round her and holding her tight to me.

'What's wrong with people?' she sobbed, tears wetting her cheeks. This from a woman not greatly given to crying. 'First those awful letters to you, calling you all sorts. Now, the world going mad and nothing but talk of war. Where will it all end?'

'Now don't you fash yourself, Ann,' I told her, wiping away her tears. 'It will turn out alright in the end.' Desperately trying to sound more confident than I felt. 'The talk is that it will be all over by Christmas,' not that I believed it for a moment, but I would have said anything at that moment to console my wonderful wife.

'And the bairns, Robert. What about them? The laddies are of army age.'

'They'll do what they know to be right,' I tried to assure her, hoping in a silent prayer that they would not be foolish enough to enlist.

We talked for ages and I was eventually able to coax a wee smile out of her. Then she settled down to preparing a meal while I had a pipe by the fireplace. Over the next two days before I returned to London, we did not again broach the subject of war. But both of us knew that things would never be the same again.

XVII

Turmoil

AS THE EARLY engagements of the war took place, I found myself full of conflicting emotions. Chief among those was my horror at the thought of young men marching into battle, many of them likely to be maimed or killed, without even having had a say in whether there should be a war or not. A huge irony struck with me then and stays with me now. Unions had often been unfairly accused of being undemocratic. I believe I have proved to you how democratic the Miners' Federation was, citing the National Miners' Strike of 1911 for example. Other large unions were as democratic as we were. Men were consulted and their views taken into account over wage demands, going on strike, continuing a strike or returning to work. But over something even more arduous that that, risking life in a country's war, which man was ever asked to vote on that?

My anti-war stance, which had attracted so much vitriol from many quarters, was as strong as ever as troops of all countries moved into action. In spite of the fact that my country was now at war, and my countrymen were putting their lives at risk, I could not join in the general enthusiasm for the war. Far from it as a matter of fact. I foresaw only blood and death, ours and theirs, and the prospect of that chilled me. Neither did I share the popular belief, in some cases expressed by people who should really have known better, that the war would be over by Christmas. With millions of men in the field, and huge navies on both sides, how could the war end so soon? Grimly, I told myself that it might well be over by Christmas, but which Christmas of which year?

And yet, in spite of all my misgivings, there was a part of me that was so completely British that I could not help but hope that, whatever happened, we would be on the winning side. Or, to put that another way, the side which lost least, particularly in terms of that most precious commodities, the lives of men and women. I cared not one whit whether Britain gained land or more power, but I did not wish us to lose either. Mainly though, I just prayed that the conflict would be short-lived and not wasteful of human life, ours or anybody else's. But deep within myself I think I knew that that was a vain hope.

I made every effort to ensure that the Federation continued to play its main role, safeguarding the interests of our members. As a matter of fact, due to our commitment to an agreement made at the Copenhagen International Socialist Congress in 1910, our Federation was pleased to do what it could to 'use the political and economic crisis created by the war to rouse the populace from its slumbers and to hasten the fall of capitalist domination'. Those words had seemed fine, noble even, in the anticipation of war but the reality of actually being at war, with hundreds of thousands of your own countrymen directly involved, meant that they lost their impact. For example, a planned congress to be held in Paris to rally international labour against the war simply never happened. It was left to each country's national sections to behave in the manner it saw most fitting.

Honesty compels me to admit to you that, within the Labour Movement as a whole and our Federation as well, a sharp division of attitude grew during the first year of the war. The parliamentary Labour Party had come to the decision that, in a time of great emergency, the country had to be seen to be together and supported the drive to strengthen the army. Not that that official view diminished Keir Hardie's determination to take a different direction. In one particularly impassioned speech, he referred to the war as 'an appalling crime against the nations ... it is the rulers, the diplomats, the militarists who have sealed their doom.'

By this time, as well as continuing my work as president of the Federation, I had been elected Chairman of the War Emergency Workers' National Committee. This body was intended to note and predict the effects of war on industrial workers and report back to the Trades Union Congress and union federations on matters of importance. Meanwhile, in public non-Federation meetings, I continued to speak out against the war, again attracting a lot of hostile publicity. This caused me no little concern. Not on a personal level: I had my views and was more than ready to accept whatever came my way as a result of expressing them. However, I was greatly exercised by a question which occurred to me more and more often. In the view of the public, where does the man end and his office begin?

It bothered me considerably that the venom directed against me from my opponents might eventually also be directed against the Federation. That the public might think that I was speaking for the Federation, while I was not. That the Federation might be held responsible for my views and suffer a lack of public support as a result. For me, this was a crisis of conscience and no mistake. Briefly, I considered giving up the presidency of the Federation to spare it unwarranted public condemnation. I went as far as suggesting that to the committee. However, they were unanimous in their view that they wanted me to stay on. So, quite contrary to my nature, I came to a compromise. I did not stop speaking out against the war. However, I spoke less often and made it clear every time that the views I was expressing were mine alone and not those of the Federation. At the same time, I made it my business not to introduce those particular views in any statement I made to our membership.

My political opponents and many newspaper editors were, I believe, rather disappointed by 'the new Robert Smillie'. I was giving them fewer opportunities to attack me and no opportunities at all to attack the Federation. Well, not on the issue of anti-war opinions at any rate! I felt rather irked by the need to rein in my opinions but it was for the good of the Federation, and that mattered a lot to me. Among our people, as with people everywhere, there was a division of opinion about the war. I believe that the fact that I said less about it in my Federation work helped to keep the Federation together throughout the war. We had declared a truce if you like. An uneasy truce from time to time but a truce is better than war, is it not? What a tragedy that Europe's leaders could not have seen things in the same light.

For some months after the outbreak of war, little changed in the industry. In some districts, peace broke out as you might say as the owners, keen to increase production due to war demands, actually withdrew from making threatened wage reductions. However, it wasn't the same in all districts. In Durham and Northumberland, for example, almost 200,000 mines were forced to accept a reduction in wages over the winter of 1914-15. Then, in the West Yorkshire coalfield, a dispute arose over the refusal of a number of mine owners to carry out an award under the Minimum Wage Act. This dispute dragged on for several months and, following a ballot, the men were prepared to go on strike. There were signs that the mine owners were not sure how to react. Sensing this, I arranged a special conference of the Federation at which we officially sanctioned the men's intention to strike. Immediately, I conveyed that information to the mine owners. That was on January 7th. On February 9th, the mine owners conceded the Yorkshire miners' demands and a major strike was avoided.

There were some districts where, for reasons which the owners claimed were based on costs, mines were not working at full production levels, so the men were on short time and the level of unemployment grew. It was from such districts that the first large numbers of miners left their pits and enlisted in the armed forces. As this enlistment spread to other districts, coal output began to be seriously affected. As soon as they realised this, the owners began to lobby the Home Office for a suspension of the Eight Hours Act which had passed through parliament some five years earlier. Naturally, as president of the Federation I was seriously alarmed at this development.

While the owners continued to press for a suspension of the Act, we decided to describe to the public the truth as we saw it. In a series of meetings and rallies, district leaders and members of the Federation committee vigorously made the point that the reduction in coal supplies had little or nothing to do with the provisions of the Act. Our view was that the owners had become too greedy, had raised the price of coal excessively, and thus suppressed demand. On February 23rd, 1915, a Home Office departmental committee was appointed 'to enquire into the conditions prevailing in the coal-mining industry with a view to promoting such organisation of work and such cooperation between workmen and employers as, having regard to the large number of miners who are enlisting for naval and military service, will secure the necessary production of coal during the war'. All of which, apart from being one of the most unnecessarily complicated sentences I had ever read, also sounded suspiciously like an attempt to squeeze every last drop of sweat from the miners. However, I was appointed to that committee, which was chaired by Sir Richard Redmayne, Chief Inspector of Mines, so at least the miners would not be without a voice.

Throughout this period, the Federation continued discussions with the railway and transport unions. The outbreak of war had slowed down the process of alliance, but it had not been forgotten about. What with my presidency of the Federation, my role as chairman of the War Emergency National Workers' Committee and my appointment to the Home Office Committee of Enquiry, I was finding that there were not enough hours in the day. My visits home to Larkhall were rare and brief, and I missed my Ann terribly. Just to compound all this, I went on a speaking tour.

I visited all the mining districts with the speed of a whirlwind. It seemed that no sooner had I stepped off one train to deliver a speech than I was stepping onto the next one to travel to make a speech somewhere else. Some meetings were held in public halls, but just as many were outdoor rallies. Sometimes I travelled and spoke on my own, whereas on other occasions the load was shared with somebody else. Keir Hardie travelled with me several times and I was delighted to have his company. However, he did not seem to be in the best of health. He wheezed rather a lot and seemed somewhat short of breath. On the platform, I noticed that he was pausing in his speeches more often than I had ever noticed before. He would hold a glass of water to his lips as if drinking, but with his chest rising and falling rapidly. I suggested that perhaps he should see his doctor. I might have expected his reply. 'Och, no bother, Bob. I'm just getting my second wind.' I so much wish that I had been more insistent.

Throughout that speaking tour, my message was clear and consistent. The miners were doing their best. But they were by now fewer in number. At the outbreak of war, they had numbered 1,116,648 men. Within seven months, 191,170 had enlisted in the armed forces. A few short months later that figure would exceed 256,000. Output over that time had fallen in direct proportion to the declining number of miners. So the problems, such as they were in the coal-mining industry, were not the fault of the men. Rather, problems were caused by the mine owners' failure to recruit and their scandalous practice of raising coal prices at a time of national emergency. The case seemed clear enough to me.

Perhaps the most significant speech I made at that time was at a special conference arranged by the War Emergency Workers' National Committee. The conference was held in London, which meant that the newspapers gave it full coverage. Also, as well as numerous representatives of the various branches of the Labour Movement, in the audience were also some members of the Home Office departmental committee, of which I was also a member, charged with trying to restore cooperation and production in the coal industry.

Presiding over the conference was Arthur Henderson, Chairman of the Labour Party. He spoke first and spoke well, generally praising the efforts of the miners in very difficult circumstances, and insisting that the Government had to put in place strategies for recruitment and steadying the costs of coal. Then it was my turn. I do not remember every word I said: it was far too long ago for that. However, I reiterated Henderson's praise for the miners, praised the patriotism of the 256,000 of the mining workforce who had taken up arms on behalf of the country, then strongly criticised the owners for failing to recruit more men to replace those who had enlisted. But I think that the point I made most strongly was very much directed towards the wider audience outside the meeting. I urged the Government to set maximum prices for coal. I went so far as to suggest that what was being done by the owners, artificially raising costs, would be denounced as unpatriotic if the miners had caused it by a demand for higher wages. But they had not done so. I finally warned that, while the miners would do nothing to endanger the country, they would not stand by idly and watch millions made out of the coal trade.

'Well done, Bob,' Arthur Henderson said, gripping my arm as the conference broke up. 'That needed to be said.'

Perhaps those hours spent 'on the road' and making speeches to whoever would listen paid some kind of dividend after all. During the course of the Home Office Enquiry, which involved calling in witnesses from all sections of the industry, I heard all the usual solutions offered. Among the suggestions made by some so-called experts were calls for the curtailment of all holidays, the suspension of the Eight Hour Act, the introduction of labour from abroad – where exactly, given that much of 'abroad' was at war? – the employment of women and the lowering of the mine-employment age limit for boys. Happily, once we discussed all the information we had at hand, we turned our faces against such suggestions.

In our report to the Home Office, after one of the briefest, tightest-run enquiries I had ever participated in, we warned against any further recruitment of miners for the Armed Forces. We made the point that the question of holidays was one for negotiation between the Coal Owners' Association and the Miners' Federation. We ruled out the employment of women and young boys. We advised thriftier use of the coal by the general public, the setting of a maximum price for coal and the setting-up of a mechanism ensuring greater cooperation between the owners and the miners. My advocacy of nationalisation of the mines was not adopted by the committee which was no great surprise to me. Our report reached the Home Office just before David Lloyd George was made Minister for Munitions. I believe that that was in May, 1915.

Just about then, I received the kind of news that I had been dreading for some time. There was no telephone in our home in Larkhall. Ann had got one of our friends at the Larkhall Union Office to phone the message through to me. I caught the train north. Usually, if I was travelling during the day I would spend my time reading documents and looking through the window at places which interested me. But not that day. I read nothing – my mind was in too much of a whirl for that. The train sped through the lush countryside of southern England, past the big towns and cities in the Midlands, through the beautiful Lake District then, on more familiar territory to me, struggled up over Beattock Summit before reaching Lanarkshire. I saw none of those places or, if I did, I took no notice of them. Indeed, I could think of nothing but my home and family. It was not until I was pushing through my own front door that I was able to think clearly.

'Robert, I'm so sorry to bother ... ' Ann began.

'Don't apologise, Ann. I had to know,' I replied, more sharply than I had intended. I held her to me to show that I had meant no harm. 'Where is he?'

'Out the back,' she told me. 'Waiting for you. Oh, don't be too hard on him, Robert.'

Without a word, I passed through the tiny scullery into the back patch, as we called it, where Ann grew her vegetables. There he stood, standing tall but looking nervous. He was dressed in his tan uniform. I was unwilling to admit it to myself, but it suited him. What didn't suit me was the fact that this was our Daniel, and he had enlisted. That had been shock enough to me. Now, what shocked me even more was the fact that I was no longer looking at a boy, my boy. Standing in front of me was a well built twenty-two year-old man. I'd been so busy, been away so much, that I'd hardly noticed him growing to maturity. Suddenly, all the speeches and pleas I had rehearsed during my long train journey were forgotten. I could only think of one thing: how much I loved the boy.

'Hello, faither,' he said, sounding a little apprehensive.

'Daniel, my boy. Are you well?'

'Aye, fine. And you?'

'Well, thank you.' What could I say to him? 'You will have spoken to your mother about ... about things?'

'Aye, I have. I've been here a few hours.'

'Would you mind telling me why you have enlisted?'

'Well, faither, I thought it was the right thing to do,' he replied.

'The right thing to do?'

'Aye, just that.'

'Nobody forced you?'

'Of course not!' He squared his shoulders. 'You always told us that only a fool

Yours very truly.
Robt Smillie.

Smillie's portrait in the 1920 Committee of Honour for Save the Children Fund.

Six of Smillie's seven sons appear in this picture as the funeral cortege moves off in Larkhall, March 1940. Alexander is out of view.

Mourners gather outside the Smillie's home at 29 Miller Street. Again, six of Smillie's sons can be identified in this picture. In the centre foreground in the lightcoloured coat is one of them, Daniel. His son, Robert, was the last in the family to remember his grandfather. To his right, holding his hat, is James Maxton.

The cortege makes its way along Miller Street. After a simple service Smillie was cremated at a Glasgow crematorium and his ashes were scattered on ground near the Summerlee Pit.

A colliery row in Netherburn, near Larkhall, c1900. It is typical of the type of housing which mining communities had to endure during much of Smillie's lifetime.

This view of a miner's dwelling in Woodside c1900 is typical of the evidence presented to the Sankey Commission by James Robertson in 1919 and which moved many onlookers in the pubic gallery to tears.

The new Robert Smillie Memorial Primary School in Larkhall.

Coal Commission Questions Suggested

Is it the case that in the days of Robert The Bruce land in Scotland was an unsaleable Commodity?

Can you give us a short account of what is stated in "Stair's Institutions of the law of Scotland" on this question?

Lord Stair was President of the Court of Session and writer of the book?

Was it the law of Scotland that at the time of Robert The Bruce all the land of Scotland was held under the tenure of what is Called "Ward" Holding?

Explain to the Commission what Ward Holding is?

Was it this — that all the land in Scotland was practically vested in the King for behoof the Nation?

He Could not sell it but he gave it out as a free grant to his Great Vassals on Condition that they with their sub vassals turned out on military service?

Was it a Condition that the Great Vassals Could not sell any of the land but were in turn bound to give it out (as a free grant)

The first page of Smillie's handwritten notes which show his diligence in preparing for the Sankey Commission. His questions were based on the work of William Small and other experts in land ownership. Many of the phrases that appear in these notes were introduced into questions which he put to peers of the realm during the enquiry.

VETERAN LEADER HONOURED

Scots Labourists' Gifts to "Bob" Smillie

ROYAL GIFT THAT WENT TO LARKHALL

Scottish Labour M.P.'s, including the "Clyde Brigade" and trade union leaders sang and danced in merry mood in a Glasgow hall on Saturday night. They showed themselves as real sociable fellows, without a care for the General Election fight.

Along with several hundred I.L.P. members from all parts of Scotland they had gathered for a social hour to honour Mr Robert Smillie, M.P., on his retirement from Parliament and fittingly recognise his 52 years' service to the trade union and Labour movements in the country. The veteran miners' leader received a timepiece, and Mrs Smillie was presented with a handbag containing "a love token" from Scottish Labourists.

When the guests of the evening appeared on the platform and again at the presentations, they were given an enthusiastic reception, the cheering continuing for several minutes.

A Striking Comparison

For 52 years Bob and Mrs Smillie have been agitators, servants, pioneers, and legislators in the trade union and Labour movements in this country, said Mr P. J. Dollan, in making the presentations. And in illustrating the growth of these movements he pointed out that:

We will have more candidates in Scotland at the General Election this month than we had known Labourists in Scotland when Keir Hardie and Bob Smillie founded the I.L.P. in 1893.

When he instanced the recent victory in North Lanark as typical of the new spirit of youth in the party the cheering was deafening, for it was known that Miss Jennie Lee, M.P., was somewhere in the audience.

Story of a Royal Gift

Bob Smillie, who had been called the Prince of Agitators (remarked Mr Dollan) had received one mark of royal favour—an attaché case bearing the royal monogram. When Bob received the gift Larkhall Branch required a literature case, and so on Mrs Smillie's suggestion—she was the power behind the throne—it came about that Larkhall I.L.P. was the only branch possessing a literature case bearing the royal letters "G.R."

The veteran leader was, in reflective, reminiscent mood in his speech of acknowledgment. Alluding to financial problems in his early election campaigns he humorously remarked—"We were not millionaires; we were not at that stage of selling honours for money-raising purposes."

A Keir Hardie Photo

His reference to Keir Hardie made a touching passage that moved the audience. "I keep a photo of Keir Hardie, my dear early comrade, on the mantelpiece at home. Perhaps you will not understand, but we consult together from time to time. I assure him—'Yes, Jimmie, it is coming yet for a' that,' and to me at least he seems to look down and nod his head, as if he, as well as I, realised that the end we had in view is coming when people will have fullness of life."

Mr George Hardie, chairman of the Scottish Parliamentary Labour group, who incidentally recalled with some pride the night he took a verbatim shorthand note of Mr Smillie's opening speech in his first election campaign, and Mr James Maxton, chairman of the National Council, added their tributes to Mr Smillie.

"Bob Smillie," said Mr Maxton, "is one of the few real gentlemen that I have ever known."

Smillie was portrayed in the national press as a socialist agitator. His local press was more affectionate towards him as the cutting from May 1929 on the left reveals after he had retired as an MP.

Smillie sat only once for this official portrait by Mendoza which was painted in 1920.

allows himself to be persuaded to do something he believes to be wrong.'

'True enough.' Then I remembered the story about all the members of the Hearts Football Team marching to the recruitment centre to enlist together. 'I just wondered if you're doing it because your friends are.'

'No, not that,' he said, shaking his head. 'There's only Tam Meikle going with me. None of the other lads are.' A brief pause. 'As I said, faither, I'm only going because it's the right thing to do.'

'So maybe you think I've been wrong, preaching against the war this last year and more?' Finding that his opinion mattered a lot to me.

'No, faither, I don't think you've been wrong about that at all. Nobody with a grain of sense in his head wants war. I certainly don't. In your position, I would have said exactly the same, maybe more. But the plain fact is that we are at war, and I won't let other men do my fighting for me.' Standing up straight, looking as proud as only a young man can.

'Aye well, Daniel,' I said to him, 'as long as you're doing it because you think it's the right thing to do, I will not quarrel with you.'

'I'm glad of that, faither.' and he smiled for the first time.

'Just promise me that you will not take any extra risks. Your mother and I love you too much to think of you doing that.'

'I promise, faither.'

'Good lad, Daniel.' I shook his hand firmly. 'Now, let's away in. I'm sure your mother will have some dinner ready for us.'

I'd gone there to remonstrate, plead, beg even. But, seeing the honest determination on his face, I'd realised that there was no point. Besides, the lad was doing what he believed was right. What more could I have asked of any son of mine? We ate our dinner, talked intimately among the three of us for a few hours and then said our farewells. An hour later, I was leaving Glasgow on the overnight southbound train to London.

On the train, I caught up on some of the reading which had escaped my wandering attention on the way up. As ever, the newspapers were full of the war, which was hardly surprising in the circumstances. Some time after crossing the border, I put down my newspaper and reflected on what had happened in the conflict so far. I supposed that you would claim that we had been successful in destroying what the Germans called the Schlieffen Plan, a strategy to fight the war successfully on two fronts. Thanks to British troops at Mons and French troops at the Marne, the German advance had been halted and they had to dig in. By and large, so did we and the French as well. This meant that any idea of a war of movement was over. Great trenches were dug which eventually stretched all the way from the English Channel to the Alps. At the same time the Russians mobilized far quicker than expected on the Eastern Front. The pattern for much of the war was set. The horrors of trench warfare had begun. My eyes were stinging with the salt of imminent tears as I thought of the details of the battle at Ypres where our soldiers defended that city and prevented the Germans moving on the channel ports. But at what a cost! Casualties at Ypres were horrifying. Over half of our men were wounded and one in ten died. No doubt many of those casualties were brave miners who had volunteered for the armed forces. This was precisely the kind of carnage I had foreseen. If there is one truth about warfare, it is that men over time develop more and more efficient ways of killing large numbers of other men. The horror of Ypres and the establishment of trench warfare just proved how ridiculous the notion had been that the war would finish by Christmas.

At the war office, Kitchener was of the view that there was nothing much amiss with British tactics. What we desperately needed was more men or, as I bitterly thought of it, more cannon fodder. He tried to persuade Asquith that conscription was required, but Asquith would have none of it. Instead, Kitchener mounted a propaganda campaign in an attempt to attract recruits and bring the British Army up to seventy divisions. Yes, seventy divisions. Soon, recruiting posters were everywhere. On that journey back home from Larkhall, even the smallest of stations we pulled into bristled with those posters of Kitchener, pointing his finger at any onlooker, with the words 'Your Country Needs You'. Frankly the response staggered me. By February of 1915, a million men had volunteered, my Daniel among them, and more were flooding in from the Commonwealth.

On the Eastern Front, things were going badly for our Russian allies. They had been fast out of the blocks, surprising the Germans by advancing westwards. But Hindenburg came out of retirement and led the Germans to two crushing victories over the Russians, who suffered particularly dreadful casualties at the battle of Tannenberg. Then, the Germans moved eastwards after the retreating Russians and occupied Poland. At that point, their Turkish allies blockaded the Dardanelles, cutting off one of Russia's most important supply routes. This led to one of the worst conceived expeditions in the history of any war.

Churchill was at his effervescent best, or worst, depending on your point of view. He came up with an idea to re-open the supply route to Russia and, at the same time, deal such a heavy blow to the Turks that they would be knocked out of the war. There were two attempts at this. Both were failures. First, an Anglo-French naval attack through the Dardanelles to capture Constantinople came adrift because the Turks had laid so many mines in the sea lanes. Then, in April 1915, Australian and New Zealand troops, followed by British troops, were sent ashore and slaughtered. The entire force had to be withdrawn. How the War Office was ever persuaded by Churchill's boyish sense of adventure was a mystery to me, and many other people. What the parents of the dead thought is unimaginable.

One single tragedy caught the attention of the world. In April, 1915, the British liner, the *Lusitania*, was sunk by a single torpedo from a German submarine. Over a thousand passengers and crew died. Much later, it turned out that the ship had been carrying vast quantities of arms and ammunition, which made it a legitimate target, if you accept such a thing, but this was not known at the time. There was an international outcry, particularly strong in the United States. One hundred and eighteen of the dead were Americans. The president, Woodrow Wilson, protested vigorously to the Germans who, for their part, were worried about the Americans entering the war against them. So, for a time at least, there was a reduction in German submarine activity. That was some relief to us, even if the reason for it stemmed from ignorance of what the *Lusitania* was really up to. Personally, I found the whole episode yet another blemish on civilisation.

During the spring of 1915, the coal industry was not in the most robust condition. The miners were doing their level best. They had made sacrifices such as curtailing their due holidays and were under enormous pressure due to the fact that virtually all mines were seriously undermanned. I felt enormously proud of the men's efforts but it was clear that, to meet the demands of the war effort, more coal had to be produced. In parliament, Lloyd George had been appointed Minister of Munitions and he had on his desk the report from the Home Office departmental committee enquiry, of which I had been a member. It was evident that, armed with that report, Lloyd George was going to have to take action, and the sooner the better. At that time, coal production was falling three million tons a month below requirements and some voices were calling for the return from active service of those miners who had enlisted in the armed forces. I did not lend my voice to those calls. It never seemed to me to be a serious option.

Under the chairmanship of Sir John Simon, the Home Secretary, conferences of employers and the Federation were arranged in London in July, 1915. At the first of those, Simon hinted that the Government was considering the suspension of the Eight Hour Act. I protested against that and, for a while, the conference was in danger of falling into two broad camps. On the one side, the employers not only supported the suspension of that Act, but also re-introduced the ideas of the employment of women and younger boys. Naturally, I reacted against that so, on our side, there was rejection of each of the tired old suggestions made by the employers. However, I took the opportunity to remind our people that, if production was not increased, then the demands of the war effort might mean that millions of poor folk might go cold during the coming winter.

The debate grew more and more heated and, from time to time, Sir John Simon was having trouble maintaining order. I even found myself close to losing my temper, which annoyed me. I had always set such store by retaining a calm demeanour and only using facts rather than heated opinions in the course of an argument. Frankly the conversation was going nowhere. I cannot comment on anybody else's feeling but I know that I felt mightily relieved when Lloyd George, who had been remarkably quiet up until this point, made an intervention.

'Gentlemen,' he said, in that rich Welsh voice of his, 'we must remain calm. I beg you to remember that what we are discussing here is the national interest and not an industrial dispute. I must ask you to remember that we are working together.' From anybody else, that might have sounded rather schoolmasterly, but his words had the habit of catching people's attention. They certainly caught mine. The meeting fell silent to listen to him. He reminded us of the need for speed and a spirit of cooperation then, through the chair, arranged a further conference later in the week. It would give us all, he suggested, a chance to clear our heads and return to the table with renewed determination to succeed. I wholeheartedly agreed with him. As the conference broke up, he came over to me.

'Well, Mr Smillie,' he said, offering that lop-sided grin of his, only just visible beneath his heavy moustache, 'perhaps we have hope of making some progress now.'

'I certainly hope so, Minister,' I replied. 'And it won't be before time.' I meant every word of that. Not only did the needs of the country have to be served but I had no intention of seeing the already over-stretched miners having their hours increased or, even worse, witnessing women and young boys working in our pits.

When I got back to my hotel that night, awful news awaited me. Keir Hardie had been taken ill and rushed to hospital. There was concern that he might not live. Without bothering to wash or shave, I dashed back out into the night and hailed a taxi. Odd, isn't it, how inconsequential things stick in your mind? Equally odd how other things don't. For example, I can't remember the name of the hospital where Hardie was being treated, but I do remember that the cabbie couldn't understand my Scots accent and I couldn't understand his London accent. However, both of us understood the words for money and I paid him off after what seemed like a never-ending ride.

Hardie was in a bed at the far end of a long, narrow ward. At first, the matron was unwilling to let me see him, saying that the doctor was treating him. However, when I explained who I was, and my closeness to Hardie, she relented and asked me to wait in an office. The doctor would see me and he would decide if I could visit my friend or not. He arrived some five minutes later. A youngish man with pleasant features though tired eyes, he was prepared to be helpful.

'I'm afraid that Mr Hardie has suffered a stroke,' he told me.

'Oh heavens no,' I cried, then hardly dared to ask the next question. 'Will he ... is he ... '

'We think he has been lucky,' the doctor smiled. 'It is a relatively minor stroke and we do not believe his life to be in danger.' Then he frowned. 'Though I have to warn you that such minor strokes can often predict more serious ones. Your friend will have to take things easy for a long time to come.'

'I see, doctor. Thank you for being so frank. May I see him?'

'Yes, but not for more than a few minutes. He is very weak.' He shook my hand. 'Now if you will excuse me, I have more patients to see.' He hurried away.

'Thank you, doctor,' I called after him, then I went into the ward to see my old friend.

'Bob, it's yourself. It's good of you to come.' Hardie was pale and looked and sounded tired, but there was no sign of the droop in his face I had been expecting and dreading. He patted the top blanket. 'Here, sit yourself down on the bed.'

'How are you, Keir?' I asked, sitting gently on the side of the bed. My friend looked so small and vulnerable that I had fears of breaking him.

'Och, not so bad, man. Not bad at all.' He looked around him with some disfavour. 'I can't wait to get out of here, mind you.'

'You just take it easy, Rob Roy Hardie,' I laughed at him. 'You do just what they tell you.'

'Aye, I suppose you're right Bob, as usual.' Then the eyes lit up in his pale face. 'So how did the conference go today?' This was absolutely typical of the man. Lying in a hospital bed, seriously ill, yet still absolutely immersed in politics.

So I told him what had gone on, how arguments had grown heated, and how Lloyd George had saved the day. Then I noticed that his eyelids were fluttering and shortly he fell asleep. Well, I'd always been a more boring speaker than him. The matron came over and told me in a kindly enough voice that I should leave. I gave my sleeping friend's hand a quick squeeze, then left to find a taxi back to the hotel. This time I was lucky. The cabbie hailed originally from Lockerbie and we understood one another just fine!

I wouldn't say that I paced the floor of my bedroom that night, but I certainly found sleep hard to come by. My head was buzzing with problems. On a personal level, I was worried about Daniel. Where was he by now? Was he in the thick of the fighting? Was he ... was he ... still alive? Was dear Ann able to sleep with worrying about her son? I suddenly felt very far from home. And what about Keir Hardie? Would he come through his illness? I prayed that he would. Unable to do anything about Daniel, Ann or Kier, I tried to concentrate on something I might be able to affect, the imminent conference with Lloyd George. By the time that I fell asleep, I had reminded myself several times that my first duty was to the miners, and it would be in that spirit that I would approach the conference.

XVIII

Bearding The Dragon

BY NOW YOU will know that I have always been interested in politics. What may surprise you is that there are certain politics I have never had any interest in at all. If that sounds Irish, as the saying goes, well I can hardly help that as I was born there. To be serious, what I mean is this. I have always been interested in that kind of politics which involves debate and argument about ideas. In particular, I have always been able to argue for the furtherance of Socialism. However, I have never had any great interest in the 'who's who' kind of politics. There are some men who, if asked, would be immediately able to tell you who held the post of Foreign Secretary in Gladstone's first term. Well I couldn't, and I'm not ashamed of that fact either. For me, politics was always about ideas rather than the men who held office. Personalities have never greatly interested me, except that knowing something of how a man thinks and works may help if you are arguing with him. However, given the complexity of what was happening politically in the early stages of the Great War, it might be as well to reflect on those matters for a minute or two.

Asquith did not prove to be a competent war leader. An able enough man, he had managed peacetime affairs well enough, even if I had seen at close quarters signs of personal weakness in his handling of matters during the National Miners' Strike and the emergency Minimum Wage Act. But as the early months of the war passed, it was clear to anybody who had the eyes to see that he was ill-suited to leading the country in a time of greatest need. He had always been pleasant and civil in his dealings with me, and I was not alone in believing that the basic gentility of his character would be his undoing in time of war. And so it proved.

Perhaps his one great gift to the war effort lay in his use of people. Faced by growing criticism of his performance, he brought Conservatives like Balfour, Lord Curzon and Bonar Law into the cabinet, as well as our own Arthur Henderson, leader of the Labour Party. In effect he created what was called a 'Coalition Government' which, in my opinion, was good news for the country even if it did irreparable damage to the Liberal Party. Most people felt that the most significant move that Asquith made was to appoint David Lloyd George to the post of Minister of Munitions. This move would eventually backfire on Asquith, but it was the single most important appointment in the early stages of the war.

Lloyd George quickly became seen as the outstanding member of the cabinet. Arthur Henderson told me that, in spite of their political differences, he saw that Lloyd George brought to his cabinet role the qualities which had previously been lacking. His vigour and adroit handling of people contrasted sharply with Asquith's sense of detachment and seeming lack of energy. Henderson and others felt that, in their new Minister of Munitions, the right man was at last in place.

It was in Lloyd George's role as Minister of Munitions and the munitions conferences that I first got to know him well. Over the years, I would have many dealing with him and found him a complex character. He could charm when he wanted to, and I must say that, on most occasions when we dealt with one another, he went out of his way to exercise that considerable charm on me. Of course, in those early days in charge of munitions, he was fully aware of the fact that, as President of the Miners' Federation, I was one of those people he would have to pay some attention to. That may have persuaded him of the need not to offend me. Nevertheless, over the years and in different circumstances, he would continue to be generally amiable when we met, even when our ideas were diametrically opposed.

He was among the most quick-witted and best organised senior politicians I ever came across. He was also decisive, on occasions I thought almost too decisive, and he had a justified reputation for getting things done. Within days of taking the office, he requisitioned a hotel to house his new ministry and appointed several men from outside politics, businessmen in the main, to the ministry because he believed them to be more decisive than politicians. He cut through red tape like a hot knife through butter, and rumour had it that he scarcely bothered to let Asquith know what he was doing, far less ask his permission to do it. Oh, he was a regular whirlwind alright, the Welsh Wizard, as the popular press named him.

You will be thinking that I thoroughly admired Lloyd George. Well, I certainly found much to admire in the man, particularly back then when his qualities were much needed. And yes, on the whole I liked him. He had a most engaging life force about him which was difficult to resist. However, it would not be true to say that my admiration for Lloyd George was absolute, for it was not. Apart from the obvious political differences which lay between us, there were aspects of the man I never took to. In his personal appearance and dress, he was somewhat foppish. As if he was saying to the world, 'Look at me!'. Not that that matters at all in the general run of things. However, it pointed to a certain egocentricity and ambition in his make-up. Also, it indicated something which was kept quiet for years: he was something of a womaniser. I find none of those traits admirable. But more importantly I was never quite sure that I could trust him. Over time, I would have good reason for that but, in the beginning, it was just a feeling I had.

That was the state of affairs in June, 1915, shortly after Keir Hardie's stroke. That lovely, silly man spent less than a week in hospital then, quite contrary to his doctor's advice, immediately returned to constituency matters. Meantime, I was heavily involved in the second of the Munitions Conferences. Or, should I say, I was busy not being involved in it. Let me explain that rather odd statement.

Unwelcome rumours had reached us at the Federation's office in Russell Square. I never found out the source of those rumours but, as Arthur Henderson was by then a member of the British cabinet, your thinking on the matter may well take the same direction as mine. But that is irrelevant. What is relevant is that it was alleged, and later proved to be true, that Lloyd George had convened another conference to which the miners had not been invited. As this story unfolds, you may guess at the reasons for that. At that conference, Lloyd George told the others, who included representatives of other unions, that he intended to present a Bill to parliament which, when enacted, would be called the Munitions Act. The provisions of this Act would allow the Government to take control of all factories, and therefore the men who worked in them, which produced armaments and other goods essential to the war effort. Further, strikes and lockouts were to be prohibited. It was further alleged that, in our absence, the position of the miners was discussed. Would we, or would we not, be included in the provisions of the Act? Now, the people who attended that conference were asked to maintain secrecy about the discussions until the next conference, due in a few days, at which I would be present, representing the Miners' Federation. But, men being men, and bearing in mind that those attending the conference were our fraternal co-unionists, it wasn't long before we heard the details. We were not entirely surprised that the unions present had taken the view that, if their men were to be covered by the provisions of the proposed Act, then the miners should be as well.

A moment ago, I told you that, however much I might have admired the man's qualities, there was something about Lloyd George that I could never quite trust. Here was the first good reason to justify my reserve in that matter. The news came through to me at the end of a working day. We in the executive committee were all very tired and, as you might imagine, the news did not improve our mood. Within two days, I was due to represent the Federation at what I would call the official conference, but it seemed that the major decisions had been agreed in principle in our absence. We talked long into the night and eventually came to the view that we would send two delegates to the imminent conference, but with a watching brief only. I would not go. The reason for that was simple enough. We felt it likely that there would be a majority in favour of the provisions of the proposed Act. If I were to go, and even if I spoke out against the miners being included in the provisions, the majority view would prevail and Lloyd George could always claim that I had been present at the conference when the principles had been laid down. I was not prepared to allow myself to be used like that, which was why we sent two delegates with strict instructions not to participate and, under no circumstances, to vote on any motion.

Our delegates duly attended the conference at 6 Whitehall Gardens, then reported back to the Executive. I was appalled at what they had to say. The proposed Munitions Act, the details of which were fully explained by Lloyd George, would undoubtedly and seriously interfere with the hard-won rights of trade unionists. We all realised that sacrifices had to be made in time of national emergency, but miners and other trade unionists had already made considerable sacrifices in terms of levels of work, wages and time off, and I found it hard to imagine how any more could be squeezed out of them. Lloyd George had not discussed the position of the miners but, when asked by a delegate from another union if he intended to exclude us from the provisions of the proposed Act, he replied that if it was the common view of the conference and the other trade unions that we should be brought in, then he would see to it that we were.

Our executive committee meeting broke up in a sombre mood, our members making their way home for the weekend. I was due to go home myself the following morning. Indeed, I had been looking forward all week to seeing Ann and Larkhall again. But, for the moment, I was too consumed by anger to think about the homeward journey. To be told that the miners were to be included in the Act when we had not taken part in the initial conference which more or less decided that was a bitter pill indeed. Lloyd George, and everybody else for that matter, had been well aware of our opposition to emergency legislation which did away with the trade unionists' basic rights. No doubt that was why we had not been asked to attend the conference in question. In an absolutely foul mood, my colleagues all on their way home, I forgot about my own travel plans and put a telephone call through to Lloyd George's office, demanding to see him. In fairness to the man, who was no doubt expecting trouble from my direction, he agreed and, next morning, my journey home to Larkhall forgotten for the moment, I made my way round to Whitehall Gardens. There Lloyd George was waiting for me, alone in his office. I was in such a temper, that I forgot my manners and laid straight into him even as he was rising to greet me.

'For the love of heavens, man,' I blurted out, 'what kind of devil's spite do you hold against the miners?'

'Why, Mr Smillie,' he replied, 'whatever is the matter with you?' He looked more puzzled than angered by my brusqueness.

'I think you know very well.' In my temper, I had quite forgotten myself. There again, I had always taken the view that no man, of whatever rank, meant anything to me when the freedom of trade unionism was threatened. 'In fact, I expect that you have been rather expecting me to call.'

'Please sit down, Mr Smillie,' he said, as calm as you like. 'Perhaps you would care for a cup of tea or coffee?' Seeing the shake of my head, he leaned across the desk and laid his somewhat untidy head on top of his knuckles. 'Perhaps we could start again,' he said quietly, his bushy eyebrows arched. 'Please be good enough to tell me the purpose of your visit.'

'If you wish,' I replied, in rather quieter tones, reminding myself of the old axiom that he who loses his temper also loses the argument. 'I understand that you have agreed, in spite of everything that I have ever said to you, that the miners will be included within the provisions of your Munitions Bill.' I paused to see if there was any reaction. There wasn't, so I continued. 'You have been fully aware all along that we were determined not to be included. Yet you have seen fit to include us.' Still no reaction. I pressed on. 'I am given to understand that there is one clause in the Bill which will make it a criminal offence to incite workers to strike.' There was a flicker on his face, but he still maintained his silence. I gave him what I believed to be an obvious and fair warning. 'You can take it from me, Sir, that if that clause becomes law, and the miners are included in your Act, then there will not be enough prison space in this country to accommodate the miners' leaders who will lead strikes.' I paused for breath and to control my voice, the tone of which had been rising again.

'Please go on, Mr Smillie. I do assure you that I am listening.' Spoken like a man without a care in the world.

'All the leading men in the Miners' Federation are determined on one thing,' I told him. 'We would rather face imprisonment than have our recognised rights stripped from us by your proposed Act.'

'But, Mr Smillie,' he said, 'I can assure you that I have never had, nor do I have, the slightest intention of putting your fellows in prison.'

'With respect, Mr Lloyd George,' I told him, 'that is ludicrous.' He stiffened slightly at those words. A ruffled feather to go with his unruly hair? 'If the circumstances were to demand it, if the miners were being ill-treated, we would have no option but to lead strike action. In which case, given that clause in your Act, the law would have no option but to imprison us.'

'I ... eh ... I take your point,' he admitted.

'I can put it no more clearly than this,' I continued. 'The miners are more than willing to giving full service to the country in the present emergency conditions, but they are not prepared to suffer the coercion which your Bill proposes.'

'I see. Yes, I think I really do see.' He gave me one of those quick grins of his whose meaning I never fully understood. 'But let me be perfectly frank with you. I have absolutely nothing against the miners themselves, Mr Smillie. You must believe me when I say that.' He certainly sounded genuine enough. 'I know the miners very well and I bow to nobody in my belief that there is no finer body of men in the whole country. And no man can be of greater service to the country than them at the present time.' Then he sighed. A genuine sigh or a theatrical one?

I could never tell with Lloyd George. 'Personally, I was quite happy to leave your men out of the Munitions Bill. Believe me, Mr Smillie, I am not wholly to blame for their inclusion. But many of the delegates at the conference, your trade union colleagues in particular, insisted that your people had to be brought in and it was at their request that I decided to bring the miners under the provisions of the Bill.

'I am aware of that.' That seemed to come as something of a surprise to him. 'But I will be straight with you. No other trade union leaders can speak on behalf of the miners. We are absolutely resolved not to go under that Bill.'

There was a fairly uncomfortable silence for a moment. Lloyd George was tapping his fingers on the desk in some agitation, while I simply stared at him. Then he smiled and said, 'Mr Smillie, I am re-drafting some of those clauses to which you object. Perhaps you will find them less objectionable in their final draft than you expect them to be.' He rang a bell to summon Sir Herbert Llewellyn Smith, his senior civil servant. 'Here, Smith,' he said, with a distinct lack of respect, 'where are the new draft clauses of the Bill?' Sir Herbert happened to have the papers with him and handed them to Lloyd George who studied them, becoming redder in the face as he did so. Finally he barked, 'This is not the way I intended these clauses to be drafted!' Crestfallen, Sir Herbert picked up the papers and left the room.

'It really makes no difference, Mr Lloyd George ... ' I began.

'Damned draftsmen!' he snapped, apparently oblivious to the fact that I had begun speaking. 'Never do what you ask them to do. I sometimes wonder if they understand words properly.'

'As I was saying,' I went on calmly enough, 'it really does not matter how the clauses are reworded. We in the Miners' Federation are not prepared to go under the Bill in any form.'

More tapping on the desk, another silence. Then he asked, 'Can I have a meeting with your Executive here?'

'No, Sir. They have all left London for their homes around the country.'

'Then could you call them together within a few hours?' How he thought I could do that was another matter.

'It would be impossible to get them together for at least three days,' I told him. 'Besides, it would be a waste of time. I am already representing the executive committee's views, not merely my own.' I allowed the briefest of silences for effect. 'I repeat that the miners will not go under your Bill.'

'I see,' he said. He suddenly sounded tired, almost defeated. It was plain to see that he had been expecting this sort of opposition from us. 'Very well, Mr Smillie, I can see that you are determined on the matter. If the miners are not willing to be party to this then, when the Bill comes before the House of Commons, I will give some kind of explanation and the miners will be excluded.' He stood up and offered me his hand which I took gladly enough.

Dealing with anybody other than a politician, particularly one as wily as Lloyd George, you might have thought that that was an end to it. But there are heaven knows how many proverbs warning us that we should never celebrate until victory is assured. I was particularly convinced of that where ministerial promises were concerned. From bitter experience, I knew that they were often made to be broken.

That may explain to you why, when the Munitions Bill came before the House of Commons, I found myself in the faintly ludicrous position of waiting behind the Speaker's Chair with the MP, Stephen Walsh. We blocked Lloyd George's entry to the Chamber and I reminded him, quite forcibly I believe, of the promise he had made. The place had been buzzing with the rumour that he intended to include the miners in the Act after all, and I warned him that he was hatching trouble if he did so. He absolutely promised that he would not refer to the miners, then entered the Chamber to lead the debate on his Bill.

I think I mentioned the fact that he was clever. In fact, he was very clever indeed but, however you look at it, not to be trusted. In the debate, he played what he probably regarded as a trump card. He would no doubt claim that he kept his promise to me by not including the miners in the Act. However, to countermand the effects of that, he introduced an extra clause. That clause provided that the king could proclaim that any workers not covered by the Act could, at any time, be covered by it by his proclamation. Knowing how these things work, I realised that this mean that, faced by a dispute, the Government in the shape of Lloyd George could quickly persuade the king to issue a proclamation and thereby bring any workers, by which Lloyd George meant the miners, under the Act's regulations. Well, there are promises and there are promises, are there not?

I read the details of the Commons' debate and the passing of the Act as I was on the train heading home for the first time in a month. Naturally enough, I was sickened by what I read. The miners were not named in the Act. To that extent, Lloyd George had kept his word. But the provision for a proclamation by the king at the Government's request in any emergency situation meant that the miners might as well have been included. I think I read the report more with frustration than anger, but what could I do? I had intervened to the best of my ability and, even though that intervention had not won the day, there was little else I could do about it. On the way home, I forgot about Lloyd George's Munitions Act and thought about Larkhall. Somewhere over the border I fell asleep, dreaming about Ann.

The day after I got home, I visited the local union headquarters and phoned the people in Russell Square to tell them I was taking a few days off. People of my class rarely enjoyed what their betters would call holidays. A day at the seaside or the races perhaps, but not much more than that. And in wartime, even those occasional delights were denied to most working families. As for myself, I hadn't had time off, far less a holiday since ... well, I couldn't remember. In truth, I desperately needed a rest and, of course, I wanted to spend time with Ann. For rest, I slept later than usual. For relaxation, Ann and I visited some of her relatives and mine, and went for long walks in the countryside around Larkhall. I was no spring chicken by then, fifty-eight years old, and Ann was only two years younger. But those long walks reinvigorated both of us and, by the time I returned to London, I was ready for anything that Lloyd George, or anybody else, could throw at me.

It was just as well that I was feeling refreshed because big trouble was brewing in South Wales. For several months the union there had been in dispute with the owners. The main areas of dispute were over rates of pay for surface workers and night shifts and various other related matters. The President of the Board of Trade, Walter Runciman, son of a millionaire ship owner, tried to intervene when negotiations broke down. However, his interpretation of the situation was so one-sided as to be unhelpful and the leaders of the South Wales miners could not see a way to prevent a stoppage. They tried again to persuade Runciman to amend his views and enter into the negotiations as an intermediary between the union and the owners' association, but to no avail. Left with no choice, the union proposed to its members the following resolution:

We do not accept anything less than our original proposals and ... we stop the collieries on Thursday next until these terms are conceded.

That proposal, put forward on July 12th, 1915, was carried with a Federation membership majority of 42,850 votes.

Up until this point, I had played no part in the proceedings. The Federation's representatives in South Wales were competent men and they had followed all the normal procedures. But then the Government contacted the king and the proclamation allowed for in the Munitions Act was duly issued. How it was envisaged that with that proclamation some 200,000 Welsh miners would be fired and their leaders imprisoned was a mystery to me, one which pointed up the folly of the particular clause in the Act. Nevertheless, it was an affair which demanded the attention of the national executive committee, and me in particular.

You have to understand that this was a very serious stoppage indeed, and not just for miners. South Wales provided almost all the steam coal for our navy and not a little for our allies. So, I was not at all surprised to receive a message from Lloyd George, asking me to see him and other representatives who were in conference. This was the day after the strike had begun. Accordingly, I made my way over to the Ministry of Munitions in Whitehall Gardens. Entering the conference room, I found a large number of rather agitated gentlemen sitting around a large, oak table, with Lloyd George sitting at the head. Present were Sir John Simon, the Home Secretary, Runciman of the Board of Trade, and the leaders of several other departments. Typically, Lloyd George fired a question to me even as I was sitting down.

'Look here, Mr Smillie,' he said to me, in a tone I didn't greatly care for, 'we are discussing the crisis in South Wales.' There were harrumphing noises from around the table. 'It has reached a serious stage, you know.'

'I am fully aware of that, Minister.'

'Well, sir, is there anything that you or your Executive can do to resolve the matter?' Perhaps I misunderstood his tone, but he sounded like a man in a panic.

'I rather doubt that,' I told him. His face fell. 'It might have been possible to have secured a settlement by joint conference but ... ' I let my words hang in the air for a moment. I had their full attention, no doubt about that, ' ... you have taken the unwarranted step of having the matter proclaimed by the king. Therefore, I have to advise you that I now believe it to be impossible to secure peace by any means other than conceding the terms demanded by the men.' I saw a few jaws sag at that, but none of the men round the table seemed able to find anything to say, so I carried on. 'Thus far, the Federation has not interfered in the dispute. But let me tell you, gentlemen, that we believe in the justice of the men's claims. We will not intervene to amend those claims. If I were you, I would instead talk to the mine owners.'

'Meaning what exactly, Mr Smillie?' Runciman put in. Of all the men there, he seemed the one in the worst mood. 'Concession, sir, is that what you want? Well, I don't like it!'

'Now, now, Walter,' Lloyd George said, 'let's hear Mr Smillie out.' He turned back to me. 'You were saying, Mr Smillie?'

'You have to get the owners to make concessions,' I told him. 'Because if you don't, and any effort is made to use the powers of the Act against the South Wales miners, then it is my opinion that the dispute will spread to other mining districts.' I let them digest that for a minute. 'Not so much because of the points involved in the dispute itself, but because of the Munitions Act being used again the men.'

'And that is your advice, Mr Smillie?' Lloyd George asked.

'It is indeed, Minister.'

'I am sure we are all very grateful to you.'

Two days later, Lloyd George travelled to Cardiff in the company of Walter Runciman and Arthur Henderson. After twenty-four hours of negotiation, an agreement was reached. That agreement conceded most of the points which the men had made, and the proclamation was lifted. After six days, the miners returned to work. I was left to reflect on the fact that, had it not been for the Munitions Act, the strike would probably never have taken place and the navy would not have been starved of six days' worth of steam coal. As far as Lloyd George and I were concerned, it was perhaps honours even, as the saying goes. He had outflanked me on the Munitions Act but then he had been forced to take my advice to resolve the South Wales strike. I cannot vouch for his view on that but I cared little for the swings and roundabouts of our personal relationship. I was simply content that the more dubious clauses of the Munitions Act would not in future be applied to the miners.

We got a very bad press over it, of course, and no surprise there. Apparently, we were using our power to secure for ourselves a position of industrial privilege. This was absolute nonsense. We had simply secured our rights as free men and trade unionists. But what caused me rather more alarm was my dawning realisation that press reports always accurately reflected what Lloyd George said in meetings with us, whereas our case rarely got more than a few lines. In the interests of fairness and in order that the public should more fully understand our position, I was anxious to redress the balance. However, I was at my wit's end to know how to go about doing so.

I found out what was going on by sheer chance. I was talking to one of our few friends in the national press and he told me how Lloyd George was able to secure the best publicity for himself. Each Friday, towards the end of the working day, he invited journalists over to Whitehall Gardens for what he apparently called a 'press briefing.' I had never heard of the term before. At those briefings he would feed to the journalists such pieces of the latest news as he felt able to release. Naturally, that news tended to cast him in a favourable light. The journalists, delighted to be given a view of what was going on in the corridors of power, were only too pleased to report his version of events. Given the timing of the briefings, their reports were available to the Sunday newspapers which enjoyed huge circulations. In this way, Lloyd George was able to ensure that his views were given full coverage.

When I heard all this, my back was up. I felt a strong desire to ensure that when the miners were in discussion with Lloyd George, which we frequently were at that time, our view of events was fairly reported. So I arranged an appointment with Lloyd George and once more went round to Whitehall Gardens to broach the issue with him. Man, I was inside his office so often in those days that they should have put in a camp bed for me!

'Why, Mr Smillie,' he said, all innocence, 'you surely don't believe that the Government has the power to make the press print what we wish, do you?'

'In some circumstances, Minister, I believe that you do,' I told him, then went on to describe in some detail what I knew of his Friday briefings to the press. 'Perhaps the Government can't decide what the press will print, but you have some success in the matter.'

'Mr Smillie, I do believe that you may have made an excellent newshound yourself,' he said, laughing, 'and I do freely admit that I hold press briefings. I feel it important that the public should know not only what is being done, but why it is being done. I think they have a right to know our views.'

'I don't mind that,' I said to him. 'What I do mind is the fact that our views on any particular matter are never fully reported to the public. My executive committee has asked me to let you know that our willingness to take part in future discussions will not be readily provided if you are not prepared to assure us that our views will also be fully represented in your briefings.'

'You make your point very clearly as usual, Mr Smillie,' he replied, still smiling. A wizard himself at manipulating people, he could easily tell when he was being manipulated. 'Let me think about it. I will see what I can do.'

A few weeks later, an opportunity arose to test his even-handedness. There was yet another conference at Whitehall Gardens, again on the subject of coal production. As usual, there were shorthand writers there to take notes. Lloyd George spoke for almost an hour about the need to increase coal production. In reply, I spoke for just as long about the difficulties the miners were facing, the sordid conditions in which they lived and worked, and their crying need for shorter hours and decent pay. At the end of the meeting, we had our Frank Hodges and one of his secretaries pour over the notes of the meeting. Then, after we had all gone, Lloyd George held his usual press briefing.

On the Sunday, I was delighted to discover that the quality Sunday newspapers had reported the speeches by both Lloyd George and myself almost verbatim. Quite a few of the provincial papers picked up the reports too. This was the first time I was aware that the miners' case had been fully covered across the newspaper world. There was a quite remarkable response from across the country and letters poured into Russell Square. All kinds of people wrote to say that, for the first time, they had an understanding of the living and working conditions of the miners and that now they were more appreciative of the stance that the Federation had taken on many issues.

It is my opinion that the way in which that report was handled, and the great wave of public sympathy which followed it, had an important long-term effect. I am certain that Lloyd George took the lesson to heart and was mindful of that lesson when, a few years later, he instituted a major enquiry into the whole mining industry. I would play a major part in that, as I will tell you later. For the time being, I was just very pleased to have held Lloyd George to his word because, as I knew to my cost, it did not always work out that way.

During the second week of September, 1915, I received the most dreadful news. Whilst visiting Glasgow, my great friend, Keir Hardie, had suffered yet another stroke. This time there was no recovery: it had been too massive for that. Keir died on September 9th. By the time that I received the telegram with the sad details, the arrangements for his funeral were under way. At the time, I was chairing a meeting between the Federation and our erstwhile allies, the transport and railway unions. I simply could not get away, much though I wanted to. I got a message through to Ann, asking her to represent our family at the funeral then, with a heart heavier than I could ever remember, I returned to the meeting. In all honesty, I can remember little of what was said there.

It was more than a week until I could return to Scotland. Almost overcome with emotion, I went with Ann to pay my respects at Keir's grave. He had been buried in the Old Cemetery, Glaisnock Street, Cumnock. Ann told me that she had never seen so many people at a funeral. No more room in the cemetery itself, people had stood in the streets and roadways outside. Very few of them had not been in tears. The miners had been well represented. By and large, such men, toughened by the hardest of lives, are not given to great outbursts of emotion, but the cheeks of most of them had been glistening with unashamed crying as Keir had been laid to rest.

On the day of my visit to the Old Cemetery with Ann, the place was quiet. Silence punctuated only by occasional birdsong. I laid down a single rose, Keir's favourite flower, on top of the grave where hundreds of other flowers were already withering. Ann and I stood in silence. I thought deeply about the times I had shared with my late friend. And not merely a friend – he had been my guide and mentor as well. Though I was feeling sentimental, I did not cry. Back in London, I had already cried my tears for Keir. I merely reflected on the fact that, in his absence, the world would be a colder, lonelier place. I would miss my dear friend. I believe that a part of me died with him.

Before I returned to London, Ann showed me two letters she had received from Daniel. For security reasons, he could not say exactly where he was, but as he ended his letter with the phrase 'vive l'Ecosse,' it was reasonable to assume that he was somewhere in France. Ann was heartened not only by the letters, but also by the fact that he was in the Veterinary Corps, and his work was tending to the artillery horses. She seemed to think that this would mean that he would not be at the front line. I did not point out to her the distance that could be covered by German artillery shells. Why shatter her dreams of our son's safety? My pleasure at reading Daniel's letter was diminished when Ann told me that during my last absence from Lanarkshire, James had also enlisted. Probably the brightest of our sons, he had been selected for officer training which he was then undergoing somewhere in England. For me, the only crumb of comfort that day was Ann's news that young Alexander had told her that there were no circumstances in which he would enlist. He was convinced of the rightness of my views about war and, dearly though he loved his brothers, he would not follow them into the forces.

For reasons you will no doubt understand, those few days in Larkhall were not among the most pleasant I had ever spent there. It was wonderful to see Ann again, of course, but with Keir dead, Daniel serving in France and James about to go there, it was not a happy time for the Smillie family. For the first time, I was beginning to feel my age.

XIX

News At Home And Abroad

THE WAR HAD an effect of some kind on the lives of most people. Young men enlisted, many were injured or killed and their families lived in perpetual fear of receiving a telegram from the war office. At certain periods, unemployment rose and, for those in work, wages were reduced. For many, there were shortages of food and fuel. Hardly anybody was immune. Well, hardly anybody of the people I knew best at any rate. There were those who escaped the rigours of war, of course. There always are. The kind of people who, through wealth or position or both, are forever protected against the rigours of life. Plus those to whom the war was an absolute boon. The kind of people who owned workplaces and whole industries whose goods were in high demand. They made a profit from the war and shared none of it with the general run of the population. I was frequently reminded of my dear brother James' view, expressed to me in Glasgow way back in 1873, that there are two kinds of people, the owners and the owned. More than four decades on, there was plenty of evidence of the truth of that during the Great War.

There was also the effect that the war had on our attempts to unify the interests of the Miners' Federation with those of the unions representing the transport workers and the railwaymen. As I have told you, initial negotiations among us began before the outbreak of war and had continued on a fairly informal basis for a year or more after that. It took us that long and more to become used to the routines of war and, in our case, there had been the Munitions Act and the South Wales Strike among other issues to deal with. The other two unions had had their problems as well. Hence the slow progress towards a formal agreement.

In the summer of 1915, I had tried to stimulate progress by an article which I wrote for the *Labour Year Book*. In that article, I pointed to the commonality of structure among the three unions, their shared positions as front-line workers' representatives, their common desire to ensure the best possible conditions for their members, and much more in a similar vein. I inserted into that article the following sentence: 'In every case the results of joint action on a large scale should be rapid and decisive and all the suffering and loss inseparable from trade troubles of the past could be avoided in the future.'

The article in general, and that sentence in particular, went down well with the leaders of the railwaymen and the transport workers. To the extent that informal discussions went on at a more rapid pace than they had been for the previous nine months or so. In those discussions, one major stumbling block arose. At our conference in November of 1915, we were resolved to move ahead with our proposed alliance but there was concern expressed over the method by which the other unions normally decided on strike action. Our rules were framed by our strong belief in democratic procedures. It was laid down that, before a strike could be called, there had to be a ballot vote of all our members. We wished to make this procedure a binding part of the constitution of any new alliance. However, this did not suit the railwaymen who strongly believed that the delay inevitably caused by arranging a ballot would endanger a potential strike. Not only that, they simply had no provision for a ballot in their union rules.

In our discussions, we bore down on that issue time and again. Eventually an agreement was reached which you will see reflected in the Alliance's constitution, given below:

THE TRIPLE INDUSTRIAL ALLIANCE

1   That matters submitted to this joint body, and upon which action many be taken, should be those of a national character or vitally affecting a principle which in the opinion of the Executive making the request necessitates combined action.

2   The co-operation of the joint organisation shall not be called upon nor expected unless and until the matter in dispute had been considered by and received the endorsement of the National Executive of the organisation primarily concerned, and each organisation instituting movement which is likely to involve the other affiliated organisations shall, before any definite steps are taken, submit the whole matter to the joint body for consideration.

3   For the purposes of increasing the efficiency of the movement for combined action periodical meetings of the three full Executives shall be held at least half yearly.

4   There shall be appointed a Consultative Committee of six, composed of two members chosen from the Executive Committee of each of the three bodies, whose duty it shall be to meet from time to time, and who shall be empowered to call at any time a special conference of the Executives of the three bodies if in their opinion such conference be necessary. That a meeting be called on application made by any one of the three bodies.

5   With a view to meeting all management expenses incurred, each affiliated body shall contribute a sum of 10/- per 1,000 members per annum, or such sum as may be decided upon from time to time.

6   Simultaneously with these arrangements for united action between the three organisations in question, every effort shall proceed among the three sections to create effective and complete control of their respective bodies.

7   Complete autonomy shall be reserved to any one of the three bodies affiliated to take action on their behalf.

8   That joint action can only be taken when the question at issue has been
before the members of the three organisations and decided by such methods as
the constitution of each organisation provides, and the conference shall then be
called without delay to consider and decide the question of taking action.

9   No obligation shall devolve upon any one of the three bodies to take
joint action unless the foregoing conditions have been complied with.

In December, 1915, the Triple Alliance was finally brought into being.
Thomas Ashton was our Secretary, J.H. Thomas MP was treasurer, Harry Gosling
of the Thames Watermen was Vice-Chairman, and I was elected as Chairman. I
was confident in my view that, with a united voice, we could never again be dictated to by any owner, or owners' association. That the future of industrial negotiation would occur on a much more level playing field.

We needed some optimism in our lives just then, because much of the news
from the battle fronts was quite horrific. For example, there was the interminable
Battle of the Somme, which began in February 1916, and continued throughout
the year. The Germans attacked the fortress town of Verdun which the French
defended with great courage. To relieve the pressure on the French, Field Marshal
Haig launched an offensive near the River Somme. That campaign began on July
1st and the results were disastrous. Our artillery bombardment failed to dent the
heavily fortified position of the Germans. When our boys went in, incredibly
ordered to advance at a slow walking pace, they were slaughtered. On the first day
alone 21,000 men were killed and 35,000 were wounded. Unbelievably, Haig continued these attempted advances until November. At the end of it, along a thir-
ty-mile front, we had advanced by a few hundred yards in general, and by seven
miles in one small sector. Our dead and wounded numbered 418,000. And all for
next to nothing. That butcher Haig came under severe criticism in some quarters
for his suicidal tactics yet, unlike millions of others, he survived numerous campaigns and, no doubt, got a few more medals to stick on his chest. A pity nobody
stuck something in his brain, if indeed he had one.

As the reports on the Somme action came in, the nation was visibly moved.
Of course, bereavement was commonplace as was the incidence of homecoming
soldiers with grievous wounds. But the despair was not confined to those most
directly affected. The excited clamour in favour of war had evaporated like mist
destroyed by a downpour. I lost count of the number of people, few of them being
among my natural friends, who contacted me to say that I had been right all
along in my stance against war. I suppose it was fairly gratifying to hear that, but
it was no real consolation. Ann and I were as worried as the next family, over our
sons Daniel and James. When I got home briefly now and again, it was all I could

do to stop Ann worrying about the arrival of a dreaded telegram from the War Office. When I got back to London, I told an official there that, in the event of the worst news, I was to be informed at Russell Square and no telegram should be sent to Larkhall. Just a gesture, of course, and nothing that would alter the awful reality if the worst happened, but I would rather Ann heard from me rather than from a telegram.

If there was one positive outcome of the Somme, it was in the world of politics. But let me first tell you what happened in that murky domain earlier in the year. In July 1916, Kitchener was drowned at sea on the way to Russia, when HMS *Hampshire* struck a mine. Lloyd George was moved from munitions and became Secretary of State for War. I am told, though for obvious reasons I cannot personally vouch for this, that morale among staff rose considerably with his arrival. That would not surprise me. Although I may have had reservations about the level of his trustworthiness, Lloyd George had energy and charm, whereas Kitchener had had neither. It was well known that Lloyd George and Asquith were not on good terms. The most recent reason for that was the Conscription Act of May 1916, while Lloyd George was still at munitions. Apparently Asquith had been totally opposed, believing it to be against Liberal principles but, such was his shaky hold over the Government, that Lloyd George got his way.

Lloyd George believed that the conscription of all males between 18 and 45 was the only way to raise enough troops to see Britain through the war. Asquith was not alone in believing it was wrong. This compulsion brought a wave of protest on religious and moral grounds. Several movements were born to protest over it. For example, there was the Conscription Fellowship, led by the great Liberal thinker, Clifford Allen. Then there were the Quakers, who argued that a man's deepest religious or moral convictions entitled him to refuse obedience to the State. Many individuals took a stand. Some simply refused to fight and were used as drivers or stretcher-bearers. Others, known as 'absolutists' refused to having anything to do with the war at all. One of those, Howard Marten, was sentenced to death in 1916 but had his sentence commuted to ten years in penal servitude. My own dear son, Alexander, refused on moral grounds to wear a uniform and, as a result, spent the war in Wakefield Prison. Though worried for him, I was proud of the stand he took.

For myself, I vigorously opposed conscription. I believed it to be a moral outrage that one man's rules could force other men against their will to wear a uniform and do things they did not believe in. At any other time, I would probably have been vilified for speaking out in this way. However, it was around that time that news of our losses were becoming clear, so I received very little negative reaction at all. Indeed, the very reverse was the case. A large number of people contacted me, some of them very prominent citizens, and suggested that we form an anti-conscription movement with a wider base than Clifford Allen's NCF. Shortly after that, many of us met and made the decision to form the National Council Against Conscription. It attracted the attention of many from the arts world, people like GL Dickinson, Philip and Ottoline Morrell, Duncan Grant, Virginia Woolf, Bertrand Russell and Clive Bell who described the war as 'purposeless horror'. I was elected president and, on behalf of our body, made numerous speeches against conscription. I regret to say that our movement had little practical effect. Perhaps it pricked the consciences of some of those in the corridors of power, but I cannot be certain of even that much. Perhaps the greatest boon to mankind of our body's work lay in its legacy. It later became known as the National Council for Civil Liberties.

The first full meeting of our new Triple Alliance was held in April, 1916. It may seem strange to you that that meeting did not concentrate on the issues of that year. Rather, it looked to the future and considered what might happen after the war was over. There were two reasons for that. First, the war itself was beyond our control. Not only that but we were not in a position to do anything significant about legislation like the Munitions Act and the Conscription Act at a time when the country was in danger and all working men, one way or another, were doing what they could for the war effort. Second, and probably more importantly, those of us who had been engaged in union activity for many years believed that we would always be in a state of relative weakness as long as we were always reacting to events. Much better, we felt, to have a strategy for the future and, in that way, to influence events.

So, at that meeting in April 1916, we decided what our position would be on a number of issues in the postwar world. We would demand the full restoration of trade union rights, rules and regulations, demobilisation of the armed forces by industry rather than by military unit, full maintenance support for discharged members of the armed forces workers, among other things. I would have liked to have seen a demand for the permanent nationalisation of key industries, the mines included, but around the table it was not seen as a priority for that meeting so it was not included. A deputation was sent with a copy of our programme to present to Asquith, Kitchener (who was still then Secretary of State for War), and Walter Runciman, the President of the Board of Trade. Later, on the day that our deputation was received, it became clear to me that the old government practice of briefing its friends in the press was still in operation. Hardly had our feet touched the steps of 10 Downing Street on our way out than *The Times* editorial was strongly attacking the Triple Alliance. It claimed that we were introducing something new and alien into public life. Its report included the ridiculous assertion that ' ... this body of trade unionists is formally attempting to supersede constitutional Government and to frighten the appointed Ministers of the Crown into doing their will.'

My colleagues from the other unions were quite horrified by this. They couldn't understand how *The Times* had got the details of our programme so quickly. Neither could they understand *The Times'* vicious attack on us when all we had done was stated what we wanted to happen after the current emergency was over. I was much less surprised than they were. Unlike them, I had been dealing with senior politicians for some time and fully understood how they used the press to convey their own views. I reminded them that when Asquith had received us, he had been reasonably agreeable. He had promised to consider everything we had proposed, not that I set too great store by that, but specifically vowed that, after the war, full union rights, rules and regulations would be restored. I urged my colleagues to return to their union bases to discuss with their members all that had been said. When we parted, we agreed that our next full meeting would be in December.

At the front, the war had become one of attrition rather than the dashing infantry advance and cavalry charges of old. As even more news came in of losses on the Western Front, there was mounting criticism of Asquith's leadership. The press accused him of being vague, lacking direction and having no control over affairs and not much more over his cabinet for that matter. As the press campaign against him intensified, I began to feel rather sorry for Asquith. One way and another, I had had considerable dealings with him over the years and had found him to be a decent man who always treated me with the utmost civility. Having suffered a great deal of press vilification myself, I could sympathise with the anguish he must have been feeling as his reputation was soured by the quality newspapers and lampooned in the popular press. Having said all that, I tended to agree with the thrusts made against him.

Asquith had made his name in peacetime. Even when I had not agreed with him, I had thought him competent enough. But even back then there had been signs that he was not a strong leader, particularly if you looked behind the newspaper headlines and saw him close-up in action, as I had on a number of occasions. I'd seen him vacillate on a number of trade-union issues and would never forget his tears and mental anguish at the time of the Minimum Wage Act. Whatever else, I did not see him as a man capable of dealing with great pressure. At war, there was always that.

In the climate of criticism, it was also common knowledge that his relationships with his most brilliant minister, David Lloyd George, had broken down. Asquith disliked Lloyd George's egocentricity and his habit of making public pronouncements without seeking the prime minister's advice, far less permission. For his part, Lloyd George had been heard to make some less-than-flattering remarks about Asquith's leadership qualities. Then, in December 1916, all this broke into the public domain. Asquith resigned. There was a general feeling that he had been unwilling to do so but had been manoeuvred into that position by senior supporters of Lloyd George. So, Lloyd George became prime minister. I believe it was the position he had always aspired to. For what little it may be worth, my opinion was that the change at the top was for the good of the country. In spite of the fact that I had reason to mistrust Lloyd George on occasion, he had a justified reputation for getting things done. If his appointment as prime minister would mean a quicker end to this disastrous war, then so much the better.

On the morning of the next meeting of the Triple Alliance, I was about to leave my hotel when a porter pushed a letter into my hands. Wonder of wonder, it was a letter from James. It had been posted to Larkhall and Ann, not expecting me home for weeks but understanding that I would be anxious to know of James' safety, had posted it on to me. Inside, there was a wee letter from her as well. Ignoring the time and the fact that I was soon due at the meeting, I found a seat in the lobby and read James' letter.

Dear Mother and Father,

I write to let you know that I am safe and well. After completing my training, I was sent onto here, arriving three days ago.

I am a lieutenant these days, but I am afraid that that's all I am allowed to tell you about military matters. Where I am and the regiment I serve in will have to wait until our joyous reunion, which I fervently hope is not too far away.

I am in good health and feeling 'as fit as a fiddle,' as the saying goes. The weather is cold but our uniforms are heavy and our stores are warm. Our food is not as good as yours, dear Mother, but better than I believe than some of the poorest folk at home are eating.

I have not yet come across Daniel but I know from his absence from casualty lists that he must be safe. There are so many men here that it will be difficult to find him but, if my duties permit, I will try.

Please remember that I am here because I believe it is my place to serve. Most of the other officers feel the same way. I cannot vouch for the views of the men in general. Perhaps some of them feel differently, but I do not really know. All I can tell you is that they behave and work well.

If you are writing to Alexander, please convey my best wishes to him and assure him that, although we have taken very different positions in the matter of war, I still love and respect him.

I will write again when time and my duties permit.

Your loving son,
James

Having read his letter over, I read it again, and felt the rising of tears. I composed myself, read Ann's wee letter, then went out and hailed a cab. On the way to the meeting, I told myself that this was just about the best early morning I had experienced for a long time. I was some twenty minutes late for the start of the meeting but they had waited for me. I apologised then briefly explained the reasons for my late arrival. Our own men and those from our two colleague unions were very pleased for me. I would have expected no less of such decent men.

At that second formal meeting of the Triple Alliance, we passed a number of resolutions. Given a recent considerable rise in the cost of living, we proposed that the amounts due under the Workmen's Compensation Act should be increased and that farm labourers' wages should be raised to a minimum of 30/- a week. We also worded a strong proposal against the proposed introduction of Chinese labour, which had been mooted by a number of owners' associations across industry. We saw that as not so much an attempt to expand the workforce but, much more likely, a means to undercut British workmen's wages. We protested long and loud about that and little more was heard again about the use of Chinese labour.

For once, the press was on our side, certainly on the Chinese labour issue but also, at least to a reasonable degree, on the matters of compensation and farm labourers' wages. The Times even ran an editorial praising us and singled me out as a 'far-sighted humanitarian'. It made a considerable change from the more typical 'Socialist agitator' epithet. Even more important, the Labour Movement as a whole saw our Alliance as a developing success. It was confirmed that our new powerful grouping was more likely to achieve greater success on industrial matters than the parliamentary committee of the Trades Union Congress, with which I had some association, and which tended to submit proposals to little effect.

We were beginning to find that the Triple Alliance, which had at its disposal the final weapon of strike action, was beginning to obtain a more respectful hearing from ministers. This raised hopes among union members everywhere that, by working together on a more formal basis, we could help to shape the future. Of course, time would be the test bed of that view.

As 1916 moved into 1917, Lloyd George was busy extending his grip on the nation's war effort. He had set up a war cabinet of only five men. With him presiding, there were Bonar Law, the Conservative leader, Lord Curzon, a man of great and varied experience, Arthur Henderson, our Labour parliamentary leader and Sir Alfred Milner, the former Governor of Cape Colony. These men took all the major decisions much to the disquiet, so I was told, of other cabinet members. Lloyd George also surrounded himself with men from outside parliament to head important ministries. For example, Sir Joseph Maclay, a Glasgow ship owner, became the shipbuilding organiser and Lord Beaverbrook, owner of the Daily Express, became the Minister for Propaganda.

Worried about poor communications among the various government departments, Lloyd George appointed Sir Maurice Hankey to organise cabinet business. He also appointed his own private advisors, including Waldorf Astor, owner of the *Observer*. Very quickly, with his usual dynamism, Lloyd George built up a reliable and effective governing team.

He also put in place numerous government controls, one of which had a direct effect on the Miners' Federation. All merchant shipping was brought under government control in an effort to counteract German submarine warfare. Farmers were ordered to cultivate extra land to meet the food shortages and, in some case, factories were told which goods to produce, items such as army blankets and khakis for uniforms being in great demand. The new Ministry of National Service decided which men should be called up, depending on whether their jobs were vital or could be done by women. Food was rationed and there was an attempt to control prices and wages. Of greatest interest to me was the fact that the coal industry was taken under government control. Well, well, well!

To an extent, these various controls mirrored what I and other Socialists had been advocating for years. The State was intervening on a large scale on behalf of everybody. Lloyd George's measures did not go so far as to establish the nationalisation agenda which I wished to see but, in my opinion at least, a platform for that had been established. Given the progress which the Triple Alliance had made towards a postwar Socialist programme, I felt that the omens were good for the future once this damnable war was over. I hasten to add that I was not so naïve as not to recognise that the role of the State had been increased as a wartime emergency measure and there were plenty of influential people around who would wish that they would call a return to normality as soon as hostilities had ceased. Well, we would have to see about that!

I could see one other fly in the ointment as far as the eventual postwar situation was concerned, and that had to do with domestic politics. Asquith's supporters were unforgiving towards Lloyd George who only enjoyed the support of about half of the Liberal members of parliament. He relied heavily on Conservative and Labour MPs for his majority in the House of Commons. Not only that but some of his policies and certainly his confrontational style was making as many enemies as friends. It seemed highly likely that, once the war had ended, he would be unable to command the support of the whole Liberal Party, and what would happen then? Of the leading political figures of the day, Lloyd George was the most likely to be supportive of what I believed to be necessary change. What if he was no longer prime minister? What if he led a Conservative-dominated coalition? Worst of all, what if the Conservatives were returned to power? I was very concerned that any of these political changes would be likely to make real reform of industry and society much less likely. However, at that stage there was nothing that could be done: certainly nothing that I could do. I tried, not entirely successfully, to push the matter to the back of my mind.

I was unable to get home to Larkhall for the Christmas of 1916 or, for that matter, for the New Year celebrations which heralded 1917. With all that was going on with the Federation and the Triple Alliance, and responding to Lloyd George's various initiatives, there just wasn't time. By getting permission to use the local branch's telephone line, Ann was able to talk to me briefly on Christmas Day. But that was as far as it went. Our joyful reunion had to wait. I'm sure that Ann understood – I certainly hope that she did.

It was when I was busy working on some Federation papers a few days after Christmas that an idea occurred to me. I went to one of our secretaries, a pleasant lassie from the Tilbury area of London, and asked her to try and find a particular telephone number for me. It was late in the day when she came through to my office, where I was still busy with paperwork, and told me that it had taken her ages but she had found it. I wondered if it might not be too late in the day to make a call, but I decided to try anyway. My luck was in. The gentleman I wished to speak to was still in his office. Not only that but he knew me. Or, should I say, he knew of me. His father, now retired, had been a miner during the 1912 National Miners' Strike and had spoken of me in flattering terms. No doubt this helped when I made my request of the gentleman. He agreed immediately and said he looked forward to meeting me.

A few days after the New Year, I caught the northbound train. For my own reasons, I travelled on the East Coast line. My excitement mounting, I felt that the journey was never-ending as we headed north past Peterborough and Lincoln. It was an express service which meant that I had to get off at Leeds then take a local train back south again for just over ten miles. At the station, I hailed a cab and told the driver my destination. At the mention of it, he gave me a quizzical look but said nothing. It was but a short journey following which he dropped me off and I paid him.

Wakefield Prison looks much like any other, I suppose, though I am happy to be able to deny any real acquaintance with prisons. Dreadfully grey, high-walled, an imposing edifice which led into the administrative area. There I was met by the prison governor, the gentleman to whom I had spoken on the telephone. He could not have been more cordial and said that he was proud to meet me. He asked me not to be offended but he had to ask for my word that I had not about my person any items which would be used for any subversive purpose by any prisoner. I assured him that I had not, that the only unusual item I had in my possession was a letter from overseas. I showed it to him, he thanked me, then walked me along an echoing corridor to a small room.

I was in that room for only an hour but it left a lasting impression on me. Perhaps about ten-feet square but very high-ceilinged, it had a cold flagstone floor and a small barred window to one wall at a height which would prevent any man, however tall, from looking out. It was clearly a disused cell, a horrible claustrophobic place. Its only furnishings were a small square table and two chairs. There was an unpleasant odour about the place, a mixture of damp and something else which I could not identify. I had barely had time to take in my surroundings when the door opened and a young man came in, and the door slammed shut behind him.

'Alexander! Alexander, my boy.' I rushed towards him.

'Faither, it's you,' he gasped as we embraced one another.

'It is so good to see you,' I told him, wanting to hold onto him forever. 'Come, let us sit down.'

I asked him how he was getting on and, as we blethered, I took a good look at him. Twenty years old now, he looked as if he had maybe lost a little weight, but otherwise looked well. His hair was cut very short, no doubt prison fashion. That hair of his had always made his familiar name seem rather odd. Formally named Alexander, he inevitably was called by the Scots abbreviation, Sandy. Yet his hair colouring was very dark, as far from being 'sandy' as you could imagine.

'And how's mother?' he asked me.

'Doing fine, Sandy, just fine.' I prayed that that was the case for I had not seen Ann for more than a month, though she had sounded well in her telephone call on Christmas Day. I added a harmless white lie. 'She's asking after you.'

'I do miss her terribly,' he said, his voice choking. 'And you too, Faither.'

'No more than we miss you, laddie.' It was time to cheer him up. I drew out the letter from my pocket. 'You'll want to read this. It's a letter from James and you are mentioned.'

While he read then re-read James' letter, I took stock. My son seemed well. He claimed that the wardens were not unkind towards him and that his cell mate was a quiet young man, something of a poet from the Lake District, in for the same offence. 'Conshies' they were called, short for conscientious objectors. Sandy had been worried that his refusal to fight might have caused problems with other prisoners, but they had said little about it, telling him instead that he was well out of it, meaning the war. It seemed to me that, though his present position was both degrading and unfair, Sandy was at least safe and less of a worry than either Daniel or James.

'Tell me something, Faither,' Sandy said sombrely, returning the letter to me, 'have I embarrassed you? Being sent to a place like this I mean.'

'What?' I was genuinely shocked by his question. The notion had never occurred to me. 'Why ever do you ask that?'

'Well, with Daniel and James at the front, I thought that perhaps ... perhaps ... ' He broke down in tears.

'Oh Sandy, laddie,' I said to him, putting an arm around his shoulders, 'never think such a thing. The three of you have made decisions based on what your hearts have told you. No man can do any more. I am proud of all of you.'

I had to leave after the hour was up. I believe that Sandy was better for seeing me. I know that I was better for seeing him. The journey back to Larkhall was a dreadful one. The train was late getting to Leeds, so I missed my connection. The next available train to Edinburgh suffered some kind of engine problem, so it was the early hours when I got to our capital city. I sat freezing in an unheated waiting room for the first train to Glasgow then I changed for a local train to Larkhall. By the time I was embracing Ann, I had been on the move for twenty-four hours. However, given the fact that I had some good news to give her for a change, it was well worth it.

XX

An Offer I Could Refuse

BY NOW YOU will be clear on my views about war as a means of doing anything other than defending your homeland. Therefore, it will hardly surprise you to know that I never contemplated a military career. However, living through the Great War as I did, I occasionally found myself wondering how I would have measured up if I had been of an age to be conscripted. I did not dwell on such thoughts for very long but I did come to one conclusion. The war weapon which horrified me the most was the submarine. I could not imagine myself being trapped underwater in those metal coffins without quickly going mad. Neither could I imagine what it must have been like to serve on a surface vessel passing areas where enemy submarines were gathering. The tension that knowledge caused must had been extreme.

From January 1917 onwards, the nation was caused great anxiety by the activities of German submarines. U-boats as they were called. For over a year the German dockyards had been concentrating on the manufacture of U-boats rather than surface vessels so they had a plentiful supply of them which they deployed to destroy the convoys carrying much-needed supplies to this country. I did not realise it at the time, but the Germans were taking a daring and calculated risk. Following their sinking of the *Lusitania* in 1915, they knew what the Americans' attitude was towards the sinking of merchant and passenger ships. That if the Germans began the strategic sinking of non-military ships, then the United States was likely to enter the war against them. The German High Command decided to risk everything by sinking so many British and French merchant ships that we would be starved into submission before the United States could make any effective move.

The news in April 1917 was horrifying. In that one month, 430 merchant ships were lost. I found out through somebody who knew Arthur Henderson well that we were down to our last six weeks of corn. Thankfully, the new convoy system strongly proposed by Lloyd George was just coming into operation, and the losses were never so bad again. At the same time, horrified by Germany's strategy of unrestricted submarine warfare, the United States entered the war on our side. There were many of us who hoped that the worst was now behind us and that the end was not too far away.

However, throughout the year the conflict on land was still mired in unrelenting trench warfare. In this country, there were calls from many quarters for a negotiated peace because the war was in a state of total stalemate. Later, we would find out that there had been similar calls in Germany. Even among our politicians, such as Lord Landsdowne and most of the parliamentary Labour party who wished to see an attempt made to establish a peace conference. During 1917, there were offers to host such a conference from Russia, the Pope and other quarters, but nothing came of these offers. The German High Command still believed they would win and, in this country, Lloyd George was proving himself to be a hardliner who believed that we were still capable of delivering a 'knockout blow' against the Germans. And so the war dragged on.

In March 1917 came amazing news. Nicholas, Tsar of all the Russians, had been deposed. Lenin was back in Russia, the red flag was being raised all over the country, and the Socialists were in control. News filtered in on an almost daily basis, much of it conflicting, and it was virtually impossible to gain a clear picture of what was happening. The Tsar was dead: no, he was a prisoner. The Russian armies were surrendering to the Germans: no, they were fighting on. The Russian aristocracy was raising a peasant army to rise against Lenin: no, they were fleeing the country. Most ludicrous of all, one popular newspaper claimed that they had it on good authority that Lenin was to be crowned Tsar. It was hard to separate the wheat from the chaff.

In fact, much of the so-called 'news' was sheer supposition. The Tsar had indeed been deposed, he and his family being held prisoner. But the position of Lenin and his supporters was by no means secure, particularly outside the cities. It was true that a revolution of sorts had taken place, but it was only the first of two that year and the real situation over all of Russia was very much in the balance. An interim government was set up, by all accounts a fairly-elected one, and Lenin and his people were meanwhile making every effort to secure the Socialist Revolution across Russia. That much was well known: the rest was mist.

None of which helped me much with a particular problem which I was facing. Towards the end of March, I was already promised to speak at a large conference in Leeds. The audience would be mainly trade unionists but, with respect for the spirit of wartime togetherness, there were also invited guests from industry, commerce and politics. Originally, the conference was due to bear down on wartime industrial matters but, with the news fresh in from Russia, it was clear that there would be an expectation of some comments on events there. As main speaker, that dubious privilege would rest with me.

Before leaving for Leeds, I sought the opinions of my executive committee colleagues. That turned out to be of little use to me because there was a sharp division of opinion around the table. Some of my colleagues were as Socialist as I was, others less so, For that reason, opinions varied from three cheers for Lenin at one extreme to saying nothing at all at the other. On my train journey to Leeds,

I scribbled note after note in preparation for the Russia part of my speech. I had at least decided to offer an opinion, believing that it would be cowardly and suggest a lack of leadership on my part if I said nothing at all. However, actually deciding what I was going to say proved rather harder, and I was still unsure of my exact message when I got to my feet in front of 500 men in Leeds.

Most of my speech that day was well prepared and I believe that I delivered it well enough even if, as was the usual case with me, there were no flights of great oratory. In brief, I talked about the nation's need for high production and industry's need for cooperation between employers and employees. It was fairly uncontroversial stuff which was politely received. However, I could tell that, given the events of the past fortnight, the men in the audience were less interested in my comments on production and cooperation than in anything I might has to say about Russia. I saw a number of reporters, notebooks at the ready, obviously hoping to hear something controversially newsworthy. To this day, I do not believe that I gave them that, though they may well have seen things differently.

I started off my comments about Russia in a fairly predictable way, warning my audience about the danger of drawing conclusions from limited evidence. I also reminded them that, up until that point, Russia had been our allies, and we should all be concerned if developments in Russia were to alter that. I also told them that great social upheaval of the kind which was being reported from Russia brought dangers, perhaps mortal dangers to the civil population. I suggested that they should pray for the safety of the Russian people. By this stage, though everybody was listening attentively enough, I am sure that people were wondering if Bob Smillie had lost his fire, that he had become too old to offer any stirring words. But I hadn't finished.

It was reported in the press in the days which followed that I had welcomed the Russian Revolution. Those reports were not strictly accurate because I went further than that – I embraced the Revolution. I told my audience that though the details were unclear and the dangers were very real, there was real evidence that a people had risen against a class of rulers who had oppressed them so badly as to almost make slaves of them. I suggested that this was the first time in history that an oppressed class had thrown off the shackles of their masters, and I congratulated them for having done so. I concluded by observing that the Russian people had shown people everywhere what could be achieved, and that one day Socialism might offer salvation for the oppressed wherever they were.

I didn't believe that I was ever cheered so loudly in my life. Men were standing all over the auditorium, clapping, shouting and waving their meeting papers. There were exceptions of course. Some of our invited guests were looking rather glum, and the newspaper men were too busy scribbling to register an opinion of any kind. As a matter of record, my views were heavily criticised in a number of newspapers but, in the middle of a hellish war as we were, my speech didn't get as much adverse press reaction as it might otherwise have done. Not that I cared one way or another. I had spoken from the heart and given my views as clearly and honestly as I could. I believe that that is as much as any man can do.

I am finding it quite impossible to keep David Lloyd George out of this part of my memoirs. It seemed as if some strange destiny had joined us at the hip. A rather bizarre episode began when I was at home in Larkhall. After yet another hectic period in London, I was actually celebrating a belated 60th birthday. My date of birth being in March, I had not been at home during that month or April and had frankly forgotten that milestone birthday. The circumstance in which I was reminded of it still makes me smile.

My train was rather late getting in and, quite unusually for her, Ann was waiting for me on the platform, looking somewhat agitated. I felt a brief panic. Bad news? A telegram from the War Office?

'Hurry along now, Robert, or we'll be late,' she said rather sharply.

'Late? Late for what?' as I embraced her.

'Never you mind. You'll find out.' She looked me up and down. 'Och, but you're not very tidy.'

'Not tidy for what?'

'Come along now,' she told me. 'There's a pan of water on the fire. You can have a wash and put on a clean collar.' And she wouldn't say any more as she virtually dragged me through the evening-quiet streets of Larkhall.

Obedient soul that I was, I washed and generally tidied myself up, then we were off out again. Still she wouldn't tell me what the fuss was about. To my surprise, she was leading me towards the Larkhall Miners' Meeting Hall. Was my memory letting me down? Was I supposed to be speaking there tonight? Then she was pushing the doors open and leading me inside, me feeling uncommonly like a lamb being led to the slaughter. Once inside, what a sight greeted me!

There was a crowd of people there including my beloved children, Jeanie, Mary, John, William, Robert and Joseph. The married ones had their husbands or wives with them as well as several of my grandchildren. Behind them, arranged in a deep horseshoe were dozens of my friends, mainly miners but also my minister and doctor. Then, Tam Lang, Secretary of the Larkhall Miners, was pushing forward and placing in my hands a large wooden box, and an accordion player was belting out 'Happy Birthday' with everybody joining in the singing. I was quite overcome.

I was pressed to open the box. Inside there were six beautifully crafted clay pipes in my favourite style. Totally embarrassed, I stuttered my thanks and then the fun began. From the back room there appeared tray after tray groaning with food. There were cordials and ale in huge jugs. Tam Lang persuaded me to have a nip of whisky from his flask and suddenly the world was a wonderful place. The accordionist struck up 'Sweet Afton' and, with Ann in my arms, I had to lead off the dancing. She was as graceful on her feet as ever and I was perhaps a little less clumsy than usual, no doubt enlivened by Tam's whisky. It was a wonderful evening, full of fun and laughter. It was the most enjoyable time I'd had in years.

Then the very next day a telegram arrived for me, dated May 28th, 1917. It read:

Treasury – Could you kindly call to see the Prime Minister here tomorrow? Matter Important. – Sutherland, Private Secretary, 10 Downing Street.

There was no indication of why Lloyd George wanted to see me, so I assumed it was to be another lecture on the need for greater coal production. Having only just arrived home with the promise of a few days with Ann for the first time in almost three months, I did not feel at all inclined to return to London so quickly, particularly for a lecture. I sent back a wire:

Apologies but am unable to see a reason to travel to London at present time – Smillie, Larkhall.

The very next day, that would have been May 29th, I received yet another telegram:

Could you call here and see the Prime Minister tomorrow? – Sutherland, Private Secretary.

What on earth was going on? Ann asked me the same question so I showed her the telegram. I suppose that some wives might have been pleased, even flattered, at the thought of the prime minister asking for an appointment with her husband. However, Ann had been trained in the Robert Smillie school, and was obviously suspicious.

'What on earth can the prime minister want that's so urgent?' she demanded.

'Well, it's either the jail or a job,' I joked.

'Aye, well,' she replied, 'if it's the jail that's one thing, but if it's a job for that man you can pack your bags and not come back.' From which you will deduce that she had no great fondness for the Welsh Wizard.

'I'm due to speak to the parliamentary committee of the TUC in the afternoon,' I reminded her. 'I could call in at Downing Street before then if I take the overnight train. It would be very disrespectful just to ignore the man.'

'Aye, maybe,' she said. 'But you mind what I said, Robert Smillie.'

A further exchange of telegrams saw me booked in for an appointment with Lloyd George at 10:30 the following morning. Cutting short my time in Larkhall by one day, I caught the overnight train and travelled south, Ann's warning words ringing in my ears. I made Downing Street with only minutes to spare and, somewhat dishevelled after my long journey, I was immediately ushered into the Cabinet Room where the man himself was waiting for me. There was a brief exchange of the customary greetings, then he got straight down to business.

'I won't beat about the bush, Smillie,' he told me, his whole body seeming to quiver with nervous energy. 'Perhaps you have heard that Lord Devonport, the Food Controller, is unwell?'

'I had heard as much,' I replied, wondering where the conversation was heading. 'I trust that he is feeling better.'

'I regret to say that he is not. Indeed, he feels considerably worse.' He fixed me with a searching stare. 'He has told me that he can no longer continue, so I have to find a suitable successor. I have sent for you to ask if you will accept the post?'

'As Controller of food?' I gasped.

'Exactly that.'

I was totally taken aback. After the series of urgent telegrams, I wondered if I was about to be offered a post. But Controller of food? You might as well have asked Ann to become a royal lady-in-waiting! Stunned though I was, I tried to formulate a reasoned answer. I reminded Lloyd George that my life's work was with and for the miners, and I had no desire to move away from that. I also pointed out that I was unqualified for the task he had in mind for me. I had absolutely no experience in connection with the work Lord Devonport had been doing. I also freely admitted that my formal education was very limited and was unlikely to be up to the task.

'Oh come now, Mr Smillie,' Lloyd George insisted. 'Do not talk yourself down. In your role as President of your Federation, you have done sterling work in one of the most difficult and important tasks that any man could undertake. Don't forget, sir, that I have witnessed your talents at close quarters.' He allowed himself a brief chuckle. 'Sometimes to my disadvantage, I have to admit. Come on man, what do you say?'

Well, he could be a persuasive fellow, that Lloyd George, but his charms were not going to work on me. I thanked him for his good opinion of me and for the offer he had made, but told him that my real work lay with the miners and I was not going to give it up, no matter what position he might offer me.

That was not quite the end of our conversation. I told Lloyd George that if I had seen fit to accept his offer, trouble would have followed.

'Trouble? What kind of trouble, Mr Smillie?'

'Because I would have demanded full plenary powers to deal with the food profiteers,' I explained.

'And what would you have done with them?'

'Send some to prison and hang the others,' I told him.

'Granted that there are profiteers out there, Mr Smillie,' Lloyd George said, 'but do you not think your measures might be considered extreme?'

'What? For people who want to make a bit rather than doing their bit?' I shook my head. 'Not extreme at all. But that's why I said there would be trouble if I accepted your offer. And you would be castigated for employing a reprobate like me.' I couldn't help but laugh out loud. 'Believe me, Prime Minister, you should be glad that I am turning down your offer.'

Leaving Downing Street, and still with time to spare before my afternoon meeting, I made for the offices of the Labour Party at 33 Eccleston Square to see my old friend James Middleton.

'Hello, Bob,' he said, pumping my hand. 'What brings you back to London so soon?'

'Oh I had a meeting at Number Ten,' I told him, trying to make light of it.

'Aye, we'd heard a rumour you might be going there.'

'What?' I gasped. 'I know news travels fast but this is ridiculous.'

'It's been on the grapevine for a few days,' he told me. 'Like enough he offered you a post?'

'Yes he did.'

'I'll bet I know what it was,' he claimed, grinning.

'Go on then, tell me.'

'Pensions,' he said. Not a bad guess because it was well known that it was one of my pet subjects.

'You're wrong, Jimmie,' I told him. 'I was offered Food.'

'Food?' He shook his head. 'Food?' He said again. Plainly, he was as bewildered as I was.

In the afternoon, I attended a meeting in Aldwych of the parliamentary committee of the Federation congress. Will Thorne and James O'Grady had just returned from Russia where they had been undertaking an investigation into the state of affairs there on behalf of the Government. They reported their findings, which were more up-to-date than anything the newspapers carried, and concluded their report by saying that it was their opinion that, at that time, no real revolution had taken place at all and it was impossible to say what the eventual outcome would be. There were plots and counterplots all over the place and the future of Socialism there was by no means assured. I was not particularly surprised at the tenor of their report. Barely two months had passed since the overthrow of the Tsar and there was bound to be confusion. On his way out, O'Grady leaned over and whispered to me that he urgently wanted a word in private. Shortly afterwards, we met in a quiet office.

'I haven't much time,' O'Grady said. 'Tell me Bob, do you know George Barnes?'

'The Minister for Pensions? Yes, I know him quite well.'

'Fine,' James said, glancing at his watch as if in a hurry to be away. 'Well, I saw him yesterday and he told me he was giving up Pensions.'

'Is that right?' I asked. 'I hadn't heard anything.'

'Well, he is, and that's a fact. The point is, he wants to know if you'd be interested.'

'Interested in what?'

'God, Bob, but you're slow on the uptake at times!' he growled. 'Interested in taking over from him at Pensions.'

'Me?' I gasped.

'Aye, you,' he replied. 'His exact words were that there is no more suitable man for the role in the country then Smillie.'

'It's not in his power to offer me the post,' I pointed out.

'Don't be so wet behind the ears!' James snapped. 'You don't think he'd have made the offer without consulting him upstairs, do you?'

'You mean Lloyd George?'

'Well, I don't mean God Almighty.'

I laughed out loud. 'Well, James, this is quite a day for me.'

'How do you mean, man?'

'Two job offers in one day!' I told him about Lloyd George's earlier offer and he was so surprised at that that it was clear he knew nothing about it. I asked him to convey my thanks to George Barnes but, given my role with the Miners' Federation and other responsibilities, I would not take over at Pensions, whoever was suggesting it.

What had already been an intriguing and confusing day was not made any simpler or clearer by the arrival of a visitor to my hotel, The Imperial in Russell Square. I was sitting in the lounge waiting to go in for dinner, when a journalist approached me. He must have told me which newspaper he represented, but I do not recollect which one it was.

'May I get a little information from you, Mr Smillie?' he asked.

'What about, laddie?' I asked, motioning him to sit down. I assumed he wanted to ask me something about the coal trade and I was never slow to talk to reporters about that subject if I felt that I could get favourable coverage for the miners. 'Ask away.'

'It's about the offer of the Ministry of Food which you received today.' Notebook at the ready.

'What!' I said. 'And how do you know about that?' Even as I asked the question, I felt that I knew the answer to it.

'Oh, I have a source,' he replied. 'I'm sorry, but I can't reveal it to you.' As if I didn't realise that it came from an address beginning with the number ten. 'I just want to know if you have accepted or refused the post'

'Well, laddie,' I told him rather gruffly, 'if you have the source you are suggesting you have, they can answer your questions. Now, if you will excuse me, I'm going to have dinner then catch the overnight train to Scotland to resume my interrupted holiday.'

There are two postscripts to this story. The first is brief. When I got home to Larkhall and told Ann what happened, she was delighted that I'd turned down not one but two posts. Which meant that she didn't throw me out and I still had a bed to go to in Larkhall. The second concerns Lord Rhondda, originally DH Thomas, who as I am sure you probably know became Controller of Food after I turned down the post. Shortly afterwards, I had cause to lead a deputation to him in my capacity as Chairman of the War Emergency Committee. We were very concerned about the shortage of sugar and wanted to discuss the matter with him. After the official business of the meeting was over, Lord Rhondda asked me to stay behind. He eyed me from over his desk.

'Well, well, Mr Smillie,' he said, 'had things gone as I firmly believe they should have done, you would have been sitting in this chair and I would have been a member of some deputation coming to see you.' He was smiling broadly as he said this.

'Well, sir,' I told him, 'I believe things are better as they are. Knowing you as I do, I am confident that you are better suited to the post than I would ever have been.'

Perhaps I should say that my knowledge of Lord Rhondda went back some years. My Welsh mining friends knew him well enough when he was plain DH Thomas, owner of a number of collieries in South Wales. He was renowned as a fierce negotiator who would fight to the last of his breath in any dispute, yet there was a side to him which endeared him to the men. Several times in the middle of strikes, while arguing bitterly with the union, he contributed handsomely to a fund to provide for the children and women. In fact, in my time I knew a few decent owners who did that, and one or two who quietly contributed to strike funds. DH Thomas, as he was then known, was once rebuked for his generosity by another coal owner and was alleged to have replied, 'I will fight the miners as hard as I can when I think I am right, but my quarrel is not with the women and children.'

What's this, I can hear you thinking, that agitating Socialist Bob Smillie surely doesn't have a good word for a mine-owning aristocrat? Well, as I have said before, I tried never to judge a man by his status, but by his actions. And while Lord Rhondda was a tough a negotiator as I ever came across, he was also honest, a man of great integrity. As soon as any dispute I was involved in was settled, he would do everything he possibly could to ensure that his part of any bargain was fulfilled.

It was no surprise whatsoever to me that he went on to be a great success in his new and difficult post. If Lloyd George had searched the country from one end to the other, he could not have found a more capable man. He found it extremely difficult in his new post to give entire satisfaction to everybody because so many conflicting interests were involved. But you can take it from me that Lord Rhondda made a far better job of it that I could ever have done.

For a while, I puzzled over Lloyd George's attitude towards me. He had directly offered me one post, and was clearly behind the offer of a second. But why? What on earth did he see in me that made him imagine that I was Ministerial material. Had Arthur Henderson pushed him in my direction? I rather doubted that, if for no other reason than the gossip mill was full of rumours that Lloyd George and Henderson were some way from seeing eye to eye on a number of things and that Henderson was coming to the view that he had only been invited to join the War Cabinet as a sop to the Labour Movement. And I doubted very much that Lloyd George had been so impressed by my work for the Miners' Federation that he believed that I was a suitable candidate for a post in government. He, above all others, must have realised that the sort of skills required to run a government department in the face of multiple vested interests were very different to those required to run an organisation, however large, which represented the interests of one group of men.

So the question kept recurring: why me? In the end, I could only come to one conclusion, a conclusion which no doubt makes me as cynical as I believed him capable of being. I decided that the real reason that he wanted me in government was not so much for what I could do inside the corridors of power as what I would have to leave behind in order to do so. I would have had to give up the presidency of the Miners' Federation and the chairmanship of the Triple Alliance. For whatever reason, and I believed he was wrong, I think he was of the view that my absence would have weakened those organisations and made life more comfortable for the Government. I could be wrong about that – it would hardly be the first time – but I believed it then and have found no reason to change my mind in the years since.

Mention of the Triple Alliance reminds me of the fact that our three unions had been working together without any real authority to do so. We had met informally for two years then, in 1916, held two major meetings in which we had produced policy proposals for the short and long terms. We had even developed a proper constitution. What we had not done, and not only as chairman but also as a democrat I felt totally embarrassed by it, was have our very existence validated by our memberships. This was put right in June 1917, when a joint conference of the three unions finally ratified the Alliance's constitution. Ah well, better late than never! I took rather a lot of ribbing from all quarters for that lack of attention to detail.

Domestic matters, and even the course of the war, were briefly forgotten between October and November in 1917. News seeped in of further revolutionary fervour in Russia. As far as we could tell, the interim Government had been swept aside by Lenin and the Bolsheviks who then proclaimed a Workers' State. In itself, that development made Socialists like me happy enough but, as I had long feared, there was a potentially serious outcome as far as the British war effort was concerned. The new regime in Russia signed a peace with Germany and withdrew from the war. This meant that the entire weight of German forces would now be thrown against the Western Front. It was as well that the Americans had now arrived in great strength, or our battle-weary troops would have been sorely pressed to hold back the Germans. It was clear that 1918 would be a very difficult year at the front.

The events in Russia caused me some anguish, I have to tell you. And I know that many others of a Socialist leaning felt the same way. While there was a brief feeling of euphoria at the thought of a Workers' State, incoming news told us that the matter was not resolved and that a state of civil war existed in many parts of that huge country. People were dying. Some reports suggested a mere trickle of deaths; others reported fatalities in huge numbers. Whatever the actual figures, I felt very uneasy. For me, Socialism was an ideal, something to be achieved through debate and persuasion, certainly not by the point of a sword or a bullet from a gun. In that respect, perhaps I was naïve. I wouldn't be at all surprised. But I was obdurate in my view that if Socialism could only be achieved by killing, I would not play any part in it.

Shortly after that period, Arthur Henderson resigned from the Government and his cabinet duties. During his period in office, he had more than once been offended by what he considered to be Lloyd George's high-handedness. His resignation in August 1917 meant that, by the time that the news from Russia was making the front pages, he was working with Sidney Webb on the development of a new Labour Party manifesto. On several occasions, I worked with them, as did many others, on that exciting project. Henderson firmly believed that the splits that Lloyd George had caused in the Liberal Party provided a great opportunity for Labour to overtake them at the next general election, whenever it came. I was of the same view myself. For reasons of wanting to preserve life, I wanted the war to end. Now I also wanted it to end so that the Labour Movement could establish itself as a significant political force.

XXI

A New Dawn

OUR DEAR SONS continued to write home, Daniel and James from the Western front, and Alexander from Wakefield Prison. It was always a great relief to me to hear from them. For Ann, it was like an answer to her prayers. What the poor woman was going through was beyond description. Her husband hardly ever at home, two sons in the front line, another in prison. How she bore it all I did not know. Yet Ann was a woman of deep faith and eternal optimism. Those qualities must have been what carried her through it all. Of course, we both realised that the letters from Daniel and James were only signals of their safety at a given time. Between their writing and our receipt anything dreadful could have happened. I fully realised that and Ann must have done as well but we never discussed it. We simply pored over the letters which Ann kept in an old sewing box and retrieved for re-reading from time to time to keep our spirits up.

Our position was no better than millions of parents up and down the land. For people who have not lived through a major war it will be difficult to understand how it felt to do so. At home there were fears of unemployment, low wages, hard toil and privations, bad enough in themselves. But try to imagine the added horror of being a parent of a boy away fighting. Praying for a letter, dreading that damned telegram, it was just terrible. The one good thing you can say about 1918 was that it was the last year in which people had to suffer torment in that way. For the time being, that is.

I will not bore you with all the final details of the war; they are well enough known anyway. However, in keeping with the rest of these memoirs, let me just refer to the main points and you may imagine what it was like for the people of Britain to receive news of them and wonder if their sons were alive and well. Bear in mind that, although reporting of events was extensive, there was a widely held suspicion that some of the details were not fully released at the time for the sake of morale. Such decisions were in the gift of the Propaganda Minister.

In March, there was a massive German offensive aimed at defeating Britain and France before the Americans were able to make a maximum effort. They got to within forty miles of Paris before Marshal Foch steadied our troops and Lloyd George organised the transportation to the front of 88,000 British troops who were home on leave. This was the last great German offensive. Our counter-offensive began on August 8th. For the first time, we used our new tanks in great numbers. The Germans were driven back with great losses. In spite of the fact that German soil was never invaded, their senior man Ludendorff was convinced that that was only a matter of time. On October 3rd, he requested an armistice. Fighting continued for a further five weeks but eventually an armistice was signed on November 11th, 1918.

I believe that I have remarked before that, even in the most awful of situations, a grain of humour can still be found. Such was the case with the armistice which signalled the end of the Great War.

It is perhaps hard to believe but those who signed the armistice agreement for both sides actually signed papers which were largely made up of gibberish. We have the work of Monsieur Henri Deledicq to thank for this ridiculous state of affairs. He was a clerk attached to French Headquarters. On November 7th, he was posted to the railway carriage at Rothondes in the outskirts of Paris where the armistice was signed. At the dictation of Marshal Foch he took down the words which would mean world peace. Unfortunately, it had been a long day, Monsieur Deledicq was very tired, and he made a great error.

He put some of the carbon papers into his typewriter the wrong way round. At 5am whole chunks of it came out, completely unreadable. Ten minutes later, all the war leaders signed the armistice. None of them noticed the error. Deledicq was given a glass of port, then went on leave. It was not until some time later that Marshal Foch reread the document and found that much of what was signed was pure nonsense. All of which put my failure to ensure the ratification of the Triple Alliance's constitution from the beginning into some perspective.

Such an amusing story was rare indeed at that time. Europe was weary, battle-scarred and bloodied. Britain alone had lost 745,000 men and 1.6 million wounded, many of them so badly that they could never work again. My God, 745,000 dead! That is a figure which I found difficult to comprehend due to its size. To make it more comprehensible, think of it this way. On average, there were 500 British deaths for each day of the war! Very quickly, people began speaking about the 'lost generation', something of an exaggeration but understandable enough. Without question, due to those dreadful losses we were an emotionally-scarred country.

As I have suggested before, the war affected the political landscape. The Liberals went into decline. The seriousness of the divisions in that party were revealed in the Maurice Debate of May, 1918. General Maurice had accused the Government of holding back army reserves during the German spring offensive. In a brilliant speech in the Commons, Lloyd George proved Maurice wrong but the opposition insisted on a vote being taken: the only time this happened during the war. Lloyd George won his vote but 98 Liberals voted against him. The split was there, it was very real, and it would continue.

The split in the Liberal Party offered great hope to those of us who dreamed that one day there would be a Labour Government. That was too much to hope for at the time, but I thought that there was a real chance that we could replace the Liberals as the main opposition to the Conservatives. My hopes were boosted when I saw the fine job Sidney Webb had made of the manifesto which we intended to present to the public at the next general election, which could not be far away. Given the title *Labour And The New Social Order*, it contained several of the policies which I had pressed on Webb and Arthur Henderson in late 1917. Among its main policies were:

Common ownership of the means of production
a statutory basic wage for men and women
full employment
unemployment insurance
abolition of the Poor Law
development of health services
special tax on capital
abolition of conscription
freedom for Ireland and India.

I thought it was a wonderful document and one which Labour candidates could support with confidence.

Shortly after the armistice was signed, Lloyd George announced the dissolution of Parliament. Given the problems he had with his own party, it was clear that he would advocate the continuation of Coalition Government. The question then arose within the Labour Movement of whether we should continue in the coalition or not. There were differing views, of course. There always are when there are major issues to decide. In general, those who supported the view of the Coalition Government during the war were in favour of continuing with it. Those who had opposed the war from the beginning and had been uneasy about Labour's participation in the wartime coalition were against continuing with it. You will readily grasp which side of the argument I was on.

A special conference was quickly arranged to decide our position. I decided to 'jump the gun' as the saying goes. After consulting the executive committee of the Miners' Federation, I released a statement saying the MFGB would not support Labour's continued participation in coalition. Apart from political considerations, I pointed out that the Labour Party had to be free to contest mining constituencies held by the Liberals and the Conservatives, and that campaigning on a coalition platform would make it impossible to do that. I said as much at the conference itself. I virtually begged delegates to allow the Labour Party to mount its own campaign. At first, I found it hard to sense how well this appeal had gone down.

Strong opinions were expressed that day. Willie Gallacher of the Paisley

Trades Council, a man very much after my own heart, argued that the overthrow of capitalism should now be at the top of our agenda. But then older leaders like Will Thorne MP and James Clynes MP urged the view that Labour aspirations could only be achieved in the short term by remaining within the coalition. I could tell that many delegates were wavering, leaning first one way then the other. Frankly, I was convinced that my view would not prevail, we would lose the vote, and Labour would remain in the coalition.

Then I heard one of the most remarkable speeches I have heard in my life. Bernard Shaw stepped forward to the platform. It was to be his last speech as a delegate of the Fabian Society at a Labour Party Conference. I listened enthralled as he employed humour and great rhetoric to destroy the pro-coalition argument. He poked fun at Thorne who was given to making speeches which travelled widely rather than to the point. Shaw said that he enjoyed hearing Thorne hammering away with words because, on the law of averages, he might hit the nail on the head now and again. Which was pretty insulting, of course, but it drew a great laugh at Thorne's expense and eased the tension in the hall.

Shaw then derided Lloyd George's promise to show 'utmost sympathy and consideration for the claims of Labour', saying he had heard that kind of thing too often before. He finished with a great appeal to loyalty and received a standing ovation. After that effort, there was never any doubt of the outcome and by an overwhelming majority the Labour Party decided to leave the coalition and fight the general election as an independent party. At the end of the meeting, Shaw and I embraced one another and said that we believed this to be a milestone in the history of the party.

Lloyd George having called the election, it duly took place on December 14th, 1918. He campaigned vigorously, promising 'a fit land for heroes' a reference to the home-coming servicemen. That was a phrase which would come back to haunt him. To all coalition candidates he issued a piece of paper or certificate as evidence that they were approved. For this reason, that election became known as the Coupon Election. There were more votes than ever before thanks to the provisions of the July Representation of the People Act. This gave the vote to all men over the age of 21 and, for the first time, women over the age of 30. This Act increased the size of the electorate from about eight million to twenty-one million.

Several constituencies in the Glasgow area asked me to consider becoming a Labour candidate on their behalf. There was a certain attraction to the idea, but I politely declined all their offers. There was a lot of serious work going on as far as the Miners' Federation was concerned and I was too heavily involved in that to spend weeks on a campaign. Besides, my track record in elections was such that I felt that the Labour Party could well do without my candidature. I did lead some rallies in support of the candidates in the London area but I was too busy with union work, as I will shortly explain, to contribute much more.

The result of the Coupon Election was a disappointment to us and a disaster for the Liberal Party. The coalition won very comfortably, we secured only 59 seats and the Liberals only half of that number though, of course, there were Liberal members in the coalition grouping. The reasons for the coalition's victory were easy enough to identify. The main reason was Lloyd George himself. In spite of weaknesses to which I have already alluded, he also had many strengths. The public admired his oratory and fiery character. He had lifted the mood when he had taken over from Asquith, he had made the Government more professional, he had deployed talent with great success and, perhaps most important of all, he had been in charge when Britain emerged victorious. In comparison, we were seen to be untried and untested, and the separate Liberals suffered badly from years of public squabbling. From our point of view, the only real compensation was that the Labour Party was the biggest non-government party and therefore the official opposition. But, like everybody else, I suppose I was pretty tired of war and politics, so I headed north to Larkhall and the first proper Christmas break I had had in years.

And what a Christmas it turned out to be! I have never had a better one. Things were pretty much as usual to start with, Ann greeting me warmly at the front door, pushing me into my seat by the fire, and giving me one of my favourite clay pipes. Then, to my great surprise, she announced that we had visitors, called through to the scullery, and in trooped three young men. One was dressed in jacket and flannels, the other two in uniform. I could hardly believe my eyes. Alexander, Daniel and James were home. I will draw a veil over the next few minutes. Let me just say that emotions were riding high and not a few tears were shed.

We ate a proper family meal that evening, the first if its kind for a long time. If memory serves me correctly it was an excellent mutton stew but – and with no disrespect to Ann's fine cooking – I remember more about the conversation that the food. As we sat there, chatting away nineteen to the dozen, my mind flew back over the years to the days when our three fine sons had been much younger, just three boys among a group of nine children, our pride and joy. Mealtimes then had generally been sparse affairs, with a broth as the most likely main course, but there had always been the excited chatter of young bairns to keep us warm. In recent years, that excited chatter had disappeared, as is the way of things, but, albeit briefly, it had returned.

Alexander had been released as a result of a general amnesty for conscientious objectors signed shortly after the armistice. Daniel and James had finally met up in France shortly before the end of hostilities and had been among the lucky first batch of servicemen to be repatriated. I had little doubt that James' pleasing manner and status as an officer had somehow or other gained them a place on the ship, but he never said anything and I never asked. Alexander had a fair bit to say about his ordeal as a prisoner in Wakefield Prison. He offered no complaint about his imprisonment, which he had expected as a result of his stance. Neither did he have anything bad to say about the way he had been treated in prison. It had hardly been a pleasant time, he told us, and he had missed his family and girlfriend, but he had had plenty of time to think and had concluded that, if the same circumstances were to arise again, he would behave no differently. Also, he had been allowed a few books. He had read with interest the poetry anthology he had been provided with and enjoyed much that he read in there. He was particularly full of praise for Burns who he described as 'an early Socialist.' And maybe he was right too. In all, he had tolerated imprisonment with great fortitude and, in my opinion, he had come out of the experience a stronger man.

Daniel and James were less forthcoming about their experience. In part, I think that that was out of a natural desire not to upset their mother. But also I think it was due to unwillingness on their part to relive the horror. That is an understandable trait I have experienced among many ex-servicemen. There were occasional references to battles and skirmishes and places I had never heard of in spite of some visits to France on Federation business. But the nearest they got to any details was on the subject of food and football, of all things. That night, they ate Ann's stew with a vigour that suggested that they hadn't eaten properly in years. I think Ann was quite sickened when they described the different ways in which a dead horse could be cut up and the many different ways in which it could be cooked. One of them, I think it was Daniel, added that dog could make a decent meal in an emergency. That comment turned my stomach a wee bit, I have to admit.

They told us about the games of football played between British and German soldiers the previous Christmas. James poked fun at Daniel by saying that as a mere sergeant Daniel had had no choice but to play whereas, as an officer, James had refereed from the side lines and managed not to get dirty. It was all said in good fun and well taken. But most of the three boys' conversation was about our family, how everybody was, what we'd been doing and all the rest of it. Also, of course, about their plans for the future. James was much taken by Lloyd George's promise of 'a fit land for heroes' and asked my opinion on that promise. Well, I could have said a lot at that point, but chose not to. Why on earth would I wish to dash the aspirations of my young sons? I simply suggested that we would have to wait and see. It was getting late and Ann and I were weary. We left the three boys deep in conversation as we made our way to bed.

'Oh, Robert', Ann said, her hand finding mine after we had settled in, 'we have been so lucky, haven't we?'

'Luckier than many, without a doubt.'

'Did you ever fear that ... that ... '

'That we would never see our sons again, you mean?' I replied. 'That Daniel and James would be killed, that Alexander would become a twisted recluse? Every single day, Ann. Every single day.'

'And what will become of them now?' she asked. 'What of Lloyd George's promise?'

'I don't think we can invest too much trust in that', I told her. 'I have no doubt he means well but that's not enough. And with his coalition packed with Conservatives, I doubt if the fate of working men will be too high on the agenda. Was it ever?' Then I laughed. 'But don't worry about the boys. They're good, decent men. They will make their way whatever the Government does, or doesn't do.' I held her tight. 'They're Smillies remember, just like us, and we've always managed, haven't we?'

I had a wee lie-in the following morning. After spending the night sleeping in chairs, Daniel, James and Alexander came in to see me before leaving. We embraced, I reminded them to keep in touch with their mother, and they were gone, off to be with wives and girlfriends. It was the holiday, after all and they had their own lives to lead now. Much heartened by our sons' return to normal life, Ann and I had a pleasant walk together. We walked a lot and visited old friends where I was pleased to pick up on the local gossip. We attended the Miners' New Year Party where, I had to admit, I got a 'wee bit fou' and was gently chided by Ann. On January 2nd, 1919, I headed back to London where a great deal of Miners' Federation work awaited me.

As far as the whole industry is concerned, 1919 was a dramatic year. Some writers described it as a year in which Britain, as it had been known, almost came to an end. You will have to make up your own mind about that. It was certainly a very complex year as far as trade unions and Government were concerned, so complex that it is difficult to separate out the strands and make sense of them. I think it would be best to consider the Miners' Federation business first, then place that in the context of the wider events.

Even as the war had been drawing to a close, we had been considering our position on a number of issues for the postwar period. There were three main issues: wages, hours and ownership. We had talked long and hard about all three. We had high hopes that, given the contribution made by miner volunteers on the battlefields and by coalface men working to keep British Industry moving, those efforts would be rewarded with government generosity after the war. We waited until the armistice was signed and the general election was concluded, then met again during the first week of 1919 to finalise the demands which we intended to make.

Even as we held that first meeting of 1919, we heard of a great deal of unrest in the country. During that month alone, there were some fifty mutinies, generally small-scale, in the army. Something seemed to be stirring but I was not quite sure what it was. At our meeting, we finalised the demands we were to make of the Coal Controller. You must remember that coal, like other major industries, was still under government control, much to the chagrin of the Mine Owners Associations. Our demands were finalised as follows: a wage increase of 30%, a six hour working day and nationalisation of the mines.

These demands were duly presented to the Coal Controller on January 9th. While we were waiting for a reply to our demands, we held a special conference in Southport on January 14th. At that conference, I came under pressure from certain quarters for not having submitted a 50% wage increase demand. Perhaps you have been of the view that the president's or executive committee's views and proposals always went through unchallenged. If you had thought that, your mind would have been changed if you had heard the debate that day. It was vigorous, to put it mildly, and tempers were not always in check. Before a vote was taken, I had the chance to make a final statement. In it, I reminded the men of my thirty years and more of wages negotiations and pointed out that I had seen many wage demands fail because of what our opponents had been able to describe as 'workman's greed.' I challenged them to consider whether they wanted to submit a demand which had a chance of success, or a wild one which would not get anywhere. The argument simmered down and the vote was overwhelming in favour of the 30% increase demand.

We met with Sir Robert Horne on February 10th to hear the Government's reply. Rather condescendingly, in my opinion, he had no wish to enter into a discussion with us. Rather, he simply read out the Government's response from a memo. It was not a response which we welcomed. As far as wages were concerned, all that would be granted was an extra 11d a day on top of the additional war wage of 3/- a day we were already getting. As far as hours and nationalisation were concerned, all that was promised was a Committee of Enquiry – yet another one! – to consider those matters. We had also asked if early demobilisation of miners could be ensured to return the workforce to its pre-war size, but that was denied. To my great consternation, that was the Government's response and, with Horne presiding, there was no discussion, far less negotiation. As calmly as I could, in spite of the anger I felt surging within me, I told him that I would submit the Government's response to the next Federation Conference.

Shortly before that conference, which met on February 12th and 13th, Lloyd George was up to his old tricks. First making sure that the press had advance notice and copies of his words, he made a statement in the House of Commons. A statement which was aggressive towards us and bordered on the offensive. I can remember sitting in my Southport hotel, reading the report of his speech, and wishing that he was within striking distance. Apparently, we were holding the country to ransom and trying to use our industrial power irresponsibly. There was even a reference to the miners' leaders behaving like demagogues. I knew, beyond a doubt, that that was a reference to me. I had heard them before: no doubt, I would hear them again. But the fierce attack on the miners from a man who had frequently claimed to be the working man's friend was hard to hear.

However, if it had been Lloyd George's intention to intimidate the miners, he failed miserably. In fact, his political posturing had the very opposite effect. In a lengthy and largely unprepared speech, I reminded the conference that our demands had been submitted with the full support of the union behind them and urged them not to bow down to what I called unreasonable pressure. Also, I was at pains to point out to them that this was no longer the Liberal Party in government that we were dealing with, hard enough though that had often been in the past. Rather, it was a Liberal prime minister whose political wings had been clipped by his need to satisfy the views of Conservatives who were the majority of his support in government. Again, I urged conference not to yield to the oppressive response of our political opponents.

In the event, there was total unanimity. The wording of our resolution could not have been clearer or more determined:

This conference rejects the terms offered by the Government as being no answer to our claims.

Given the attitude of the Government, and the tenor of Lloyd George's speech, only one option remained open to us. We decided to take a ballot vote of the whole membership to see if it was the collective view of the men that the situation warranted strike action. Accordingly, a ballot paper was drafted, which read as follows:

1. Application for 30% increase in wages.
2. Six-hour day.
3. Full maintenance at Trade Union rates of wages for mine workers unemployed through demobilisation.
4. Nationalisation of mines.
5. The Government have failed to grant any of the above proposals. Are you in favour of any of the above proposals? Are you in favour of a National Strike to secure them?
   Yes   No

These ballot papers were immediately distributed around the districts and were to be returned by February 22nd. I thought at the time, and still do, that we had behaved in entirely the right way. Lengthy discussions had preceded our demands which were then ratified by a full conference. The Government's response had been fully discussed and an agreed position taken on that. Then, without taking any precipitate action, we had consulted all our members, as was always the way we did things. To judge by Sir Robert Horne's reaction, you might have thought that we had thrown away our own rulebook. He wrote to me in the strongest possible terms, advising that any strike action would be ruinous to the country and, in the long term, ruinous for the miners. He implied that I was wittingly leading the men down a path which would destroy our industry, and much more of the same. Interestingly, before I received his letter, it was published in the press. And that man was accusing me of foul play! You may not be surprised to learn that I did not dignify his letter by providing any response.

The Government's intention to discredit the union, and me in particular, became clear when they spent thousands of pounds of public money on an advertising campaign. In national and regional newspapers, there appeared lurid warnings and strongly worded advice to the miners to vote against the conference resolution. Through a friend in the press, I found out that the Coal Controller's office had supplied all newspapers with a mountain of alleged facts suggesting how our demands would ruin the industry. Again, I did not respond to this tactic, which amounted to nothing less than intimidation, and neither did any other member of the executive committee.

By this time, I would estimate that Lloyd George was in something of a panic. Under huge pressure from his coalition members on one side, yet now recognising that the Government's shabby tactics were not succeeding with the miners, he was caught between two irreconcilable forces. So I wasn't surprised that our Federation Executive received an invitation to Downing Street to talk to him. I noticed quite a change in him. He looked tired and had aged considerably. Of course, leading the country for two years of war had taken its toll. But there was something else, almost a nervousness, which was quite unlike the man.

'Mr Smillie,' he began, 'I wish to ask you for a delay.'

'A delay, Prime Minister? A delay to what?'

'The date by which you might call a strike,' he replied. 'As I understand it, your ballot returns are due on February 22nd, in just over a week's time. Am I right?'

'Indeed you are, Prime Minister.'

'And if your men vote in favour, which I am told is likely,' permitting himself a weary smile, 'and you issue a strike notice, then a strike could begin on or around March 15th.'

'That would be more or less correct.'

'Well, Mr Smillie, I would like you to consider delaying any such action for a fortnight.'

'To what purpose, Prime Minister?'

'I wish there to be a Commission set up, bound to report by March 31st,' he told me. 'A fortnight's delay in strike action would permit that.'

'A Commission is it?' I asked. I looked round at my fellow Executive Committee members. They were pretty stony-faced at the suggestion. 'Let me remind you, Prime Minister, that our proposals were lodged with Sir Robert Horne as long ago as January 9th. I believed then, and still do, that the claims we made were just and fair. Let me bore you for a moment with the background details.'

In fairness to Lloyd George, he listened attentively in spite of the fact that I spent ten minutes or more describing the deplorable nature of miners' living and working conditions. Of course, I knew that he had an almost romantic sympathy with the miners' lot, but he can't have enjoyed the experience much, virtually being lectured to by a man he had recently described as a demagogue. I moved on to one of the main issues, ownership of the mines.

'The mine owners have always told us, and you tell us now, if you hand the mines back to them for free competition amongst each other, that we have no right to a voice in the commercial side at all. They say: "We invested our money in those mines and they are ours; you are merely our hands." Now, I say we invest our lives in those mines, which is of greater importance than the capital of the employer; and to that extent we have a right to have a say as to what the conditions shall be, not merely the working conditions, but we are entitled to have some information on the commercial side of the industry also. I believe, sir, that you have the data at hand, if you cared to use it, to be able to give us a reply on the wages question as to whether or not the claim which we put forward is unreasonable.'

There was a brief silence, during which the only sound was the ticking from a splendid clock on the wall behind Lloyd George. My colleagues were nodding their heads while Lloyd George looked ... well, almost shocked, I was not entirely surprised. In our long acquaintance, it was probably as Socialist a statement as I had ever made to him. I broke into the silence by remarking that all the necessary information on wages was already in the hands of the Government, and that I could see no good reason why a decision on that matter needed scrutiny by any Commission.

Finally, Lloyd George snapped out of his reverie and told me that, whatever his personal feelings might be, he had been advised that all matters relating to our demands should be referred to the proposed Commission. I sensed the hand of Bonar Law behind that, but did not pursue the matter. Lloyd George said that the miners could be fully represented on the Commission and there the matter was left for that day. We left, promising to consider his suggestion. Then, back at Russell Square, we decided to call a special conference to consider what the prime minister had said.

In the meantime, the result of the ballot of our members became known. By February 25th, the votes had been counted and the following figures published.

For stoppage	615,164
Against stoppage	105,082
Majority for	510,082

In spite of the Government's public vilification of me and their expensive advertising campaign, this ballot was a weighty endorsement of the Executive Committee's position. No doubt, this gave Lloyd George further food for thought.

On February 24th, Lloyd George pushed ahead with his plans for a Commission. The Coal Industry Commission Bill came before the Commons. After debates for several days, and some changes made to it, the new Act gave wide powers to the Commission it established. The Commission was empowered to:

Look into the position of, and conditions prevailing in, the coal industry and in particular as to:

the wages and hours of work in the various grades of colliery workers and whether and, if so, to what extent, and by what method, such wages should be increased, and hours reduced ...

any scheme that may be submitted to or be formulated by the Commissioners for the future organisation of the coal industry, whether on the present basis, or on the basis of joint control, nationalisation, or any other basis ...

Other areas for enquiry included the cost of production and distribution, selling prices and profits, social conditions of the miners, mining royalties and:

... the effect of proposals under the above headings upon the development of the coal industry and the economic life of the country.

This was wide-ranging indeed and, at first glance, impressive. I could not help but wonder if it was simply a governmental delaying tactic but, given firm report-back dates provided, I was inclined at the time to think not. However, everything hung on a decision from the Federation. Would we participate in the Commission or not? This meant yet another conference – my diary seemed to be full of them – which took place on February 26th in London. I really don't know how my voice had not given up by then!

As you may imagine, the conference was a lively affair. A number of strong arguments against representation came from a number of delegates. I could fully understand their reasoning. What would happen if the Commission produced a report adverse to the miners and we had participated in the work of the Commission? In effect, we would be seen as the authors of our own downfall and might prejudice our position for years to come. However, I was convinced that there was an alternative view to the whole matter.

I reminded delegates that there was the promise of an interim report by March 20th, and a final report as soon as possible after that. Our mandate to strike was still available to us. If the interim report offered nothing to us, we could then invoke the strike. If the interim report was favourable, we would see what the final report had to say. If that was unfavourable, we could issue a report of our own as long as we participated in the enquiry, and could still invoke the strike if we wanted to. If we did not participate, I argued, we would be portrayed as obstructive men and, if we were to go on strike without participating, ran the risk of arousing public condemnation. Finally, I reminded delegates that, as of that moment, wages, hours and nationalisation were still very much on the table. I was persuaded that we could lose nothing by participating in the Commission and, that if our case was put clearly and strongly, we might gain much.

In the event, there was still some dissent but it was agreed to postpone strike notices until March 22nd at the earliest and to participate in the Commission's enquiry. On March 1st, the membership of the Commission was published. The coal owners were represented by Evan Williams, Richard Cooper and John Forgie. The Government nominees were Arthur Balfour, Sir Arthur Duckham and Sir Thomas Royden. Richard Tawney and Sidney Webb were members agreed between the Government and the Miners' Federation. Representing the Federation itself were Sir Leo Money, Frank Hodges, Herbert Smith and myself. The Commission's Chairman was the Hon. Mr Justice Sankey. Forever more that group, which first met on March 3rd, would be known as the Sankey Commission.

I headed home to Larkhall for a few days to rest, clear my head, and prepare for work on the Commission. I will return to that enquiry shortly but, for the moment, divert your attention to other events in the year 1919. If it was a momentous year for coal mining, it was also a year in which the whole of Britain was shaken by a series of events which, in my opinion, came close to causing mayhem, as I will now try to explain.

XXII

Ferment

AT THE END of the war, there was a brief celebration. It never turned to euphoria, certainly among people whom I knew, because the entire nation was simply too weary for that. Yes, there were parties, services of thanks, and probably far too much alcohol consumed, but that didn't last long. Most people were just desperate to get on with their lives and lived in hope of the better future promised by Lloyd George and his Coalition Government. In many quarters, that sense of hope did not last out the winter.

Our front-line troops were the people who should have been best looked after but, in many cases, weren't for many long months. The Government took the decision to first release troops who held key civilian jobs. As precious few miners were repatriated during the first few months, it led me to wonder exactly what was meant by a 'key-worker.' This meant that many rank-and-file troops spent up to ten months waiting to get home, just proving how lucky Daniel and James had been to return in the first wave.

As I have mentioned before, the level of unrest among troops stuck in France grew to the extent that there were numerous 'protest demonstrations' as they were referred to by the Government and reported in the press. However, from sources inside Parliament, where I had numerous contacts, I knew that the truth was more serious than that. In fact, there were over forty incidents where serving troops refused to obey their commanding officers. Some of those incidents involved large numbers of men and were, in fact, mutinies. How could you blame the men for their insubordination? They had given everything, had been prepared to die for their country, yet were being treated with the utmost insensitivity.

Naturally, the Government did not broadcast those details. In spite of the fact that I knew full well what was going on, I kept my silence. I could not see how airing the matter in public would help anyone. But some incidents could not be kept out of the public domain. There was a new issue which angered the already-irate troops. It concerned Russia. Lloyd George's cabinet, in which I suspect Bonar Law was the real hawk, decided that they were fearful of revolution. It was decided that troops should be sent to Russia to join an international force to fight Bolshevism. There was uproar at this.

In many cases, troops mutinied and refused to go. Not even the Government could deny the fact that in Folkstone, on 3rd January 1919, 2,000 troops flatly refused to board the troopships destined for Russia. I may tell you that took some courage as the punishment for such behaviour would have been only too well known among the men. Ignoring the blandishments and curses of their officers, they turned round and headed back into the town where they headed a huge protest march of troops and civilians together. At its height, the numbers involved in that protest march exceeded 10,000 people.

The next fortnight saw many more incidents of troops refusing to be sent overseas. Some of those incidents were reported because they were very public. Others which occurred in garrisons were not reported because the Government imposed a press blackout. Some of the troops used friendly journalists to publicise their position. Their priorities were always much the same. They wanted speedier demobilisation and no fighting in Russia. There were also frequent reports of mistreatment by officers. Though much did not reach the ears of the public, evidence of unrest in the army was building up. I wondered what the Government's reaction was going to be.

In fact, the Government was in a state of panic. They realised that some of these mutinies were well organised and they began to suspect Communist agitation. They may well have been right, to a degree at least. There were plenty of men with Communist leanings in the mining industry and others, so why not in the armed forces? But the notion that somehow all of this was the result of some dastardly Bolshevik plot was risible. The men wanted release from the army, they wanted it quickly, and they certainly didn't want to be sent to Russia. Who could blame them?

It transpired that the army's Commander-in-Chief, Field Marshal Haig, had ferocious rows, first with Lloyd George and then with Churchill. Haig's view was entirely clear and he didn't much mind who knew about it. Men who refused to obey legitimate orders were mutineers. The penalty for mutiny was death. Haig was adamant about that. Of course, I was not privy to his heated discussions with Lloyd George and Churchill but, from a reliable source, I heard of the tenor of them. Lloyd George simply disagreed with Haig on principle and, when Haig lost his temper, ordered him from his office. He found a more sympathetic audience in Churchill who tended to agree with his view of things. However, as a politician, he saw the situation in terms of end results and was worried about the reaction to any executions. So, for political rather than humanitarian reasons, he turned Haig's suggestion down. I was led to believe that Haig offered to resign, but had his offer rejected. For obvious reasons, I cannot vouch for that.

The army was not the only branch of the services to be affected. The Royal Navy suffered some mutinies as well. These tended to be even less well reported than the army mutinies for the obvious reason that any ship is almost a self-contained world of its own. However, some reports filtered out. One of the most serious incidents occurred on board HMS *Kilbride* while she was berthed at Milford

Haven. Ordinary seamen point blank refused to go on watch. They were protesting about their dreadfully low pay. Some men actually raised the red flag on HMS *Kilbride*. No details were ever released of the punishments meted our though I did hear that several men were court-martialled and sentenced to lengthy prison terms.

As far as our armed forces were concerned, unrest was rife throughout the first half of 1919. It was largely due to Lloyd George's direct involvement that the situation was quietened down. In the late spring, he ordered a change in the demobilisation process. He insisted that men should be released from service on a 'first-in, first-out' basis. Though late in coming, this was seen to be a fairer way of doing things. By October, over four million troops had been released and gone home, so the tensions of the earlier part of the year were eased. However, there was an undoubted feeling of lingering resentment over what had gone on.

Of course, when you talk about national security, it is not just the armed forces you have to consider. Naturally, in times of national crisis, they are in the forefront of our thinking. However, there is another branch of domestic security which is always there to protect us and who should never be forgotten. I mean, of course, the police force. Incredibly enough, in my experience, there was great unrest in their ranks as well. And that unrest lasted throughout the year.

There was the usual dispute over pay and, in truth, lower ranks in the police force were poorly paid. Perhaps more importantly though, rank and file policemen up and down the land were aggrieved because successive governments had refused to permit them to form a trade union. In 1913, in liaison with prison officers, policemen had formed a trade union, the National Union of Police and Prison Officers, but the Government refused to recognise it. Even the Metropolitan Police Force refused to recognise the union and threatened to dismiss any officer who joined it. So, by 1919, this ridiculous situation had existed for some six years. Matters came to a head in the summer when a NUPPO organiser was sacked.

NUPPO called a strike, set for August 29th. The Government sat back, confidently expecting that the action would enjoy limited support. However, they were to be proved wrong. Even the strike organisers were surprised. Out of a Metropolitan Police Force of under 19,000 men, over 12,000 came out on strike. The extent to which Lloyd George was shaken by this can be gauged by his comment that, 'This country was nearer to Bolshevism that day than at any time ... ' That was fairly typical Lloyd George hyperbole of course. If indeed there were Bolsheviks in their ranks, they would have been few in number. I would question the extent to which there were many Socialists of any kind that day. But what was clearly true was that organised Labour was taking its toll on the Government.

Lloyd George was well and truly caught. With industrial unrest all around, soldiers disaffected and sometimes mutinous, and now the police on strike, he did not have far to look for his troubles. He felt that he had little choice but to give in to police demands, in spite of many Conservative members of his coalition urging him not to. In fact, in several respects he gave the police officers more than they had been demanding. A large wage rise, the introduction of a widow's pension, and the reinstatement of more than twenty NUPPO officers who had been sacked in the course of the year. It appeared as a great victory for the police officers and bore all the hallmarks of a government in trouble.

However, even as the men returned to duty only forty-four hours after the strike had begun, Lloyd George proved that he was as wily as ever. This was over the issue of union recognition. That recognition was finally granted but with the exception of wartime. That exception would ensure that the Government would have full control over the police in a time of national emergency. To many people, policemen included, that seemed reasonable enough. I was not so convinced. After all, how simple would it be in future for any government to redefine 'national emergency'? Would a strike be open to such a definition? Perhaps you can understand why I had reservations.

It must seem an amazing statistic but, in the course of 1919 and the first part of 1920, there were more than 2,000 strikes called in Britain. I was involved in some of those. Many were relatively small and localised, whereas others were on a much larger scale and more widespread. And of course, the success of any one strike would tend to inspire more. That is the nature of things. No worker in any industry will simply and quietly applaud the success of workers in another industry. Why should he? He is as likely to be as poorly-paid and starved of the comforts of life as the other man was before he gained some marginal improvement in his situation.

The first major industrial confrontation of the year took place in Glasgow and Belfast, beginning on January 27th in a coordinated action. It became known as the Forty Hours Strike due to the main demand for a forty-hour working week. Briefly in Larkhall at the end of that month, I addressed a huge rally on Glasgow Green, offering support from the miners for the cause of the engineering workers. In Glasgow and Belfast, over a third of all workers were employed in engineering, much of it directed towards munitions, and the workers were heavily unionised.

The Clyde Workers Committee (CWC) had been formed during the war, in late 1915 I think, and was made up of shop stewards from a variety of factories. Those stewards were all Socialists and led the men in all disputes. It was at this time that Glasgow and its immediate environs attracted the description of 'Red Clydeside'. At the end of the war, engineering faced two big problems: unemployment and the absorption of demobilised workers returning from the armed forces. To maintain jobs, the CWC proposed a reduction from fifty-four working hours a week to forty hours a week, thereby alleviating unemployment. It was the employers' refusal to countenance this that sparked off the strike.

There are those who would say that such strikes are led by hotheads whose views command little support among the men. That strike, which began on January 27th, illustrated how off the mark such a view can be. The response from the men was overwhelming. Around 100,000 came out and turned this into one of the most active strikes Britain had ever seen. Each day saw mass picketing and huge open-air rallies. It was a response to gladden the heart of any trade unionist.

However, the strike had weaknesses and was raised on rather shaky ground. The composition of the strike committee was a major flaw. In addition to the official and solidly Socialist members, there were others from factories with little experience of industrial action and no great commitment either to striking or to Socialism, their main aim being simply to keep control of their members. Also, there was another union, the engineers' ASE, which had been pro-war and led by non-Socialists, which quickly negotiated with the Government and whose workers in Glasgow and Belfast returned to work before the end of the strike.

Another problem was that there was disagreement among the strike leaders about whether the strike would be presented to the public as having political aims or not. The majority decided that it would be unwise to portray it in this way, leading the renowned Socialist union man Willie Gallacher to reflect later, 'We were carrying on a strike when we should have been making a revolution'. Meanwhile, the Government realised that they held most of the cards. The war was over and there was no great demand for munitions. The strike leaders were not wholly united in their aims. So Lloyd George decided that this was a time for the stick rather than the carrot. After only a week of strike action and no end in sight, the troops were sent in. By Saturday, February 1st 1919, Glasgow was virtually an armed camp, occupied by troops with bayonets, machine guns and tanks. There was even a flight of aeroplanes sited in a field outside the city. The strike leaders were searched out, attacked and arrested. Nearly all of them were sentenced to prison terms. The men returned to work having gained nothing and, with a significant reduction in the demand for munitions, only the prospect of lower wages and more widespread unemployment in the industry to look forward to.

The railwaymen who, of course, were one of our partners in the Triple Alliance, were also threatening action, even if their leader, Jimmy Thomas, was miles away from being a Socialist and was very keen to avoid strike action. So he was very happy to negotiate for whatever he could get. The men wanted an upwards standardisation of all wages. The lowest grade workers were very poorly-paid by the standards of any industry. Given all that was going on around the country – and bear in mind that we in the Miners' Federation were just beginning to participate in the Sankey Commission – the Government was desperate to avoid further industrial unrest. Besides, they knew that in Jimmy Thomas they were dealing with somebody who hadn't wanted a strike in the first place. So, they made some concessions. They awarded some extra wages at certain grades, a shorter working week, a guaranteed week's holiday a year, and a method for men to make complaints about the management. They also said that they recognised the need in principle for upwards standardisation of wages which they would consider very carefully. That was enough for Jimmy Thomas who persuaded his committee to call off the threatened strike on March 27th.

The folly of being bought off so easily was brought home to the railwaymen in September. Far from upwards standardisation of wage rates, the Government announced substantial reductions for 100,000 men. Not even Jimmy Thomas could tolerate that. A strike began on September 27th and it was solid. A number of other unions, the miners included, offered to come out in sympathy but Thomas, who had already ignored the constitution of the Triple Alliance, declined all those offers. In the event, given the solidarity of their action, the railwaymen won through. All the reductions were rescinded and the lower grades were awarded pay increases.

The discontent which simmered among railwaymen throughout the summer, and the strike which followed, might well have been avoided had Thomas been stronger in his negotiations back in March, though of course we cannot be certain of that. But the whole affair illustrated how important it was for strike leaders to remember that they only exist to represent their members' demands rather than their own views. An interesting footnote was that, during the strike, troops were called out to keep order and reduce the incidence of mass picketing. However, even though by then most soldiers had been repatriated from France and morale should have been restored, there was a great deal of evidence that the troops felt that they were there on sufferance. Many fraternised with the strikers and had to be recalled to their barracks.

That summer, waves of strikes continued to rock the Government. There was one of some 450,000 cotton workers which lasted for eighteen days, the biggest single strike of the year. However, I do not feel there is need to go into great detail about more strikes. From what I have told you, you will begin to see that it was a year of great volatility across industry, within the armed forces, and even the constabulary. There are many sources which provide full details of the unrest of that year and attempt to offer explanations of it. That is not my business. I simply wish to portray the overall picture and have you understand how tense things were.

There was one other major event that year which may have contributed to the general feeling of unease. I only say 'may', because I wasn't certain then and am no clearer about it in my own mind now. In July, news came through that Tsar Nicholas II and his entire family had been executed. Naturally enough, this caused a great deal of furore here in Britain. The consensus view in the press and among politicians was that it was an act of terror and desperate villainy. It was frequently alleged that it was no more than could be expected from barbarian

Bolsheviks or Socialists, the two terms being used indiscriminately. In truth, I was sickened by the news but not everybody of my acquaintance felt the same way.

Shortly after the news came through, I was home in Larkhall, a joyful experience which did not come my way very often that year. I was only home for a few days so Ann and I made the most of our time together. There was a lot of talking, of course, to catch up on our news, and visits to friends' homes to renew acquaintances. How I loved such times, being with people I loved. Immersing myself in the ordinary things in life, escaping the pressures of London, albeit too briefly.

On the Saturday afternoon of my visit, we went for a long walk and ended up at the cricket ground where I had enjoyed a brief career as a 'flannelled fool' so many years earlier. We sat on a bench outside the boundary rope and quietly watched a match in progress. By now August, the early Scottish summer was drawing to a close and there was the slightest suggestion of a crispness in the air, but it was pleasant sitting there, watching something entirely unimportant and wholly transient taking place.

'I'm not that impressed,' I finally remarked after watching a slow passage of play. 'I'm sure we played better in my day.'

'Spoken like a true old man,' Ann laughed. 'Men! You've got more vanity about sport than anything else.'

'Well, maybe.' It was hard to disagree with her, and I never wanted to anyway. 'But I don't think I was ever that vain about my time as a cricketer.'

'Och, away with you, Robert Smillie,' laughing out loud this time. 'I remember well when we were courting you used to rush me down to the newspaper office to pick up the latest edition so you could see your name in print.'

'Only if I'd scored a few runs.' No harm in being honest, is there? I noticed her shivering slightly. 'Come on, old woman, let's carry on walking before you freeze.'

'Less of the old woman, if you please,' she said, but she got up and took my hand. We walked out of Larkhall and made a route toward the gentle hills beyond the town.

'So what have you made of the news then?' I asked her as we rested on the trunk of a fallen tree and I began scratching out my pipe.

'You mean about the Tsar and his family, do you?'

'Aye, that's right.' Finally getting the pipe going.

'It's a terrible thing right enough,' she said. 'You know that I do not believe in capital punishment, and execution is just an extreme form of that.'

'Some folk I know are saying that his people were responsible for a lot of poor folks' deaths.' I suggested. 'So maybe he deserved to die.'

'And his wife and children? Who did they ever kill, Robert?' She shook her head sadly. 'Whatever he did, I still don't hold with executions.'

'So, you're upset about it then?'

'Upset? No, not at all,' she replied. 'I never knew the man or his family, so how could I be upset about them?' She paused for a moment. 'But Rita Cunningham's boy and Sheila Armstrong's man for example. Buried somewhere in France, the pair of them. I'm really upset about them, because I knew them. And there'll be people up and down the country feeling much the same way, Robert. With so many dead in the war, everybody will have known somebody who was lost, and that's really upsetting. But somebody far away, somebody you have never heard of? That's different. It's awful news and it is to be regretted but it's not something to be upset about.'

She was right of course. My Ann usually was. So many people had suffered so much personal anguish that the deaths of strangers in a foreign land somehow seemed remote and not of personal consequence. I heard a lot of sympathy expressed for the Romanov family but there was no huge wave of emotion on their behalf. Except at the very top, of course, where there was a degree of kinship in royal circles and a fear of Bolshevism in the Government. There were those, of course, who were inspired by the executions, men in my own union and others. They saw the removal of the Russian monarchy as a necessary step in the achieving of a genuine Workers' State. I could see the logic in what they were saying but found it impossible to marry up with their views.

It was a time when many of us were forced to search our consciences and decide what kind of Socialists we were. You see there have always been many different strands to Socialism. You might not think so given the way that the press and political opponents bandy about words like Bolshevik, Communist and Socialist, among others, as if they were all one and the same thing, which they are not. In my lifetime, particularly in my work for the miners, I came across them all. They varied from men who simply wanted a better life for working men and their families, to those who actively sought revolution to overthrow the existing system by force. There were quite a few of those around in1919.

As you will know, I have often been described as 'left-wing', a 'Socialist', an 'agitator'. In honesty, I wouldn't dispute any of those. Indeed, I would go so far as to say that I am proud of them. What you may be surprised to know is that I was often described by other people as being neither left-wing nor Socialist enough, and too prone to negotiation rather than fierce agitation. Well, you can't please everybody, I suppose. But in late 1919, and quite contrary to my normal disposition, I did find myself on occasions becoming rather introspective and given to wondering who the real Robert Smillie was. I was either very left-wing or hardly left-wing, a committed Socialist or one on the fringes. What was the truth?

There were two types of Socialists I regularly came across whose views I found hard to accept. The first type was what I thought of as theoretical Socialists. Some of these were ordinary working men whose Socialism was bred from the words of others, and these others were the leaders of this type. Men whose knowledge of the reality of ordinary people's lives was gained by limited observation and considerably greater amounts of reading. Typically, they would have come from comfortable backgrounds and their Socialism was fired by their intellect, their reading of philosophers, many of them European. They could quote people like Marx, Engels and my old friends Jaurès. They understood the world from a set of theories and passed those on to others less capable of understanding them. By and large, such men ended up as Communists rather than Socialists. I do not necessarily condemn their views, and I knew many good men of their type, but I found them over-reliant on theory and untested by the cauldron that is real working life.

The second type of Socialist whose views were sometimes at odds with mine could at least claim to have had their opinions forged by real experience. Typically workers in the most arduous of industries, mining included, they were embittered by years of mistreatment by their employers. I could certainly understand how they felt. They wanted the world to change. I could understand that too. But there our views diverged. Such men were often indifferent to the methods they used in securing change. So hardened were they by their own painful experiences, that change became their only goal and any suffering caused in obtaining change was merely incidental to them. Such men would countenance chaos and destruction on almost any scale to achieve their aims. I found it impossible to see things that way.

I learned my Socialism as I made my way through life, from the bitterness of my youth to a more pragmatic view of the world as I grew older. I wanted change, saw the desperate need for it, but not at any cost. Summing up my view as best I can, I wanted to see a world in which all men enjoyed opportunity and dignity, and in which the difference between the classes eventually disappeared. Naturally, that view led onto other things such as the initial need for a political party which could over time gain such influence as to create the world I dreamed of, and state control of industry to eliminate the differences between the owners and owned. Having met men in all stations in life, I recognised that there was good and bad in all quarters. I did not wish to destroy any group. I wished people to come together in a cooperating whole. I firmly believed in democracy and wished to see the new world created by arguments, debate and the will of the people. In my view of things, there was no place for savagery and force, whatever the source.

No doubt you will think my views rather simple: perhaps they were. Indeed, maybe they still are. But I had faith in man's ability to eventually change things in the right manner. That optimism, in spite of many setbacks, has never left me. If that makes me less of a Socialist than some, and more of a Socialist than others, so be it. I have changed little in my views since then, and that is how I was back in 1919 when, for a time, the country seemed to be being shaken to its very foundations.

This brief portrait which I have painted covers the whole of 1919. You will understand now the context in which we were working. It was fraught, sometimes dangerous and always difficult. It is time now to return to the subject which exercised me and my colleagues most in 1919. The date was March 3rd, and that was the day scheduled for the first meeting of the Coal Industry Commission, better remembered as the Sankey Commission.

XXIII
Sankey Commission: Questions & Answers

LET ME BE clear about something. The remit given to the Sankey Commission was wide-ranging but there was one part of its remit which was of greater interest to me than all the others. That was, as the Commission Act put it ' ... any scheme that may be submitted ... for the future organisation of the coal industry ... ' It was my view, one shared by the Federation's Executive Committee, that national-isation of mines was our main priority. If that was achieved, then everything else from wages to working hours would flow from that. We were in a fairly confident mood before March 3rd. We led a union of well over a million men. Adding in their families, we were representing the hopes of perhaps six million people, more than 12% of Britain's population. Our proposal in favour of nationalisation had featured in the ballot paper presented to our members and had been heavily endorsed. Somehow, we just felt that it was our time.

In the days leading up to the first day of the Sankey Commission, those of us due to represent the Federation met several times to discuss strategy. Among the most important things we had to decide was who we were to call as witnesses. Each side could call as many as they wished and they would be bound to attend. Witnesses would be of two types, those whom you wished to introduce to sup-port a case, and those whom you wished to introduce to expose a weakness in your opponents' case. It was the selection of the latter which would be crucial and to which we devoted most time.

Herbert Smith, Frank Hodges and I made several suggestions but we were more than happy to be advised by Sir Leo Money, by far the most experienced of our team in these matters. Eventually we produced a set of witnesses whose posi-tions we wished to expose. It read like an extract from Who's Who. Among oth-ers, it included:

The Duke of Northumberland
The Earl of Durham
The Marquis of Bute
The Marquis of Londonderry
The Duke of Hamilton
Lord Dynevor
Lord Dunraven
Lord Tredegar

We could not be certain exactly how these gentlemen would answer all our questions, of which we composed a great list but, from information we had obtained, we knew that they would have a hard time of it to deny that, among them, they had earned over £3 million in coal royalty payments during the Great War. To us, this seemed as good a starting point as any.

The setting for the Commission Enquiry was quite splendid. It was in the King's Robing Room in the House of Lords. I had never seen such a place before – it had a magnificently carved vaulted ceiling, frescoes on every wall, portraits of monarchs, the largest of which were those of Victoria and Albert, a royal-blue carpet in which you lost sight of your shoes, and much more besides. Not exactly what Bob Smillie was used to, you might be thinking, and you would be right. In the centre was an oak witness box and, facing that in a horseshoe shape, were the tables and chairs for the twelve of us serving as commissioners. Behind the witness box, members of the press and public were crowded, many of them standing. Hundreds of people had been turned away. Sitting in my chair, believing that this was as important an affair as I had been involved in, I took a series of deep breaths to clear my head. Then Mr Justice Sankey said a few words and we were ready to begin.

The first witness called was the Financial Advisor to the Coal Controller. The coal owners' representatives provided him with a string of questions designed to prove his expertise. They did not realise it but that suited us very well: we actually wanted him to be seen as an expert. By the time our opponents finished their questions, they were satisfied beyond a doubt that their man had painted a picture of an industry aching to be returned to private control. They reckoned without Sir Leo Money.

'I wonder if we could begin by talking about coal royalties,' he began.

'Of course, Sir Leo.'

'I wonder if you would be kind enough to tell the Commission the extent of royalties earned between 1914 and 1918 by the following eight gentlemen?' He trotted out the names of the eight witnesses we had decided to call.

'Well ... eh ... yes, if you give me time to consult my papers.' He began searching through his briefcase.

'Let me save you the time.' Sir Leo then quickly detailed the royalties in question. 'Do these figures seem about right to you?'

'Eh ... yes.'

So our strategy was laid down on the first day. To demonstrate that the coal industry generated huge profits, that only a few men saw the profits from those, and that the majority laboured for very little. From that, it would be but a short step to argue that, on the grounds of efficiency and fairness, State control would be a superior system.

By the time that Sir Leo had finished with the Coal Controller's Financial

Advisor, Messrs Williams, Cooper and Forgie must have been wishing that he hadn't turned up. What he had to say about the profits made during the war had the public in attendance sneering and the owners' representatives squirming in their seats. Under Sir Leo's barrage of questions, he produced chart after chart showing increases in profits at a time of stagnant or reducing wages.

There was also evidence of inefficiency and wastefulness which had seriously hampered the war effort, particularly in the early years before government intervention. All the evidence given in the first two days of the trial were fully and fairly reported. It was, after all, a public enquiry. It was becoming clear that there was increasing public support for our case. This was in no small way helped by the further evidence of Dr JC Stamp, Assistant Secretary to the Board of Inland Revenue. He produced figures to show the profits in the coal-mining industry had almost quadrupled during the war, from 11½d per ton to 3/6½d per ton and that the total profits of the industry for the war period constituted a massive rise when compared to the pre-war years. During the war, the average wage for a miner, including overtime, was £2.5/-. These figures caused further public reaction against the owners. It was not uncommon to hear the term 'war profiteer' applied to them.

A further technical revelation was to our benefit. It was shown how often huge profits were concealed by the capitalisation of reserves or other readjustments of capital. In his evidence, Mr Emil Davies said:

'It will be seen that the most successful companies are able by these methods and by dividends, which are in reality much larger than they appear, to return to their shareholders every few years the whole of the share capital originally subscribed by them; and that the undistributed reserves are still so considerable that the present market price of the shares is several times their nominal value. It is submitted that if the coal reserves of the country were pooled, the enormous profits made – and particularly concealed – by the large companies would be available to meet part, at least, of any additional working costs that may be necessary; and the incentive to build up reserves for subsequent distribution. Which obscures the enormous profits actually being made.'

The press again faithfully reported all of this and, without naming names or levelling specific accusations, conveyed the impression that the owners were not only war profiteers but also people who were prepared to act fraudulently in the pursuit of extra profit. On our side, there was delight at the way things were going.

Let me explain at this point that the public examination of witnesses lasted for two weeks, ending on March 17th. We sat every day except Sunday and each day was long in duration. Unlike judicial proceedings, witnesses did not appear in banks: all the prosecution witnesses followed by those for the defence. Rather, and in part because these were very busy men, they appeared in random order and were closely questioned by our opponents and ourselves. For this reason, my own contribution to the proceedings was not sandwiched into one of the two main weeks of the Commission Enquiry. Rather, I was most heavily involved towards the end of the first week and the beginning of the second. The first witness I questioned at any length was Sir Richard Redmayne, with whom I had crossed verbal swords on several occasions, and who was at that time Chief Inspector of Mines and head of the Production Department of the Coal Controller. I will not bore you with the details of some of the questions I asked nor his replies to them, because they tended to be highly technical. However, and bearing in mind that Sir Richard was as impartial a witness as ever stood in a witness box, it is worth recording what he said when I asked him, in light of his great experience, if he had a particular view on mine ownership. He replied:

'That the present system of individual ownership of collieries is extravagant and wasteful, whether viewed from the point of view of the coal-mining industry as a whole or from the national point of view is, I think, generally accepted.'

He could hardly have said anything more damning about the private ownership of mines, and this from a man who had been a government-appointed inspector for some thirty years. But he went even further. He went on to describe the advantages which would stem from a system of collective production and went into some details under the headings of 'enhanced production', 'diminished cost of production' and the 'prevention of waste'. I could hardly have written a better script for him. Again, we were delighted with his testimony.

Other witnesses during the first week were less friendly towards us. Inevitably, and in the interest of fairness which I fully supported, there were witnesses produced to present the owners' case in the most favourable light. However, and particularly under Sir Leo's interrogation, their claims that the miners' position would cause ruin to the industry and the country did not stand up well. As witnesses, they seemed particularly uncomfortable when faced with questions which invited them to say whether or not the miners had the right to hope for a higher standard of life. Our feeling was that their testimony did not enhance the owners' case; quite the opposite in fact.

I think it was the first Thursday when the first of the so-called great men made an appearance. This was the Earl of Durham who owned Lambton Castle and another stately home. He owned over 12,000 acres under which lay some very rich coal seams. It had been agreed that I would lead on the Earl, with Sir Leo standing by in case I ran into difficulties. In my time, I had answered a lot more questions that I had asked and, I must admit, I was feeling a little nervous. However, I had my questions well prepared and, determined not to let our side down, I began asking them. You may wonder how I am able to remember all these questions and answers after so many years. The reason is simple. There were transcripts and I have always kept the one given to me.

'Tell me, Lord Durham,' I began, 'have you ever worked at a coalface?'

'Of course not!' he snapped, in a tone which suggested that my question was preposterous, which of course it was, but it was asked for a purpose.

'As a responsible mine owner, how often do you enter your pits to check on the men's working conditions?'

'My managers do that.'

'So, as a rule of thumb,' I pushed on, 'you leave the running of the pits to your managers.'

'Of course, that's what they're paid for.' If ever a man had looked enraged at being interrogated by one of his inferiors, it was the Earl of Durham that day.

'Tell us, my Lord, do you ever go down your pits?'

'No, I do not.'

'So, you have no idea of the working conditions of your employees?'

'I have told you already, Mr Smillie, that my managers see to that.'

'Thank you.' Then I fired a shot across his bows. 'Would it be true to say that you earned in excess of £40,000 last year in coal royalties?'

'I'm not sure that's any of your business, Smillie!' he barked.

'It is this Commission's business,' I reminded him. 'Now, my Lord, would you say that I have quoted an accurate figure?'

'Perhaps, but I would have to check.'

'So you are uncertain as to how much money you earned from the work of the miners last year, and you have no personal experience of the conditions in which those men work?' He turned red, I feared an outburst. I pressed on and changed tack. 'Would you agree that the land, which includes the minerals and metals, is essential to the life of the people?'

'If you like, I accept that.' Then, with a twisted grin, 'They cannot live in the air.' Nobody in the public audience laughed.

'Let me press you on that if I may,' I told him. 'You agree that land is essential to the life of the people, but you will not accept the proposal that if the land is in the hands of a limited number of people, practically they hold the lives of the people at their disposal?'

'Of course I don't accept that,' he replied, somewhat loudly. 'The lives of the people who live on my land are as happy as those on any other land, and it makes no difference whether I own it or not.' His tone growing sharper.

'You will have heard of Sir William Blackstone, my Lord?' I asked, while I consulted my notes.

'The lawyer? Yes, I have heard of him. What of it?'

'Not just a lawyer, my Lord,' I corrected him, 'but a great constitutional lawyer. It was his opinion that it is an undeniable principle of law that all lands in England are held immediately of the king. Would you agree? If so, you cannot lay claim to the land you say you own.'

'That is your opinion. My family has owned land for many years and no-one has disputed it.'

'We dispute it now!' I shouted, to loud laughs from the public area. 'My Lord, let me quote from another source, the greatest of them all. It says in the *Holy Bible* that the earth is the Lord's, and the fullness thereof. Would you agree with that?'

'I prefer another authority,' Durham replied. 'In the same book, in the gospel according to Matthew, it says that those things which are Caesar's must be rendered unto him, and unto God those things which are God's. Would you agree with that, Mr Smillie?'

'I would indeed, my Lord,' I told him. 'That is precisely my point. If the earth is the Lord's, it cannot be the property of individuals.'

At that point, Mr Justice Sankey, possibly fearing further ecclesiastical sessions, ordered a recess. I can't vouch for how the noble Earl felt, though the redness of his face was suggestive, but I felt drained. I asked Sir Leo if he felt it would be better for him to carry on with the questions.

'No, no, Robert,' Sir Leo insisted. 'You carry on. You're doing fine.'

'But don't forget about the vans, Bob,' Frank Hodges said.

That last comment might need some explaining. You see, largely at my suggestion, through Mr Justice Sankey we had tried to insist that all the noblemen witnesses should bring to the Commission all the title deeds and charters proving their ownership of the land which they claimed to be theirs. Deemed in some quarters as a farcical request, there were two reasons behind it. First, we thought it just possible, though unlikely, that some of them couldn't prove their ownership, and where would that leave them? Second, it was bound to anger them and, on Sir Leo's advice, we were happy to provoke them because an angry witness is rarely a convincing one. Mr Justice Sankey had in fact complied with our request but then waived it when it became clear that it would take half-a-train at least to transport all the legal papers to London. As my interrogation of the Earl of Durham resumed in the Robing Room, I decided to lead on this issue.

'On the subject of title deeds, I want to examine you as fairly as possible without any bitterness, Lord Durham.'

'About a railway van?' he replied, to some laughter.

'Would you agree that it would indeed require a large van to carry your deeds?'

'That is an exaggeration, Mr Smillie.'

'I repeat, Lord Durham, would it require a railway van?'

'A portion of a railway van perhaps.'

'No doubt having been asked to procure them,' I said, 'you have taken the opportunity to examine them. Am I right?'

'Yes.'

'And do you have any doubt, any doubt whatsoever, about their validity?'

'No, and I hope I never will have,' he replied with the air of a man who resented the direction which the questions were taking.

'Was it only recently that they were examined?'

'About two to three weeks ago, when you demanded that my title deeds should be produced here. That caused a great deal of inconvenience. Normally, they are kept in the depository and I don't read them every Sunday.' His indignation caused some stifled laughter among the public.

'They have not been sent here?' I persisted.

'No, but if the Chairman says I must produce them, I will.'

'You will be hoping that the Chairman will not say that, Lord Durham.' That brought forth a few ironic laughs. 'Now, you say that you did not read them yourself.'

'No.'

'Would it be true to say that you depend on your agent to read up on matters of this kind?'

'Yes, for many years now.'

'A good many people would be delighted to read their title deeds from day to day,' I suggested, 'if, like you, they had any.' That was greeted with some laughter and an outburst of clapping which Mr Justice Sankey quickly silenced.

'Are you suggesting I should give them my title deeds?' Even I joined in the laughter at that. Then I returned to serious matters.

'I have a feeling that you have no title deeds which justify your ownership of land and minerals, and that being the case I would suggest that you ought to give it back to the State, which is the proper owner.'

'You are entirely wrong about that, Mr Smillie.'

'Let me sum up your position, my Lord,' I continued, ignoring his rebuttal. 'You own mines, yet you never enter them but employ managers to do so on your behalf. You make huge profits, but you are uncertain of the exact figures because you employ accountants to look after those. You own two stately homes, twelve thousand acres of land and many pits, yet you have never read the title deeds to all of this because you employ an agent to do so on your behalf.' Seeing his face redden with anger, I allowed the summary a few moments to register with everybody before I spoke again. 'Tell me, my Lord, do you actually do anything?'

'I refuse to answer such a ridiculous and impertinent question.' Clearly rattled, he was grateful to Mr Justice Sankey who asked me to move along with my questions.

'How familiar are you with miners' living conditions on your estates?' I asked him.

'Not intimately,' he admitted.

'Then you will not be aware of the numerous complaints made about housing conditions there,' I suggested. 'I put it to you that you would not care to live in any of the houses which your miners live in.'

'I would prefer to live where I am living,' he replied, in as defiant a tone as he could muster. But he must have known that he was on difficult ground with these questions. The conditions in which the miners lived were described in detail by several of our witnesses and compared so appallingly with the homes of their owners and the styles in which they lived that even the most anti-miners' newspapers were forced to admit that the owners were portraying themselves in a most unfavourable light. In addition to the Earl of Durham, the Duke of Hamilton and Lord Tredegar were particularly uncomfortable with this line of enquiry because housing conditions in the Scottish and South Wales coalfields were notoriously bad.

Without wishing to predict the Commissioner's report at this stage, it is instructive to quote from the report a short passage which referred to housing conditions for miners and their families and the consequences of those conditions:

'There are houses in some mining districts which are a reproach to our civilisation. No judicial language is sufficiently strong or severe to apply to their condemnation.'

It was pointed out that there were more casualties in Britain's mines in 1918 than there had been in the Gallipoli campaign. For miners' children, the infant mortality rate was higher than in any other sector of the populations at 160 per thousand, as compared with 96.9 among agricultural labourers and 76.4 for the middle and upper classes. It would be true to say that, across the country as a whole, there was shock and repugnance at the release of these statistics.

The Commission Enquiry moved slowly into its second week. On Friday and Saturday, March 14th and 15th, several of our witnesses appeared. Among them were William Straker from Northumberland who talked about nationalisation, James Robertson from Scotland whose subject was the standard of living, John Potts of Yorkshire who gave evidence on hours and output, and Vernon Hartshorn MP, of South Wales who discussed wages. Needless to say, each of them were subject to quite severe cross-examination but they all stated their cases ably and with great conviction.

William Straker spent a whole day in the witness box being grilled by Evan Williams on the subject of mine ownership yet, in spite of the intensity of his ordeal, he never yielded an inch. James Robertson was so knowledgeable on the subject of housing conditions that Richard Cooper could make no headway with him at all. Indeed, Robertson's evidence undoubtedly made a deep impression on the Commission and the public. Quite typical of his evidence was the following statement:

'Even in England and Wales, where the housing conditions are acknowledged to be better than in Scotland, roughly one in ten persons lives under conditions of severe overcrowding. In certain mining villages of Durham this is true of four out of every ten persons.'

Potts and Hartshorn were equally strong witnesses, who refused to bow to even the severest cross-examination. On the subject of the length of the working day, Potts said:

'With a working day reduced by twenty-eight per cent (that is to six hours), it may be anticipated that the underground worker will go without an accident, on average, for nearer eight years than the present six years ... permitting every worker (and therefore to every father of a family) a longer uncrippled life.'

On the subject of wages, Vernon Hartshorn was more than a match for John Forgie, who clearly knew less about wages structures than our witness did. Forgie tried to probe him on miners' wage increases during the war claiming, as some figures suggested, that they had risen by 105%. But our man had the details at his fingertips and finally convinced everybody, with the possible exception of Forgie, that miners' wages had risen by 78% while owners profits had risen by 380%. By the time that Hartshorn put away his graphs and left the witness box, Forgie was a beaten man.

I will not relate the details of the interrogation of the other noblemen, save one. Each interrogation followed much the same pattern as mine of the Earl of Durham. Questions about rights of ownership, title deeds, working conditions, living conditions and the level of personal involvement of the witnesses. Hodges, Smith, Money and I shared the load of interrogation and these witnesses created no better an impression than the Earl of Durham had. Perhaps the Duke of Northumberland was the strongest of their men. The owner of a fine stately home, a quarter of a million acres pf land and a town house in Kensington, he was at least direct with his answers and seemed to have a better grasp of his own affairs than the others peers had.

'How much income is generated annually through coal royalties?' Sir Leo asked him.

'Sixty-nine thousand, one hundred and ninety-four pounds,' he answered clearly, and was not at all put out by the gasps from the public gallery.

'As much as that?' Sir Leo said. Then he leaned forward and stared directly at the duke. 'Don't you think it's a bad thing for one man to own as much as you do?'

'No, I think it is an excellent thing,' the Duke replied. The public and press roared with laughter. In the form of what was dubbed 'class warfare', they were being richly entertained. Then Herbert Smith, President of the Yorkshire Miners Association took over.

'If this Commission recommends nationalisation,' he asked, 'would you use your position in the House of Lords to try to defeat it?'

'Certainly,' the Duke snapped back. 'What has this Commission got to do with me?' That didn't go down well.

'The House of Lords always opposes reform, does it not?' Smith asked.

'That is purely a matter of opinion, and I do not agree with you.'

'Tell me of any reform supported by the Lords which has brought about better conditions for the people.'

'There have been many,' the Duke replied but, perhaps because he couldn't, he didn't elaborate.

'Why do you oppose nationalisation?' Smith asked calmly.

'Because it is only a blind – a stage to something more revolutionary.' Clearly the Duke believed that. It did not seem that many people present agreed with him.

The Commission's Enquiry came to a weary end on Monday, March 17th. It had lasted fifteen days, very long days indeed. Everybody was tired. Frankly, I was exhausted. Bear in mind that I was now sixty-two years old and not as resilient as I had once been. Not only that but, throughout the Enquiry, I had been worried that my lack of formal education and inexperience as an interrogator might let down not only me but the other members of our small team. They assured me that I had done well and, in truth, I felt that I had come through it alright. No great dramatics – that was never my style – but no major mistakes either.

I desperately wished to return to Larkhall, spend time with Ann, and escape the bustle of London, but that was never a possibility. The Enquiry stage was over, and we all felt as most newspapers did, that we had established our case both clearly and strongly. But now the talking had to begin within the Commission. All the evidence had to be reviewed and an interim report submitted to government within days. Following that, there would have to be a full report. Given the presence of Forgie, Cooper and Williams, and perhaps Tawney too, we knew that it would be no easy thing to produce a report to which everybody agreed. And so it proved.

XXIV
Sankey Commission: Reports & Politics

I WONDER IF there is anything in this life more frustrating than trying to talk sense into mulish, closed minds. That is how I felt after hour upon hour of debate with Williams, Cooper and Forgie, the coal owners' representatives on the Commission. In fairness, perhaps they felt the same way about Hodges, Smith, Money and myself. One thing was clear. In spite of Mr Justice Sankey's wise and benevolent guidance, the representatives of the MFGB and the mine owners were not going to see eye to eye. Everybody else was prepared to work towards an agreed report, but the mine owners' men were working towards a more limited agenda.

In such circumstances, it is natural for each group to have its own priorities. Even within any group there will be shades of opinion. For example, my main concern lay with nationalisation, while Frank Hodges' priority was miners' standards of living. However, as a group representing the MFGB, we wanted the reports to cover all issues: pay, hours, nationalisation and re-employment of demobilised miners. By and large, the chairman and the Government's nominees, as well as Mr Tawney and Mr Webb, felt the same way. However, Williams, Cooper and Forgie had little interest in the ownership issues and resisted all our efforts to draw them on the subject. I remember that Frank Hodges, probably the most impatient of our group, had to be restrained on several occasions from heaping verbal abuse on them.

Right on schedule, on March 20th our interim report was ready. Or should I say reports, for there were three of them. There was a Majority Report, a Chairman's Report and a Minority Report. The Majority Report was signed by Smith, Hodges, Money, Tawney, Webb and myself. It was a fairly lengthy report backed up by pages of argument and factual evidence gained from the enquiry. Its main conclusions were as follows:

1. The miners' claim to an advance in their standard of life is justified ... rise of wages asked for, 30% on earnings apart from war wage, is not excessive.

2. We find justified the claim to a substitution in the Coal Mines Regulation Act of 1908 of six for eight hours. A corresponding shortening of the working day should apply to the surface workers.

3. We find justified the miners' claim for a more efficient organisation of their industry ... individual ownership being wasteful and extravagant, retail distribu-

tion costly ... in the interests of the consumers as much as of the miners, nationalisation ought to be, in principle, at once determined on.

4. The case of demobilised miners would be best dealt with along with the cases of men in other industries.

Perhaps the most important of the supporting papers was the one on the working day, which I had worked closely on with Frank Hodges. It clarified a common misconception, an understandable one, which thought that eight hours meant eight hours, and six hours meant six hours. In the working life of a miner, time had a different meaning. We referred back to a House of Lords amendment to the 1908 Act which ...

'made the eight hours date from the moment the last man of each shift entered the cage to descend the shaft, until the first man of the shift reached the surface. This excluded all the 'winding time' which ... averages something like an hour, and in the most extreme cases reported to us by the inspectors takes as much as two-and-a-half hours per day.'

These facts indicated that an eight-hour shift actually meant nine to ten-and-a-half hours underground, and in that event the proposed six-hour shift would mean men spending between seven and nine-and-a-half hours underground. We felt it our clear duty to point this out to the Government on behalf of all miners.

Of course, we did not expect our Majority Report to go unchallenged. We fully anticipated that the owners' representatives' Minority Report would differ sharply from ours. What bothered us more was the Chairman's Report. We felt that it was likely to be the best represented of the reports at government level and we worried that its arguments might counter ours. In the event, we had little to worry about. That Chairman's Report, signed by Mr Justice Sankey, Arthur Balfour, Sir Arthur Duckham and Sir Thomas Royden, came to the following main conclusions:

1. We recommend that the ... Eight Hours Act be amended by the substitution, in the clauses limiting the hours of work underground, of the word seven for the word eight from July 16th 1919, and ... by substitution of the word six for eight as and from July 13th, 1921.

2. We recommend that as from July 16th, 1919, the hours of work of persons employed on the surface or about collieries shall be 46½ hours per week, exclusive of meal times.

3. We recommend an increase of wages of 2/- per shift worked ... In the case of workers under 16 years of age, the advance is to be 1/-.

4. We recommend the continuation of the Coal Mines Control Agreement Act, 1918, subject to certain suggestions indicated in our report.

The Chairman's Report also had some strong accusations concerning the conditions of many miners' accommodation and suggested that 1d per ton (worth about £1,000,000 a year) should be deducted from owners' profits and spent on improving houses and amenities. There were differences from our report. The move to a six-hour day would be gradual and dependent on the health of the industry. The pay award would be rather less than the 30% we had asked for and the mines would remain in the control of the Government but not quite fully nationalised in the sense that we meant it. Nevertheless, in spite and in much of the detail, it was remarkably similar to ours.

Predictably enough, the Minority Report, signed by Cooper, Forgie and Williams was rather different. To begin with, it was much shorter and lacked supporting argument or evidence. Its main conclusions were:

1. One and sixpence per day for persons 16 years of age and upwards, 9d for persons under 16.
2. A substitution of seven for eight hours in the Eight Hours Act.
3. Eight hours per day for surface workers.

You may reasonably wonder why this report was so short and made no mention of the ownership issue. Well, there were several reasons for this. Having taken part in the Commission's review of evidence and attempts to compile a unanimous report, the owners' representatives could tell which way the wind was blowing. They knew that if their report was totally at odds with ours, and more importantly the chairman's, it would probably be rejected out of hand. So, on hours and wages they made concessions, less than those in the other reports, but concessions nonetheless. On the issue of ownership, we would later find that they were simply 'keeping their powder dry' as the saying goes and, by concluding nothing, offering no hint as to their real tactics.

On March 20th, the same day as they were published, the three reports were presented to Parliament by Mr Justice Sankey. That same evening, in the absence of the prime minister who was indisposed, Bonar Law, leader of the coalition Conservatives, spoke for the cabinet. In his speech, he announced that the Government had adopted the Sankey Report 'in spirit and in letter'. Ominously perhaps, he did not specify which of the three reports he was alluding to, though his use of the word 'Sankey' suggested that it was the chairman's. That seemed reasonably good news, though he somewhat spoiled his otherwise reasonably generous remarks by saying that the Government would use all the resources of the State without hesitating if a strike took place. In the circumstances, that comment was both superfluous and provocative.

Events were moving quickly now. On the next day, March 21st, a special Miners' Conference took place in London to consider the three reports and

Bonar Law's reaction to them. You might remember that the earlier strike notices were due to expire on March 22nd but, after lengthy and sometimes heated discussions, it was decided that the men should continue working on day-to-day contracts until March 26th, by which time it was expected that the Government's response would become clearer. In the meantime, our executive was charged with trying to secure improvements to the chairman's proposals. Let me be quite clear, make a confession if you like. Against the heated opinions of some of our intemperate delegates who were enraged by Bonar Law's reference to 'using all the resources of the State' in the event of a threat to strike, I was the one who spoke in favour of extending the strike notice and continuing a dialogue with the Government. I was convinced that, in Mr Justice Sankey's proposals on pay, hours and ownership, there were the seeds of a very positive outcome for the miners. Along with Hodges and Smith, I argued that view against some lively opposition. However, with all the facts at my disposal, I carried the conference. For the time being at least.

We met with Bonar Law twice, on March 22nd and 24th. He promised that we would have a clarification of the Government's decision on the 25th. On that day, we again met with Bonar Law, who was accompanied by Sir Robert Horne. We were told that the Government intended to accept the Chairman's Report in its entirety and, though we had argued our case well on wages and hours, for the time being at least the Government was not prepared to go any further. On the whole, his attitude was pleasantly conciliatory and he hinted at better things to come. I had to tell him that, though Mr Justice Sankey's Report proposed a better future for the miners and the industry as a whole, it did not quite match up to our expectations and that it would be up to another Federation Conference to decide whether or not the proposals as they stood were acceptable.

So, yet another Federation Conference met on March 26th. Given that the proposals on offer had not altered in the past five days since the last conference, some delegates were still of a mind to reject them. Of course that was never a realistic option because, in any event, the whole membership would have to be consulted. This was pointed out by the wiser heads and that was the decision reached, one which pleased me greatly because it was democratic and it meant that, whatever the members felt, we could again act on their mandate. So, preparations were made for a ballot of the whole membership. The ballot was to take place on April 9th and 10th, with the results to be in the secretary's hands by April 14th.

I took advantage of this lull in proceedings to escape London and spend a few days in Larkhall. I fear that I was no great company for Ann because, exhausted by the never-ending series of formal meetings of the past few weeks, I slept most of the time, to the extent that Ann expressed concern for me.

'You're looking awful tired, Robert,' she told me as she woke me one midmorning, hours past my normal waking time. 'Do you think you should maybe see Doctor McQuillan?'

'And what good would that do me?' I laughed. 'He'd just have me rattling with horse pills.' I patted her hand. 'Don't you worry, lassie. I'll be fine once this Commission business is over.'

'But how long will that be, Robert?'

'Oh, it shouldn't be too long now,' I replied airily, which just went to prove the value of the old saying, that there's no fool like an old fool!

I arrived back in London, feeling reasonably refreshed, in time for the announcement of our ballot. Even I was astonished by the solidarity of the vote. The figures were as follows:

For acceptance of the Government's terms	693,084
Against acceptance of the Government's terms	76,992
Majority for acceptance	616,092

On April 16th, at another MFGB Special Conference, it was agreed that, at the overwhelming wish of our members, the strike notices should be withdrawn. Everybody was clear that this had been done to smooth the passage for the Government's commitment to improve the miners' working conditions and end the private ownership of mines. We had provided them with the time to honour those pledges and for the Commission to reconvene and compile its final report.

It seems incredible when I look back on it now, but the meetings which took place to produce the final report lasted for two months. Suspended for a month to allow the response of the Government and our federations, the Commission reconvened on April 24th and continued until June 23rd. Many of the sessions were public and generated wide interest. The main business was that of ownership. The Chairman's Report a month earlier had placed nationalisation at the centre of the Commission's final report and the subject almost completely dominated our discussions.

There were changes in personnel as we reconvened. Sir Thomas Royden, one of the Government nominees, resigned because of ill health and was replaced by Sir Allan Smith, Chairman of the Engineering Employers' Federation. Likewise, Mr Forgie fell ill and was replaced by Sir Adam Nimmo, recent advisor to the Coal Controllers. With no disrespect to Royden and Forgie, their replacements undoubtedly strengthened the owners' side of the Commission.

During the two months of sittings, twenty-eight days were taken up by the further investigation of witnesses, 116 of them in total. It was again an exhausting business. We heard from economists, royalty owners, Home Office spokesmen, experts in existing forms of nationalisation, technicians, coal owners, miners, miners' wives, industrial consumers, managers, administrators and various other witnesses. I can't vouch for anybody else, but by the time the last witness had been dismissed my head was reeling and my notebook contained almost as many words as the *Bible*.

Our evidence was presented between May 23rd and 30th. I conducted Henry Slesser, Standing Council to the MFGB, through our proposed draft Parliamentary Bill which contained our scheme for the nationalisation of the mines and of miners. He was supported by two of our earlier witnesses, William Straker and Arthur Winstone. To finish our consultation to that part of the evidence, Sidney Webb and Sir Leo Money also attested to methods for replacing private with public ownership. In the round, our evidence was directed at replacing autocracy in industry with democracy. Many people read into our evidence, not without justification, that we were looking beyond mining towards all major industries. As William Straker said in evidence:

'This ideal cannot be reached all at once owing to the way in which private ownership has deliberately kept the worker in ignorance regarding the industry. But as that knowledge which has been denied him grows, as it will do under nationalisation, he will take his rightful place as a man. Only then will Labour unrest ... disappear.'

This was a statement of purpose and hope which included, but extended beyond, mining. It placed nationalisation in exactly its right place, not only as the best means of running great industries, but also as a way of raising working men from the depths. I found myself nodding in appreciation of his every word. This marked the end of the process of evidence gathering.

I was not surprised that, once again, we could not produce a single common report. Given the attitudes displayed by the Government representatives as soon as we began meeting in closed sessions, that was never going to happen. As it turned out, there were no fewer than four reports submitted to government. The Chairman's Report was signed not only by Mr Justice Sankey himself, but also by Sir Leo Money, Herbert Smith, Frank Hodges, Richard Tawney, Sidney Webb and myself. There being some marginal differences in emphasis between the chairman and the rest of us, we sought his approval to submit a separate report which he readily agreed to. The third report was signed by Sir Adam Nimmo, Sir Allan Smith, Arthur Balfour, Richard Cooper and Evan Williams. A fourth report bore only the signature of Sir Arthur Duckham.

To my surprise and no little delight, all four reports appeared to agree on two things. First, they proposed State ownership of all seams of coal, and therefore of all royalties. Second, for purposes of distribution, they proposed the use of existing systems within local government and the Co-operative Movement. There were caveats, of course. On our side, we decided that ' ... no compensation whatever should be paid to the present mineral owners for the mineral rights to be acquired by the State'. After all, these men had made fortunes already from the industry. Why should they make more when the State took over?

The Chairman's Report proposed a rather longer timescale for State acquisition of the mines and developing administration for nationalisation than ours did. However, I felt that these were matters of detail rather than principle and I took the view that the differences were marginal and could be ironed out. However, the report of the Government nominees and the coal owners' representatives became more and more unsympathetic to the chairman's and our reports when you looked beyond the headlines and examined the full text. While in general they agreed that the system of individual private ownership was not the most effective, and that perhaps the State had a role to play, their real position was revealed by the following words:

'We have carefully weighed the whole of the evidence, and have come to the conclusion that the nationalisation of the coal industry in any form would be detrimental to the development of the industry and the economic life of the country.'

So, in spite of the fact that they had at first seemed to be in favour of State control, their argument rather than their headlines were against nationalisation. The furthest their rhetoric went was for the setting up of consultative Pit Committees. To a large extent, that view was supported in Sir Arthur Duckham's report which rejected full nationalisation and instead proposed a network of 'district unification', effectively a series of coal trusts, each enjoying a monopoly within its own area.

It was what you might call a 'mixed bag' of reports which went to the Government on June 20th. On the other hand, as far as I and my colleagues could tell, the majority view seemed to be in our favour. All the reports agreed on the abolition of royalties. To one degree or another, they agreed that the State should own the coal seams, even though we were fully aware of the fact that ownership of them did not mean control of production or profits. Eight of the thirteen Commissioners favoured getting rid of private production, already condemned by the majority in the Interim Report, and putting in its stead one form of nationalisation or another. Clearly, great change was favoured by the majority, including the chairman. All we could do now was wait for the Government's response.

'Well then, Bob,' Frank Hodges said, pipe in one hand, glass of ale in the other. We were with our fellow Commissioners of the MFGB in the lounge of the Imperial Hotel in Russell Square, where Frank and I were staying during the Commission's two month of talks.

'Well, then,' he said again.

'Well, what?' I asked.

'Where are we with this thing?' By 'thing,' of course, he meant the reports.

'I wish I could tell you, Frank,' I replied. 'So many views, so many bits of paper. I admit to being confused.'

'But we've got Sankey on our side,' Herbert Smith put in. 'That must count for something.'

'You would think so,' I agreed, puffing at my pipe. 'But that Balfour and his people must be up to something. What do you say, Leo?'

'I agree, Bob,' he replied. As charming as he was intelligent, he insisted on our use of his first name without the title when we gathered out of public view. 'Obviously, Balfour will have the ear of the Prime Minister in a way which we don't.' He puffed furiously on one of those odd Turkish cigarettes of his. 'More than Sankey does too,' he added.

'But our case is strong, surely?' Frank said.

'Not only that,' I added, 'but Lloyd George set up the Commission only a few months back, and Bonar Law agreed to accept the Interim Report in March.'

'True, Gentlemen, true,' Sir Leo sighed. 'But Lloyd George and Bonar Law are politicians. And where politics are concerned, who knows!'

At that point, the dinner bell sounded and we went through to eat, Sir Leo Money's words ringing in our ears.

After the submission of the reports, I returned to Larkhall for a brief holiday. Ann again expressed concern at how tired I was but cheered up when, after a few days' rest and good home cooking, I was feeling stronger. As ever, on that visit home I realised that with most of my time spent in London among senior trade unionists, civil servants and government ministers, I was less aware than I had once been of how the miners at the coalface, and their families, were viewing the matters I was working on. As usual, Ann was an excellent sounding-board.

'So, what's the talk of the steamie?' I asked her.

'Oh, nothing much,' she replied. 'Just some stories about an old man from Larkhall in a fight with the Government.'

'And this old man,' I said, 'is he winning or losing?'

'Well, opinion's divided on that. Some say he's landed some heavy blows.' She burst out laughing. 'But there's them who say he's too old to fight. He gets his fists caught up in his moustache.'

'Ann Smillie, you're a wicked woman!' I embraced her, then asked the question most important to me. 'But what do you think?'

'I think you're doing your best for us Robert,' she replied. 'And nobody can ask any more.'

I returned to London in better mood than when I'd left. Having spent some time away from the madhouse, I had convinced myself that all would be well. After all, had Bonar Law not promised to adopt the Interim Report, nationalisation proposals and all, 'in letter and in spirit'? Of course, I knew that no government is constitutionally obliged to accept any Commission's Report but, in this case, surely they had no choice. A specific pledge had been given by Bonar Law and, given the fact that the greatly respected chairman had come down in favour of nationalisation, what could go wrong? Or so I told myself.

However, the Government appeared to be in no hurry to give its final response. Whenever asked, inside or outside the House, Lloyd George and Bonar Law replied from the same script that 'the matter remains under consideration'. We did not realise it at the time but a large number of Conservative MPs, and a number of Liberals, were bending the Government's ear. So too were vested interest groups such as the coal owners' association and Chamber of Commerce. We were aware of meetings addressed by the likes of Lord Inchcape and Lord Leverhulme and other heads of big monopolies, preaching against the evils of nationalisation. But surely they were too late and too self-interested? We consoled ourselves with the knowledge that the Chairman's Report was in the Government's hands and Bonar Law was in favour of it.

While everybody awaited the Government's response, no major union, the miners included, undertook any action in an attempt to force the Government's hand. There were voices in favour of major rallies, demonstrations and even strikes to force Lloyd George to our view. I argued against and resisted any such suggestions. We were in the middle of a process, I told our people. We had willingly entered into that process and had to see it through. To do anything other would not only be precipitate, but actually dishonourable. On reflection, perhaps I was wrong, too committed to correct procedure and, beyond a doubt, too trusting. But we can never know that for certain.

In July 1919, nationalisation became an issue at two by-elections in Swansea and Bothwell. In both cases, the Labour vote increased substantially. There, I told myself, was a clear enough message for Lloyd George. Time passed slowly as the Government continued to fail to declare its position. Our men continued to draw their wage increase of two shillings per shift, which they termed 'The Sankey Wage.' Then on July 9th the Government suddenly announced an increase in the price of coal by the large amount of six shillings a ton. We saw this as a crude effort by the Government to alienate consumers who, in their ignorance of how these things are done, would blame the miners. There was also one local strike in Yorkshire, entered into against my wishes, due to an argument over piece rates. That lasted for four weeks during which time the Government took every opportunity to berate the miners. The optimism I had felt upon my return from Larkhall was fast evaporating.

Finally, on August 18th, the Government made its response. I was horrified but, given the tenor of the past few weeks, not entirely surprised when Lloyd George announced that he had come down against nationalisation. He cited the Yorkshire Strike, 'against the Government' as he mischievously put it, as evidence against nationalisation. What the connection was between the two was unclear, and he did not expand on it. His actual proposals were:

'That the minerals are to be purchased by the State; that a fund should be raised for the promoting of schemes for the social improvement and the ameliorations of the conditions and the amenities of life in the mining villages; that the State should not purchase the business of the mines, and certainly not run them ...'

He went on to provide more details of issues like amalgamation of mines within districts to improve efficiency, and miners having representatives on the boards responsible for district management. But these matters were of no great interest to me. In spite of the pledges, in spite of Bonar Law's acceptance of the Interim Report 'in letter and in spirit,' there was to be no nationalisation of the mines. How strongly we felt about the Government's broken promise was summed up by Vernon Hartshorn, speaking on the same day:

'We did not ask for a Commission. We accepted it. We gave evidence before it. Why was the Commission set up? Was it a huge game of bluff? Was it never intended that if the reports favoured nationalisation we were to get it? Why was the question sent at all to the Commission?

That is the kind of question the miners of the country will ask, and they will say: "We have been deceived, betrayed, duped".'

You may wonder why those words came from Vernon rather than from me. As president of the MFGB, I should have been the first to respond on behalf of the miners. The simple truth was that I was in no fit state to respond. Again exhausted beyond belief, every emotion torn from me, I was in despair. I do not mind admitting that, alone in my hotel bedroom that night, I wept. No doubt there was an element of self-pity in that but most of the tears were shed on behalf of the mining community. I wept for men and women who had been the victims of a heinous act of betrayal.

XXV
Sankey Commission: The Aftermath

FOR SEVERAL DAYS after Lloyd George's announcement, I was in a state of shocked despair for two reasons. First, I had never felt so let down in my life. Oh, I know you will say that from what I have previously told you that I should have had good reason not to invest much trust in Lloyd George, but this time I had really felt that things might be different. He had set up the Commission and given everybody to understand that he would abide by its recommendations. Then Bonar Law had accepted the Interim Report and promised to honour it 'in spirit and in letter'. The final Chairman's Report had been warmly welcomed and, not until the last minute, had there been any clear sign that it would not be fully implemented. So, its final rejection had been a hammer blow.

Second, and even more troubling to me at that time, was my conviction that I had let down the miners. For the best part of six months they had faithfully followed a strategy which, to a large extent, had been described by me. On several occasions, I had argued down those who wanted to take action to put pressure on the Government. I had forced votes to make sure that they did not get their way. And for what? A Government decision which had made concessions over pay and hours, though not to the levels we had demanded, and a total rejection of nationalisation which, in my opinion, had been the single most important issue of them all. I could come to no other conclusion than that my strategy had failed; that I had been too trusting of other men and due process, as a result of which the miners had been sold short and I had been humiliated. Not that my wounded pride mattered in the great scheme of things, but it certainly contributed to the despair which I felt.

No meetings immediately due, I kept to myself. I wrote a long letter to Ann in explanation of events, keeping my personal feelings out of it. She would have been worried for me. I went for long walks, my mind poring over the sorry situation. I slept little and just picked at my food. I became overwhelmingly tired. Just hours before our next Executive Committee meeting I decided that, in light of what I saw as a failure, I would resign from the presidency.

At our meeting in Russell Square, I summarised recent events as I saw them without commenting on the anguish which I was feeling. Then I offered my resignation. There was a stunned silence, then a hubbub of voices breaking out. I could scarcely credit their reaction. Not one man among them was prepared to accept my resignation. One delegate from Ayrshire advised me, 'Away an' bile yer head, Bob. Dinna be so daft, man.' That provoked some laughter and helped to ease the tension. I was greatly moved by my colleagues' reaction. They took the view that there remained much to be done and, in spite of recent events, I was still the man to lead the Federation. Humbled, I thanked them for their support, promised to continue to do my best, and the matter was dropped.

At that meeting we decided to call a special conference which was held in the Westminster Hall on September 3rd, 1919. Before the conference, all the delegates were provided with the full text of Lloyd George's announcement so that they could thoroughly familiarise themselves with his reasoning, such as it was. As president, I opened the meeting and, from the chair, I went over the events of the past few months and explained why it was the Executive Committee's view that the Federation should reject the Government's scheme for the future running of the mines. I have rarely had a more attentive audience. In my opening address, I saw fit to answer a recent claim made against me by the Duke of Northumberland whom I had recently examined as a Commission witness. He had claimed that at the head of the Federation, which meant me, there must be 'Bolshevik influence and Bolshevik gold'. I countered his claim in the following words:

'The Duke believes I am an honourable man ... but I cannot be an honourable man if behind us, knowingly, there is Bolshevik gold or Bolshevik influence. I am not now speaking against Bolshevism; the Bolshevists are merely a majority of the people of the Socialist movement in Russia. As to the rightness or wrongness of their movement, I am not dealing with this point. I have considerable sympathy with them in their struggle to free their country from Capitalism ... I would like to ask the Duke of Northumberland either to prove his charge of Bolshevik influence and money, or to have the courage to withdraw it.'

On that point at least I had an enthusiastic response. There is nothing a miner likes more than hearing a major coal owner, particularly an aristocratic one, being held to account.

The resolution to endorse the rejection of the Government's scheme for the running of mines was moved by William Brace MP and seconded by his fellow Parliamentarian William Adamson. In support of those two, George Barker of South Wales roused the conference when he said:

'I am certain that if the conference that met at the Holborne Restaurant in February could have foreseen that the Government would have abjured the findings of the Commission they would have never agreed to the Commission being set up. I hold, personally, that the Government has broken faith with the miners of this country. I have in my hands several documents that I have made. A speech by the Prime Minister in the House of Commons on February 24th, 1919:

"They will find as a result of this inquiry they will get a Miners' Charter, which will be the beginning of greater and better things for them, and if they do so, and throw themselves into this inquiry and present their case – in some respects as I know, irresistible, in others requiring undoubtedly some greater proof than I have seen up to the present; but I am not prejudiced – they will achieve great things for their industry and for the men they so ably lead. And they will have the satisfaction when they have got these things knowing that they obtained them without inflicting any hurt upon hundreds of thousands of other men and women engaged in honest toil like themselves."

'One may ask, why this reference to a Miners' Charter, if it did not specifically refer to the main principle of such a charter, namely, nationalisation of the mines with joint control by the workmen? If it did not mean that, it was a deception.

'A speech by Mr Bonar Law, March 25th, 1919:

"If this Commission is allowed to continue, interim reports will be issued dealing with subject after subject in which you are all vitally interested; and not merely will these interim reports be issued, which in ordinary circumstances might be put into the waste-paper basket, but it is the part of the Government to deal with these reports in the spirit as well as in the letter, and steps will be taken to enable these recommendations to be carried into effect."

'Though nationalisation is not expressed here, it is implied, or language has no meaning.'

Finally, after quoting also the pledge given in Parliament a scant seven months earlier by the Home Secretary ('if on enquiry it is found to be the best thing for the community, then I unhesitatingly say, of course, I accept the principle of nationalisation'), Barker concluded:

'Therefore it is abundantly proved, it is on the records of the House of Commons, that the principle of nationalisation has been conceded to the industry providing the Commission found in favour of nationalisation, and the Government have taken the responsibility upon themselves of breaking faith with the greatest Trade Union in this or any other country, and by doing that they have administered a deadly blow to the principle of conciliation and negotiation so far as it affects the industries of this country in the future.'

By this stage, the delegates to the conference were in a state of near uproar. Speech after speech was outlining the perfidy of the Government. Such was the intensity of their feelings that I believe that, if I had ordered a march to Parliament, not a man would have refused.

Vernon Hartsorn MP, one of the witnesses to the Commission and one of our most able men, then summarised the whole affair by outlining the reasons, as he saw them, why the Government had gone back on its pledges to the miners. Again referring to the records of the House of Commons, he reaffirmed the clear understanding in Parliament that if the Royal Commission were to report in favour of nationalisation, then the Government would have no choice but to put it into effect. So, he asked us to consider what had changed the situation. The coal owners had failed to prove their case, so why on earth had the Government come down on their side? He provided the answers to those questions in his own words:

'The coal owners practically purchased the Press of the country. Look at every meeting of directors that is held in the mining industry today. What do you find? You find what has never appeared before – whole pages of the daily papers are devoted to the advertisement of speeches of directors of colliery companies, and in every speech that has been delivered they are making nationalisation their one and sole topic. They have been passing resolutions, issuing circulars, and sending them to the Members in the House of Commons, practically amounting to a threat that if they wanted in the future the support of these shareholders in the mining industry they must vote against nationalisation. The Prime Minister was informed that he must not introduce a scheme of nationalisation. What has happened is simply this, that the Prime Minister and his Government have surrendered to the mass of shareholders.'

Nobody present had any doubt that Vernon Hartshorn was right in his account of what had happened. There was a very real anger in Westminster that day. Nobody present believed anything other than that we had been duped by an unholy alliance between the coal owners and deceitful politicians. I was much relieved by the fact that none of the speakers saw fit to malign me for the way in which I had managed our side of things. Indeed, a number of speakers went out of their way to congratulate me on the faith I had shown in my fellow men and the diligence with which I, and my fellow Commissioners, had prosecuted our case.

After all the speeches, there was never any doubt about the conference backing the Executive Committee's proposal to reject the Government's position. The following resolution was passed unanimously:

'Being convinced that the Government's scheme is wholly impracticable for the future working of the mines, the Executive Committee recommends the Conference to reject the Government's scheme, and records its regret that the Government have no better scheme than the creation of great trusts to secure the wellbeing of the industry.

'We are convinced that the only way to place the industry upon a scientific basis for the purpose of giving the advantage of maximum production to the community consistent with the maximum economic and social wellbeing of the miners is to at once introduce the scheme of nationalisation recommended by the majority of the Coal Industry Commission.

'We do not at this stage recommend the miners take industrial action to secure the adoption of the report of the Coal Industry Commission, but we invite the Trades Union Congress to declare that the fullest and most effective action be taken to secure that the Government shall adopt the majority report of the Commission as to the future governance of the industry.'

You will note from that resolution that, at that time, we were not minded to propose any unilateral action by the miners. Rather, we felt that the mere threat of action might be more conducive to bending the Government's will. We felt it advisable to talk to our colleagues in the other major trade unions. One problem with that was that there had been a lack of urgency on the part of the Parliamentary Committee of the TUC which, not unusually for them I have to say, had twice that summer refused union requests to call a special Congress on issues like conscription and military intervention in Russia. We felt now that we had to force that Committee into action. A meeting of the Triple Alliance was organised at which it was agreed to release a statement suggesting that nationalisation and strike ballots were very much on our minds. Then, at the next session of the Trades Union Congress in Glasgow on September 10th, I proposed a resolution which was seconded by James Thomas MP. The resolution was as follows:

(a) This Congress having received the request of the Miners' Federation to consider the Government rejection of the Majority Report of the Coal Industry Commission, and the adoption in its place of a scheme of District Trustification of the industry, hereby declares that, in conjunction with the miners, it rejects the Government Scheme for the governance of the industry as a scheme contrary to the best interests of the nation, and it expresses its resolve to co-operate with the Miners' Federation of Great Britain to the fullest extent, with a view to compelling the Government to adopt the scheme of national ownership and joint control recommended by the majority of the Commission in their Report.

(b) To this end the Congress instructs the Parliamentary Committee, in conjunction with the Miners' Federation, to immediately interview the Prime Minister on the matter, in the name of the entire Labour Movement, to insist upon the Government adopting the Majority Report.

(c) In the event of the Government still refusing to accept this position, a Special Congress shall be convened for the purpose of deciding the form of action to be taken to compel the Government to accept the Majority Report of the Commission.

Although the resolution was opposed by Harelock Wilson MP of the Sailors' and Fishermens' Union, it was upheld by as big a majority as I can remember at such a session. The figures were:

For the resolution	4,478,000
Against the resolution	77,000
Majority	4,401,000

In effect, the resolution enjoyed a fifty-five to one majority. By having that resolution passed by the Trades Union Congress, we had achieved two things. First, we had more or less bypassed the cumbersome and rarely active TUC Parliamentary Committee. Second, we had sent a clear message to the Government that not only miners but the whole Trade Union Movement was at odds with their negative views on nationalisation. Our mood should have been clear from the wording of the proposal which talked of 'compelling the Government' and a 'form of action'. But would the Government listen?

That Congress having taken place in Glasgow, I was able to take a few days' rest at home in Larkhall with Ann. Again she suggested that I should visit the doctor. I was looking dreadfully tired, she told me, and though I wouldn't admit it to her that was exactly how I felt. I was sleeping badly, suffering headaches now and again and sometimes it took a few seconds for my eyes to focus properly. But I told her I was fine, just a wee bit tired, and that I would feel like my old self again once the argument with the Government was over. Man alive, how often had I come out with platitudes like that before once again catching the train to London?

On the way south, I decided not to do much reading because my eyes didn't feel quite right. Instead I reflected on the positions we found ourselves in. We had put our trust in the constitutional process suggested by Lloyd George and had done so wholeheartedly and with the best of intentions. As I knew only too well, it had been hard at times to get the miners to accept the idea of a Commission, and then to accept its findings which had fallen a little short of our original demands. Then, while awaiting the Government's response, there had been problems reining in some men who had wanted to take direct action, but we had managed it with the exception of the Yorkshire Miners' Strike. We had not reacted hotly to the coal owners' anti-Sankey Campaign during the summer, because we had felt bound to await the Government's decision. When that decision had been handed down against our interest, we had resisted requests for strike action and, instead, referred the matter to the Trades Union Congress. In short, throughout we had honoured our commitments and respected due process to a far greater extent than either the mine owners or the Government had done.

Reflecting on these matters, I believed that I had done the right things throughout. I believed that my conscience could be clearer than many of the other participants. But where had it got me? It had brought me to the stage of relying on other unions, not just ourselves, to put pressure on the Government. Maybe I should have been more obstinate, less obsessed by democracy and due process, I told myself. By the time my train reached London, I was fairly well convinced that this particular Government was unlikely to bend to argument. If so, what other options did we have?

On October 9th, Lloyd George repeated his refusal to nationalise in spite of the resolution made by the TUC in Glasgow. At the next TUC meeting in December, there was a majority in favour of launching a 'Mines For The Nation' campaign in the belief that such a campaign would win over some public support for nationalisation to such an extent that the Government would be forced to listen. I voted in favour of the campaign but had no great hopes of it. I doubted very much whether people like Lloyd George and Bonar Law would be persuaded by public sentiment even if it could be aroused, which I doubted. The issue had been in the public domain for so long that I felt that the mass of the population outside the mining areas were tired of it. And so it proved. The campaign had been running for about four weeks and arousing no great amount of interest. In my role as President of the MFGB, I asked the TUC to consider the issue of a general strike to enforce the people's will against the Government. I sensed that the general population's support was draining away from us and, if we were to take action, it had to be done sooner rather than later.

For various reasons of illness, poor weather and other meetings, the following TUC meeting did not take place until the second week of March, 1920, by which time the 'Mines For The Nation' campaign had more or less withered. At a Miners' Federation meeting the week before that, we sounded out delegates on their committee's views about strike action. We took a vote which resulted in 524 in favour and 344 against, most of the latter votes coming from Yorkshire and Durham delegates. It was sadly clear that we were divided among ourselves.

At the TUC meeting, there was no appetite for strike action. The vote showed 1,050,000 in favour and 3,732,000 against. There would be no general strike in favour of nationalisation. What was decided was that there would be an intense campaign in favour of nationalisation in preparation for the next general election, whenever that took place.

In spite of the fact that our own Federation vote had shown a division of view, many miners felt indignant over the TUC vote. Nationalisation of the mines had been shelved and it would likely be several years until the next general election. Without question, morale slumped. I took it particularly badly. I had long advocated nationalisation and this had been the best chance we had ever had to secure it. Now, at my age, I might never see that chance arise again. For now, with the 'Mines For The Nation' campaign dead, I honestly felt that I might as well be too. Again, the Executive Committee refused to accept my resignation which I offered in late March. Instead, they suggested that I go home to Larkhall to regain my health and enthusiasm. In a low state of mind, and desperately fatigued, I was only too happy to accept their kind offer.

XXVI
Dreams

IT WAS THE worst train journey I had ever made. My mind was whirling: I couldn't concentrate on anything. My newspapers and the MFGB papers I'd brought with me lay beside me, unread. Stations came, stations went. In truth, I had little idea where I was. A kindly gentleman wearing a clerical collar stopped by several times to ask me if I was feeling ill. I have no idea what I said to him. Nothing was making sense to me anymore. When the train crossed the border and began the long climb up Beattock Summit, it hardly registered. Normally, by that stage I would have been counting the miles and the minutes to Larkhall. But not this time.

I was fixated on the treachery of Government. I was reviling myself for not having seen it coming. I was in abject misery at having let down the men. Some small part of me was trying to insist that it had not been my fault, that I had behaved honourably and done my best and that no man could have done more. But mostly I rejected that as simple self-defence. I should have been more obstinate, less accommodating, pressed our case with action as some of our people had wanted to. Lloyd George would have been more malleable if I had pressed him harder, threatened him with general strike action. Why hadn't I done that? Why, oh why? God, but I felt tired.

As soon as I got in the door, Ann told me to sit down. I tried to walk to my chair, the one with the pipe rack close by. But my legs were so heavy, like lead, and my eyes could not focus properly. Instead of the chair and the pipe rack, I saw wriggling things like small worms. What on earth? I reached for the arm of the chair, couldn't find it, and the last thing I remember is my legs giving way.

When I woke up, I was in bed. At least it was my own bed, thank God. The curtains were closed. Was it night-time? I couldn't tell. In the semi-darkness, my eyes began to focus and I made out the dim outlines of two people. One was Ann, my dear Ann, but the other one? That he was big was all I could make out.

'How are you feeling by now, Bob?' Andrew McQuillan, beyond a doubt, our doctor for more years than either of us cared to remember.

'Give me a minute to wake up and I'll tell you,' I murmured, trying to make a joke of things with no great success. And was that my voice? It sounded like mine but it seemed so far away.

'What's the time?' I asked.

'Just after one o'clock,' he replied.

'Good God! Have I been asleep for ... four hours?'

'In the afternoon,' McQuillan added quietly.

'In the afternoon?' I tried to work it out but couldn't. 'So how long have ... '

'Since nine o'clock last night, Robert,' Ann put in. 'About sixteen hours.'

'You'll be thinking I'm lazy,' I said and started to pull at the bedclothes. 'I'd better be getting up.'

'Oh no you don't, Robert Smillie.' McQuillan's heavy arm pushed me back down. 'You're staying where you are.'

'Here? But why?' In truth I was still feeling awfully tired. 'What's wrong with me, Andrew?'

'You're fatigued, Robert,' he replied, 'fatigued, exhausted!' His great booming laugh filled the room. 'Buggered, if that suits a mining man better!'

'So what am I to do ... ?' my voice trailed off.

'Bed-rest, Bob,' he told me. 'And this.' He held up a large bottleful of liquid. 'Two spoonfuls, twice a day, for a week. Ann can start the course now.'

Quite literally, I took my medicine. I had neither the strength nor the will to resist, even if I'd wanted to. Ann brought through a wee bowl of soup and spoon-fed me. I was having difficulty keeping my eyes open. She started fussing about, plumping my pillows, straightening my bedclothes, but I was hardly aware of her. I was drifting away, no longer in my bedroom but in a half-world of memories ...

... In 1909, we were faced with yet another wage reduction, an episode which led to me dealing with some very famous people indeed. The MFBG was threatening a national strike in support of hard-pressed Scottish miners and Winston Churchill, then President of the Board of Trade, got heavily involved. There was a stormy conference lasting three days at which the Scottish miners and coal owners eventually came to an agreement with some advantage to both sides. I was unhappy because the owners came out of it too well, in my opinion, so I was not among the signatories.

Churchill had contributed to several sessions of the conference and sometimes he entertained our delegates in the garden behind the Board of Trade offices. A young man then, he was an entertaining host and was full of talk about a 'new social order' which he and his younger colleagues were keen on. He was full of praise for the miners, whom he described as the best of men, and painted a bright picture of a better future for them. But he was a politician, first and foremost, and I never had any experience of him putting his words into action in the various offices he held over the years.

As a result of knowing Churchill, I was introduced to Lord Balfour. We got on rather well. It turned out that he was one of the Commissioners responsible for refurbishing an old property in Kennington for the future use of the Prince of Wales. He invited me to see it, and I was glad to accept. By this stage, most of the refurbishment had been carried out and the interior of the house was quite delightful. As we were leaving, Balfour tugged my arm and pointed to a couple who were touring the area. They were none other than the king and queen, no doubt anxious to inspect the area before their son took over his new property.

At Balfour's insistence, we hovered behind at a respectful distance as the royal couple inspected the properties of their son's future neighbours. One of them belonged to Tom Richardson, one of our people. A surprise visit without any previous announcement, the presence of the royals no doubt surprised the wee girl who answered the door. She was Annie Richardson, a slip of a thing in those days. Once she had registered who her visitors were, she invited them in, as calm as you like. Lord Balfour accompanied them while I waited outside, feeling that I was hardly dressed for the occasion. Balfour later told me that the king, queen and Annie had a lengthy conversation about the neighbourhood and its amenities, with Annie presiding over the teapot. Balfour told me that young Annie Richardson was among the finest young women he'd ever met.

Years later, I bumped into Annie in the lobby of the House of Commons. She was with her husband and was holding a wee baby in her arms. I reminded her of the royal visit to her house years earlier and she confirmed the details provided by Lord Balfour, except that the king had noticed a portrait hanging on the wall and enquired who it was. Balfour told him it was of Keir Hardie and what a terrible man he was. At which point Annie became indignant, said that Hardie was one of the best of men and, looking straight at the king and queen, added that anybody who did not agree could leave straight away. At which point Balfour revised his opinion and the king and queen smiled broadly. And Annie's verdict on the occasion? They had been very nice. 'Just like other decent people.'

... In 1916, just for a few hours, I became Bertrand Russell. I was to speak at a meeting in Glasgow, at which he was to deliver a lecture. At the last minute he was prohibited from appearing, in case his anti-war views stirred up trouble. In the land of free speech, for heaven's sake! Two days before the meeting I received a copy of Russell's speech and a request from him, written in his own hand, to read it out. I consulted Sir Daniel Stephenson, who was to chair the meeting. At first, he was against the idea, saying that it might provoke the authorities but when I threatened that I would withdraw from the event he relented, adding only that it would be my responsibility if anything went wrong.

I began my statement to the meeting by explaining the circumstances then began to read aloud Mr Russell's beautiful prose. It began: 'On dark days, men need a clear faith and a well grounded hope, and as the outcome of these the calm courage which takes no account of hardships by the way.' It was one of the most beautiful things I had ever read and it strengthened my determination to fight for justice and freedom for the ordinary people.

The Russell speech was well received. Some of the press were unkind enough to comment that it was better than any of my own speeches, which was undoubtedly true. They also reported the fact that, at the end, I had spoken vehemently against interference with the liberty of speech and the authorities' narrowness in banning Bertrand Russell.

Next day the *Glasgow Herald* ran a leader column more centred on my comments than on Russell's words. At the end, the Editor remarked, 'We are sure the War Council will not plead the Defence of the Realm Act against Mr Smillie'. I wasn't quite so sure of that. Given my anti-war stance and my work on behalf of the miners, I was not exactly the War Office's favourite son! For some time after that event in Glasgow, I half expected a knock at the door and some large peeler telling me I was being indicted for seditious talk. But that never happened, thank the Good Lord.

... I slipped in and out of consciousness. What time of day it was, I had no idea for the curtains were kept shut. Once I asked Ann to open them a little, which she kindly did, but the daylight affected my eyes so badly that I had to ask her to shut them again. I knew that I was having visitors asking after my health but, no sooner had they gone, then I was forgetting who had been there. Ann was patience itself, spending hour after hour with me, encouraging me to eat a little which, to be frank, I didn't feel like doing. And the fatigue still clung to me, so much so that I actually welcomed the idea of falling asleep and rejoining my dreams ...

... It was just after the end of the war, I'm not sure exactly when, and I was sitting at a platform in a beautiful place packed with younger people. The place absolutely smelled of history, busts of the good and the great everywhere, the beautiful heavy woodworking centuries old. Somewhat apprehensively looking around me, I saw well dressed people, many in military or naval uniform and, in the gallery above, rows of ladies and gentlemen, finely dressed. I was in the Union, the hall of the famous Debating Society of Cambridge University and I, Robert Smillie, miner, union leader and agitator par excellence was about to take part in a debate on the motion 'Would it be in the interests of the nation that the Liberal Party should come back into power?' As the clock ticked its way towards the appointed hour, I could feel my legs turning to jelly.

It was all Arnold McNair's fault. A brilliant Cambridge don, I had met him on numerous occasions when he had been Sir Richard Redmayne's secretary. He was a Radical rather than a Socialist, but had an abiding interest in Labour questions and frequently peppered me with enquires about the lives of working men and their families. Later, he became Secretary to the Sankey Commission. Over the course of some years, he and I got to know one another well. He mentioned my name to his brother, retiring President of the Cambridge Union, and I was invited to take part in the debate about the Liberals.

I was to second the motion against the Liberals and listened with great interest and not a little alarm to the opening speakers. The methods of the Liberal and Conservative advocates were new to me. Neither presented a solid case as such, each man's priority being to score points off the other. They did this brilliantly, I must add, but I wondered how on earth I would fit into this debating style.

I spoke for perhaps thirty minutes in a matter wholly different to the others. I stuck to my usual formula. Neither the Liberals nor the Conservatives could serve the needs of ordinary people because they weren't of them and didn't understand them. Both favoured private capital while only nationalisation would serve the interests of the nation and working people. Knowing my views as you must by now, you can probably imagine the rest of it. I half-expected a lynch mob to arise out of the audience for I believed it unlikely that many, if any, shared my views. But they were very kind to me, tolerated my 'extremist' views with great calm, and offered me genuine congratulations at the end, by which time my legs were more or less strong enough to support me without shaking.

I heard later that the next debate was on 'The League of Nations' and that the Duke of Northumberland, one of my main antagonists from the Sankey days, was a principal speaker against the League. He never was a man for new ideas, the old Duke! About to sign his name in the visitors' book, he paused and frowned. The last name written in the visitor's book was mine! I was told that he seemed to take an age before he condescended to sign. It must have been the only time in his life that his name followed that of a miner in any list.

... I was well acquainted with Lord Morley whom I knew when he was plain John Morley, MP for Newcastle-Upon-Tyne. He was a fine writer and his master-piece was his biography of William Ewart Gladstone, in my opinion the greatest political figure of the nineteenth century.

Although a young man of only twenty-two at the time, I vividly remember Gladstone's famous Midlothian Campaign in which he talked as a champion of working people, attacked Disraeli's policies as 'immoral and iniquitous' and called the Afghan War 'a crime against God'. Man, but he was a great orator and regularly drew crowds of more than 5,000 people to his great open air meetings.

At that time, before I had begun to take a deep interest in the Labour Movement, I leaned towards the Liberals and helped Stephen Mason, the Liberal candidate in mid-Lanark. But the country's eyes were turned towards Midlothian where Gladstone was triumphantly returned. Shortly after that, I attended a rally at the Waterloo Rooms in Glasgow, attended by both Mr and Mrs Gladstone. Well, both Gladstones spoke and, though William Ewart delivered an excellent address, it was actually the Reverend George's which impressed me more.

As I said I was a young man then and could hardly have expected that I would ever come into closer contact with Mr Gladstone. Yet I did, many years later, by which time I was playing a leading role in everything which concerned miners and, on several occasions, met the great man. On one occasion I accompanied

John Weir in a deputation to meet Gladstone on the subject of the Eight Hours Act. Weir had a broad Scots accent, to put it mildly, and apologised to Gladstone for it. The old politician simply smiled and told John not to worry because he liked to hear a touch of the Doric.

On numerous occasions, he listened to me talking at length about miners' concerns and was always patient about it. I always worried that, with his mind full of international and national affairs, he would consider our business unimportant. However, he always conveyed the impression of being deeply interested, and expressed a great deal of sympathy with many of our views. Even if in the end I did not share his political views, I always found him kind and courteous. Of all the allegedly great men I ever met, I would without hesitation place Gladstone at the head of them all.

... In a pleasant house just outside Dunfermline, I made the acquaintance of another great political leader, Sir Henry Campbell-Bannerman. Recently appointed as prime minister, he was visiting his constituency and staying at the home of his chief supporter, Iain Robertson. Sir Henry had made it known that he wished to hear the views of the miners' representatives face-to-face. In particular, he wanted to discuss the Eight Hours Act and the workmen's business stock. I imagined that he would be a typical capitalist, lacking the gift of sympathy, but I was pleasantly surprised. He invited us in, told us to draw our chairs nearer to the fire and said that he wanted us to tell him, with no formality, exactly what we thought.

Man, we were there for hours! We were afraid of outstaying our welcome but, every time we thought we had finished, he would ask another question. Not only did he show great sympathy with us on issues like social welfare, but he also had an uncanny grasp of detail. He made no promises other than doing his best, and we left with a feeling of great fondness for him. In his own way, he was a great man. Not as great as Gladstone, but who was?

Balfour ... who felt that the sufferings caused by unemployment were matters for men and employers and not the Government? Salisbury, who believed that the concerns of miners were trivial? Haldane, a brilliant organiser who lacked concern for ordinary soldiers? Bonar Law, whose mendacity became a by-word among MFGB members? Churchill, a brilliant opportunist who promised much and delivered little? Jean Jaurès, the wisest man I ever met? Keir Hardie, dear friend and inspiration? Ramsay MacDonald, his greatness limited by his fears? Lloyd George? A magician without morals. There were many more besides. I met them all, but Gladstone was the greatest of them all.

By the time that I began to feel better, a week had gone by. MacQuillan's bottle was nearly empty, the curtains were left open, and I was eating with more enthusiasm. Not yet recovered, but getting there. Which encouraged Ann to show me the telegrams which had arrived for me. There was one from Frank Hodges, another from Arnold McNair, others from Ramsay MacDonald, James

Thomas, Herbert Smith and heaven knows who else. One in particular rather surprised me:

Dear Mr Smillie,

Saddened to hear you are unwell. Do recover quickly.
Have not had a satisfying argument in some time.

Your sincerely,
David Lloyd George.

Well, I had always known that little Welshman was human, even if I couldn't trust the man. Ann gave me the last of McQuillan's bottle of medicine and it wasn't long before my eyelids began to flutter ...

... The summer of 1894 brought little warmth to Scottish miners and their families. In 1893, the Midland Coalfield of England had secured an improvement in their wages. Then in the spring of 1894, the Scottish miners were faced with a reduction of 1/- a day. The men voted to reject it. And quite right too. Why should the Scottish miners be paid less than their English counterparts? The strike began in early June and went to on October. The owners refused to concede, the strike collapsed and we returned to work on the owners' terms. Seventeen long weeks of privation, and all for nothing.

The expense of that strike taught me two things. First, that our organisation had to be improved, an issue I dealt with earlier in these memoirs. Second, that for the sake of all parties concerned, it would be advisable to have the machinery in place to consider wages and other matters on a regular basis, rather than incurring hasty reductions on both sides. Thus, the Scottish Coal-Fields Conciliation Board was formed in January 1900, under rules agreed by the owners and the mining unions. From the beginning, I served on that board. Andrew McCosh, of the owners, was appointed Chairman and I was Vice-Chairman.

For some years, that board was instrumental in setting pay rates, considering issues of safety and all the rest of it. It was not all sweetness and light. McCosh could be a very hard negotiator. In spite of that, there was less trouble in the Scottish coalfields at that time than elsewhere in Britain. There was a lesson to be learned there for all of us. Negotiation is always better than confrontation and involving people is preferable to issuing instructions. Basic rules of democracy, I suppose. It didn't last, of course. Such civilised arrangements usually don't. Why is mankind so prone to mistakes?

But I still remember most clearly from that period the pinched faces of the children during that 1894 strike ...

At long last I was able to get out of my bed and begin getting some strength back into me. It's amazing how quickly you can recuperate when you get some fresh air into your lungs and I felt so much better for getting outside even if, at first, I wasn't able to walk far. It wasn't long before I was walking further, enjoying my food, and feeling more or less back to normal. When Dr McQuillan visited me for the last time, he finally told me what had been in the bottle. A sedative, for goodness sake! My body had been so run-down and exhausted he'd taken the decision to make sure that I got as much rest as possible. Otherwise, according to him, 'a daft old bugger' like me might have spoiled the recovery process.

I began to give thought to returning to London and my duties. Ann wasn't prepared to let me go until I gave her my word that I would not exhaust myself again and I gave her my word. Then, the day before I was due to set out, as 1919 was ebbing, a final telegram arrived. It was from a very unexpected source and made me think about some events earlier in the year.

An impressive lady by the name of Eglantyne Jebb had for some time been campaigning for the establishment of an organisation which would work across Europe to champion suffering children in the aftermath of the Great War. She contacted me at the Miners' Federation Headquarters and asked if I could support her efforts. Apparently, she'd heard that I was a man with a conscience so she couldn't have read any of the newspapers which labelled me a 'Socialist agitator'!

We met in my office and I was immediately impressed by a person who clearly saw the helping of children as her mission in life. The devil of it was that setting up any organisation, particularly one with grand ambitions, was a costly enterprise and she asked me if I thought the Miners' Federation could help. Of course, I gave her my absolute promise that I would do what I could and the Federation responded magnificently when I put Eglantyne's request to them. Eglantyne and her sister Dorothy then organised a 'Famine Meeting' at the Royal Albert Hall on May 19th, 1919, and I was able to attend with some good news for her.

That day, inside the hall, the atmosphere was buoyant. Eglantyne was shaking a little because she hated public speaking and there were thousands present, but she made wise use of the guest speakers. There was Henry Noel Brailsford, for example, the well known journalist who described the indescribable rigours of life for children in Berlin and Vienna.

Then I was called on to speak. It had been agreed beforehand that I would propose the resolution which we hoped would stimulate the formation of the organisation which Eglantyne so desperately wanted. Accordingly, I proposed ' ... this meeting urges the necessity of pressing forward every measure of effective relief to meet the appalling conditions of the famine districts, and especially to stay mortality among the children'. Following that, I was able to present a cheque to the value of several thousand pounds from the Miners' Federation which, over the next few years, would donate over £30,000. That day in the Albert Hall the Save the Children Fund was born.

All of this raced through my mind when I opened the telegram that wintry morning in Larkhall. I was astonished by its contents:

UNION INTERNATIONALE DE SECOURS AUX ENFANTS

Mr Smillie,

On behalf of the Executive Committee of the above, we ask you please to do us the honour of accepting a position on our Committee of Honour.

Yours Sincerely,

Gustav Ador
4, Rue Massot,
Genéve
December 28th, 1919

'What on earth do they want me for?' I asked Ann.

'It's simple,' Ann told me. 'You are a good man, Robert Smillie. You always have been and always will be. They want you for your goodness.'

It might have made more sense to me if I had become a member of the British Executive Committee which sat in Golden Square in London, chaired by Lord Weardale. It included people like Percy Alden, Mr Philip Snowden, the Duke of Atholl and the MFGB's very own Frank Hodges, among others. Theirs was a working committee whose task was to get things done. But I wasn't to be a member of that; I was to be a member of the Committee of Honour.

Naturally, I accepted and was proud to do so. I realised that my role would be more representative than practical, but that pleased Ann no end. Given how exhausted I had been, I am sure that she would have dissuaded me from accepting if I was likely to be involved in much extra work. So it was that in January 1920 my name appeared on the Save the Children Committee of Honour list. I had to pinch myself when I realised who the other members were. Statesmen, dignitaries, church leaders, academics and me, wee Bob Smillie from Larkhall. I had never before imagined that I would be in the illustrious company of men like the Crown Prince of Denmark, the Prime Minister of South Africa, the President of Turkey, the former President of France and many others. But I was, and, somewhere in a box under my bed I still have the paperwork to prove it.

So it was that I returned to London, refreshed in health and buoyed in spirit. How long that would last would depend on many factors, many of them beyond my control. I little realised how quickly the harsh realities of the industrial and political worlds would impact on me.

XXVII
Dark Days

THE EVENTS WHICH led up to the disaster which took place on Friday, April 15th, 1921, were so complex that, if I were to attempt to report them all, they would occupy more space than the whole of this memoir. Permit me, therefore, to stick to the most important of the bare facts which, I trust, will be sufficient to convey to you the main reasons for the darkest days in the history of the Miners' Federation. Trouble had been brewing throughout the second half of 1920. As ever, the problem was wages. More specifically, our attempts to ensure a means for proper national regulation of wages. To a degree, Lloyd George was sympathetic as his correspondence with me during September of that year proves. For example, in his letter to me of September 23rd, he commented, ' ... regulation of wages in the coal industry might take a little time to arrange ... proposal of the Government which could be made immediately operative ... ' Being Lloyd George, of course, he made sure that that letter, in which he appeared very conciliatory, reached the press, if not before it reached me, then certainly no later.

One reason why Lloyd George was making apparently friendly noises was his fear of the Triple Alliance. What may have comforted him, had he but known it, was that, even as early as September 23rd 1920, the Alliance was not working as cooperatively as had been intended. At its most recent meeting, there had been a fierce debate which ended with JH Thomas of the railwaymen announcing that the NUR would not come out in support of any miners' strike on the issue of wage regulation. Also, Ben Tillett of the transport workers proposed a delegation to the Government rather than consideration of any strike action. Memories of the Sankey Commission fresh in my mind, with its failure in spite of continuous dialogue, delegations and all the rest of it, I disagreed with Ben Tillett, insisting that we had built an Alliance to show strength not weakness and that, in any event, the miners would press their claim by taking strike action if necessary, with or without the other unions' support. Between the two main days of that Alliance meeting, the Miners' Federation held its own meeting and I reported back to the Alliance on September 24th.

'We were not anxious to plunge the nation and our own men into a strike with all its effects ... some people feel their dignity so keenly that in no circumstances will they allow it to develop. Our Executive found that dignity is alright but there are times when you must set it aside. We decided practically and unanimously to advise our Conference to suspend notices for a week.'

That was about the best I could do in an attempt to hold the Alliance together. We were prepared to defer any ballot on strike action for a brief period to allow the other unions time to consider their positions, but we were making it quite clear that, in our view, there was no great room for further negotiations, so on October 11th and 12th we held a ballot of our members. I advised our Executive that the men must feel able to vote according to the dictates of their own consciences so, on the ballot papers, there was no proposal from the Executive. Rather, there was a statement, 'No recommendation is made. Everyone is left free'. There were also details of the owners' offer which amounted to a wage increase of 1/- a day given certain production totals and other considerations for greatly increased production.

By the time of our next Federation meeting on October 14th, the results of the ballot were to hand. The main figures were as follows:

Total votes recorded	816,526
For the owners' offer	181,428
Against the owners offer	635,098
Majority against offer	453,670

In short, 22% of the men voted to accept the offer on the table, while 78% voted against it. And bear in mind that that result was achieved without a formal recommendation from the Federation Executive.

Lloyd George was fully aware of the result of our ballot. My first duty at the meeting was to read out to delegates the text of the letter I had received from him the previous evening.

Dear Mr Smillie,

It is impossible to conceive of any action more likely to bring about a serious disaster to the trade of this industry, especially when it is recollected that at the present time industry is confronted with great and increasing difficulties, and the prospect of unemployment amongst the masses of our people is causing grave anxiety. Nor is it only in these isles that the injurious effect of your action will be felt. Many struggling people on the Continent of Europe are totally dependent upon the supply of coal which this country gives them.

The Government has exhausted every effort to prevent this calamity. We have suggested to your Federation two possible remedies. In the first place we proposed that your claim to an increase in wages should be referred to a tribunal peculiarly fitted to deal with the matter with complete impartiality, and experience and knowledge of similar questions. It is the means of decision which would most readily recommend itself to civilised communities. Many other of the great Trade Unions of this country have their wages questions settled in this way, and the majority of your brethren of the Triple Alliance resort to such an arrangement for the decision of similar questions which affect them all. It is significant in connection with the present difficulty that some of the most prominent leaders of your Federation favoured this method of settlement, and that their proposals were supported by a very large body of opinion in your delegates' Conference.

In the second place, we put before you a means by which your members could be assured of the increased wage which they ask by giving the country once more the measure of output which the mines yielded in the first quarter of this year. You will readily understand the position of the Government in this matter, because you yourself have acknowledged, on behalf of your Federation, the anxiety which you feel over the declining output of coal. It is very unfortunate that recent increases in wages have been followed almost automatically by a reduction in production.

If this plan had been approved by your members it would at once have benefitted them and the great mass of our people. It would have increased the revenue of the country and lowered the cost of living; it would have provided cargo for our out-going ships and helped pay for the commodities which, as an island people, we must import. I take note of the fact that our suggestion was supported by you and other leaders of great prominence in the Miners' Federation, and the whole country must deplore the fact that your advice has not been followed.

In facing the trial which the decision of your Conference has imposed upon our people, the country will no doubt be fortified in its determination to endure by the fact that the proposals made by its elected Government have received the support of the most responsible and experienced minds of your Federation. Upon our part we have explored, and are still ready to explore, every avenue that might lead to a peaceful solution of this difficulty. I can only express my profound regret that proposals which all must regard as supremely reasonable have received a final rejection at the hands of your Conference.

Yours faithfully
D. Lloyd George

It was a clever letter, naturally enough. I would have expected no less of the man. And he was right to point out that not all members of our Executive were keen on pushing for strike action. The truth was that none of us wished to move in that direction but we felt we had little choice. In truth, throughout that period, true to my principles, I had wished to give dialogue every chance. Briefly, during an exchange of letters with Lloyd George, I had thought there was promise of progress. However, his later letters and the increasing anger of our members persuaded me that only action, nor mere words, could bring us any success. It was an opinion which I reached very reluctantly. Moreover, we had learned the bitter lessons of the Sankey Commission. Besides, those on our Executive who had spoken against strike action had been silenced, temporarily at least, by the overwhelming vote of the men. I told the delegates that, in my opinion, Lloyd George's clever letter took us no further forward, and opened the meeting to debate.

I believe that, for the first time in my life, I changed my mind over something very important in the course of one short hour. The reason for that was the atmosphere in the debate. I was used enough to lively argument. That is healthy. But what I was listening to was not healthy at all. I may have been wrong, may God forgive me if I was, but as well as the usual heat and anger, I thought I detected fear. In spite of the fact that most of them saw Lloyd George's letter as a piece of 'clever politics', they were alarmed by the fact that he gave every impression of being in command of the situation and I believed that they were worried about what counter-measures he might employ against us. This particularly alarmed them because of the fragile unity in the Triple Alliance, there being no indication that the railwaymen and transport men were prepared to support us in the event of a strike. For an hour or so, I listened with mounting alarm to the developing debate.

In most debates, there are two opposing sides, those who are for something and those who are against it. That day, though, the debate I heard was nothing like that. Franks Hodges did more speaking than anybody else. There was much that I admired about Frank, and we had been colleagues for a very long time, but I never found that clear-mindedness was one of his major qualities. What he had to say that day bore out my opinion. It was hard to discover what his consistent view was. He preached against giving in to the Government. Then he warned about the unreliability of the Triple Alliance. He made further comments about the need for strength, yet warned about taking on forces who might defeat us. Other contributors joined in, normally solid men like Herbert Smith and Levi Lovett. They were calmer than Frank, but suddenly it seemed as if there were as many opinions as there were men present.

It was time for clear leadership. To my horror, I could not think of any way of providing it. I could see no way of reconciling the differences, certainly not of removing the fears which were provoking those differences. Lloyd George was beyond my control. So too was the reluctance of the railwaymen and transport workers to support us. It seemed to me that we were at the mercy of forces over which we had little influence. Not only that but, for nine years now, I had been President of the Federation. By and large, under my presidency we had stuck together. There had been differences, of course. Which organisation does not have those? But we had overcome them and shown our collective strength. Now, so soon after the huge disappointment of the Sankey Commission in which what was largely my strategy had not brought about the desired outcomes, our senior men were as disunited as I had ever seen them. Suddenly it came to me. There was only one thing I could do. I called for silence, then made an announcement:

'In this dispute you will have enough to face without carrying about with you a Jonah in the shape of your President ... I don't think I can be of service to the Federation any longer. I have reluctantly come to that conclusion. The recommendations I have made have been turned down by the men, which they have a right to turn down; that is their business. But I feel now as strongly as I have done at any time that was the way out of the difficulty, either one method or the other; and holding that view, as I do, I don't think that the Federation can afford to carry me with them in this dispute – this life and death struggle that we are about to enter.'

I added that Frank Hodges and I had an honest difference of opinion on the whole matter. I could have said that it was difficult to be quite sure what Frank's opinion was, but refrained. I concluded by saying that the Federation had to be led towards harmony, and I did not feel that I was able to do so. I fancied that I saw Frank Hodges smirking at that point, but I ignored it. I finished by saying, 'Therefore, gentlemen, I sincerely hope that you will relieve me from the position of Presidency of the Miners' Federation.' When I sat down, there was only what I can describe as a shocked silence.

In one way, I had misjudged the mood of my colleagues. It turned out that, in spite of the vast range of opinions they had just been offering, they were as mindful as I was of the need for unity, particularly given the difficult situation we were facing. One by one, they rose to their feet to respond to my offer of resignation. Herbert Smith, our Vice-President, was first.

'Well, gentlemen, this is a thunderbolt to everybody here ... I want Bob Smillie to be in his place here. We want him to be in this fight with us. We have got to fight, and we shall want all the brains and all the help we can get to come through successfully. I have been in plenty of scraps, and have come through them. I was opposed to this strike, but I shall be in it with the rest of you. I appeal here on behalf of this Conference and on behalf of the men in the districts for you to withdraw and say: Herbert, I will join hands with you and stick to you through this fight and fight it through.'

He was quickly followed by Levi Lovett and Tom Richards. Even Frank Hodges said a few words: 'If Mr Smillie should resign now, you would find a parallel in the 181,000 men who voted against a strike continuing to work, whilst the others were on strike.' Hardly gracious, even suggesting that to withdraw from a struggle was cowardly, but that he didn't want me to resign was clear enough. I suspect that Frank had merely judged the mood of the others! Then GH Jones of the Midland miners got to his feet:

'I must say, from a boy, I have looked upon Robert Smillie as a kind of hero, and there is a great deal of hero worship in our coalfields, even though our men were opposed to this datum line ... I think it will be a disaster if he goes out of the movement at this time. The Press would make a great deal of it, and therefore I trust you will reconsider your position.'

I have to confess that, by this stage, I was almost in tears. How often does a man hear so many endorsements, some of them from unexpected quarters? More men got up and spoke in broadly similar terms, and I found myself wavering. Perhaps it was when our treasurer, James Robson, spoke that the issue became clearer in my mind. James was never known as a sentimental man and his statement that morning bore his usual hallmarks of directness and common sense:

'If we are to win now it will only be by unity, and set aside all opinions, or else the consequences will be disastrous amongst either officials or local men. The Press is waiting for this; they have tried to create divisions amongst us. Why, this morning I believe that the letter from the Prime Minister was intentionally written to create division in our ranks, in seeking to apportion blame ...

'What will be the effect on thousands of people in the North of England and Scotland when they read in the press that the President has resigned? That, I think, makes the thing hopeless at the start. I do not think it ought to be raised at this stage, at this crisis, and I do hope he will not at this stage take this step, because, when this thing is over, there will be plenty of time to consider the position, and if he feels it is wise for him to take this course, that is a matter for himself, and at a time when he will be better able to judge the whole situation than he can at the present time.'

Well, I was in a real fix, wasn't I? Half-an-hour earlier, I had been convinced that the best thing I could do would be to resign and allow the appointment of a new president who might, by some means or another, manage to unify opinion. Now, I was being told that I was the man to do just that. I had my doubts, but what could I do? If you like, the meeting had spoken. Feeling much more emotional that I usually did, I got to my feet once more to address the meeting.

'I am sure you feel that I don't desire to injure this movement ... I am more convinced than ever of the justice of the men's claim. I wanted an opportunity of being able to prove it by others means. Evidently these other means are impossible. I recognised when I read this letter the prime minister was again making capital out of the advice some of us conscientiously gave to the men.

'Now, I am not so strong as I was in the last big fight we had, but I hope I still have some energy left. Well, for what it is worth, that energy will be given to our movement. We as individuals are of very little account side by side with the great movement. My dream has been to endeavour, slowly as it may be, but surely, to improve the conditions of the men, women and children connected with the mining industry, to improve their home life and raise them especially in their own estimation rather than in the estimation of other people. We are only at the beginning even now, and whether we are defeated or successful in this fight, that will have to go on.'

So it was that within half-an-hour, I had demanded that the meeting accept my resignation, then was forced into withdrawing my demand. I was not at all sure that I had done the right thing. What could I do in the future any differently to those things that I had done in the past to ensure that the Federation remained united and strong? I really had no answer to that question. Not only that but I was now sixty-three years old and no longer had the stamina I once had. Perhaps I no longer had the same vision either.

The strike began on October 16th. It was known as the Datum Line Strike because we were desperately trying to loosen the highly rigid position of the owners' proposals which linked meagre increases in wages to significant increases in production. Five days into the strike, Lloyd George called for negotiations but showed no inclination to suggest that the owners should make any concessions.

On the same day, October 21st, we received two important letters. The first was from CT Crump, on behalf of the railwaymen. It concluded with the words: ' ... unless the miners' claims are granted or negotiations resumed by October 23rd, which result in a settlement, we shall be compelled to take the necessary steps to instruct our members in England, Scotland and Wales to cease work.'

The second letter was from the prime minister and made the following offer: 'I should be glad to meet your office bearers or such representatives of your Executive as they might select, for the purpose of making an attempt to arrive at a basis of settlement ... over the weekend ... if that is convenient to you.' Clearly the conciliatory tone of his letter meant that Lloyd George had had a copy of CT Crump's letter and was fearful that the Triple Alliance might show its teeth at last. Just to show that he was as wily as ever, he also pushed through the House of Commons the Emergency Powers Bill which would have serious consequences a little later.

We met Lloyd George on five successive days, from October 24th to October 28th. After a lot of hard bargaining on both sides, he offered the following proposals:

an immediate increase of 2/- per shift
scaled increases for additional output
the setting up of a National Wage Board
guaranteed coal export prices

As an Executive Committee, we met immediately, but there was no agreement about whether or not to accept Lloyd George's proposals. As a matter of record, the decision was taken to recommend acceptance as an interim step on my casting vote. This was hardly the unity which I desired! Following a ballot of the men, it transpired that, in a total vote of 685,000 men, there was a majority of 8,459 against accepting the proposals. This was desperate stuff. The men had rejected the Committee's advice, albeit by a very small margin. It seemed to me that there was a real risk of fragmentation of our membership. I had to show leadership and I did so by referring back to our rulebook. It was clear that continuation of a strike had to be supported by at least two-thirds of those eligible to vote. Nothing like that proportion had done so and I moved that that rule had to be adhered to. There were strong murmurings at this but when we moved to a vote 121 delegates supported the rule while 46 voted to break it.

The next day, the men returned to work having gained some concessions but less than we had wanted. Most important to me at the time was that we had managed to keep the Federation together, for the time being at least. Had we pressed on with the strike, with only a tiny majority in favour of doing so, I believed that we would have caused much fragmentation within the Federation. So, the Datum Line Strike was ended but I was certain that further trials were around the corner. Again, I was finding sleep hard to come by.

The news, when it came, was no bombshell. We had been expecting it. But, rather like the death of a lingering loved one, it still had a powerful effect. A letter arrived for me on January 1st 1921, inviting a delegation to the offices of the Board of Trade. Its president wanted to discuss 'questions affecting the coal-mining industry'. We knew exactly what that meant. Removing the controls introduced in wartime and wholly returning the entire industry to private ownership, thereby eliminating any Government influence on all related matters. I wrote back agreeing to attend but advocating our view that 'we cannot acquiesce in any proposal for the decontrol of the coal trade until the coal owners and ourselves are able to present to the Government a jointly agreed plan for the national control of the industry which will effectively substitute the present arrangements'.

At the meeting on January 13th, Sir Robert Horne told us that he had considered my letter but, for a variety of reasons ' ... The Government therefore proposes to decontrol prices and distribution entirely on the 1st March, but to keep on with the pooling of profits for some time longer, say, to take a date at random, until 30th June, 1921. By that time it is hoped that the two parties in the industry would have come to their conclusions on the point'.

There was no moving him. The decision had been made. This was not a simple question of ownership. That had never passed from private hands. Rather it was about the setting of prices and regulations regarding the distribution, in which areas the profits are made. The Government had controlled these areas under the auspices of the Coal Controller for some four years and were now returning those powers to private hands. This meant that all matters relating to the mining industry, including employment, wages and safety would once again be in the hands of those men with whom we had fought so many battles in the past. Further, having decontrolled the industry, the Government would no longer be in a position to act as a broker between the owners and the Federation in times of industrial difficulties.

We wrote again to Sir Robert, pressing our case for the need to have agreement between the owners and ourselves before the decontrol order was issued. But, at a meeting with him on February 23rd, he told me, 'I have to announce to you in private conference ... that the Government has decided ... to decontrol the coal trade absolutely as at the 31st March.' I told him how appalled I was. Decontrol would mean a savage cut in wages and an attack on the living standards of miners and their families. I believe that he was sympathetic but his hands were tied by decisions taken at a higher level. I pressed on with my arguments, which were minuted by both sides:

Mr Robert Smillie: I suppose we may take it that the passing of the control, if it passes at the 31st March, means that the Government have no further responsibility in connection with wages or in connection with the profits of the employers.

Sir Robert Horne: That would be so.

Mr Robert Smillie: I think you are aware that the employers' view of the matter is that that would be a breach of a pledge given to them when the Act was passed.

Sir Robert Horne: So they have informed me; but I have done my best to disabuse them of that view.

Mr Robert Smillie: Well, we are of the opinion that it is a breach of an understanding so far as we understood the position. We recognised that you could give up control of prices, but we felt that you could not give up control of the industry so far as the national pool was concerned until the end of August ... we were strongly against that. I do not see how the Government can wipe their hands of the responsibility for the position in which the trade is now. They took upon themselves, rightly or wrongly – I think rightly – to regulate the prices of coal, the distribution of coal, and indeed largely the output of coal. They felt that it was necessary in the interests of the nation that that should be done. During the war it could not be left in the hands of private individuals who might put their own interests before the national interest. Consequently the Government took the responsibility of directing the coal trade in every direction. Well, I do not think the Government can fairly merely wash their hands of that now and hand back the coal trade into the old channels that it was prior to the war.

I notice that you are urged by the employers, before you rid the Government of the pool and of the control of the mines – a request has been made to you publicly, if not privately – to reduce wages and to bring wages down to the point which would make the coal trade on an economic footing – that economic footing meaning that the rate of wages would be reduced down to the point that would enable any colliery that continued to meet its liabilities in wages and cost of production. You have instanced a colliery to us that was going on at a loss of 53s. per ton.

Sir Robert Horne: Yes.

Mr Robert Smillie: It is perfectly plain that supposing they had been paying no wages at all, they would not go on.

Sir Robert Horne: No.

Mr Robert Smillie: So that we are in the position that wages might be taken away altogether if the coal trade is to be carried on and the colliery is to continue, but that perhaps is an extreme case.

Sir Robert Horne: A very extreme case; a very exceptional case, of course. I gave it as the most extreme example I could think if. It was a pit which was resuscitated during the war because of a lack of coal. A pit like that cannot continue it is quite obvious under present circumstances.

Mr Robert Smillie: The coal trade should be treated as a whole. Very often collieries are carried on under these conditions: that certain districts of a mine are clearly not paying, and cannot pay, their way, and other districts of that mine have to make up for the poor districts in the mine. That is an everyday occurrence in collieries in every part of the country. It cannot be conceived that every district of every mine is at all times paying, neither is it possible to conceive that at all times every colliery shall be paying.

Your remedy, if decontrol takes place, is that all collieries which are not paying would have to shut down because, after all, behind all this is the inevitability of reducing wages. I have never heard yet of any attempt being made to bring down the cost of stores or the hundred and one things that go to make up the price of the coal. All this is aiming at very substantial reductions in wages. If the mines are to go on producing coal, the miners will have to get a livelihood.

Sir Robert Horne: That is so.

Mr Robert Smillie: I think you have admitted more than once that the first claim on the price per ton of coal ought to be reasonable wages to the person who produces that coal. I know that in your inmost souls you and your colleagues are aiming at either getting rid of this industry or the responsibility for this industry in order that the colliery owners may begin to reduce wages so that you yourselves would not be forced to take that line. We cannot agree with you that the coal industry should be decontrolled and that the national pool should be abolished. We will not, if we can avoid it, I assure you, see the wages of the miners in one district of this country being reduced down to the starvation point or below starvation, while miners in other parts of the country more favourably situated are receiving fair remuneration for their labour.

He was a decent man, Sir Robert, and I could tell that he was uncomfortable with our conversation. That didn't stop him playing the old political game of trying to destroy a case by reference to exceptional cases, of course, nor from arguing the Government's position as strongly as possible. By the end, we both knew that we were not achieving anything and, when we shook hands, there was sadness on both sides.

Next day, our Federation vowed to oppose the decontrol orders which we saw as 'prejudicial to the interest both of the coal trade and the nation generally'. Though I wholly agreed with this, in my heart of hearts I could not see how we could offer effective opposition short of strike action which would have played into the Government's hands. They would have publicised it as clear evidence that we were unfit to play any part in the industry, other than hewing coal.

You may be surprised to know that the owners were not wholly satisfied with the Government either, though for different reasons. Looking after their own interests and conscious that members of the Government were their friends, they felt that a huge surplus of profits (wrung from the European consumer by fabulously high export prices and taken over by the Chancellor of the Exchequer) ought to have been used, in part at any rate, to provide more and better profits to the coal owners. They were not wrong in their belief that the Government were their friends. Their complaint was met and satisfied. The Government 'compensated' the coal owners by paying the full standard profit up to the end of 1920 and nine-tenths of that up to the end of the first quarter of 1921. With this the owners, but not without some grumbling, withdrew their opposition. There was no question raised by them of 'compensation' for the miners.

The Government, having reached agreement with the owners, could now go full speed ahead, or rather full speed astern. The legislative measure for decontrol, mentioned in the King's Speech in mid-February, took shape three weeks later as a Bill which passed through all its stages in the House of Commons in the second week of March. The Royal Assent was given on March 24th and it became the Coal Mines (Decontrol) Act. Chaos was let loose in the mining industry and the mining community was burdened with all the evil consequences.

On the night of February 23rd, 1921, I sat alone in my hotel room in the Imperial Hotel and considered the wreckage of the negotiations with the Government. Could I have handled it differently? What else could I have done that could have produced a better outcome for us? I honestly could not think of anything. That conclusion forced me to a bitter truth. Which was that a man who cannot see a way forward in a difficult situation should step aside and allow somebody else to do so. On hotel stationery, I wrote a letter of resignation in such clear terms as to prohibit anybody from even considering trying to dissuade me.

Next morning, I rose early, packed my bag and made my way to Russell Square before other Committee members arrived. I handed in the letter, addressed to Herbert Smith, then caught the first train north. It was over.

XXVIII
A Battle Lost

I FIND IT difficult – perhaps impossible would be a better word – to describe how I felt on the train journey back to Scotland. I'm tempted to say that I felt happy because the problems of dealing with the Federation's opponents would in future be somebody else's responsibility, but that wouldn't be the right word. I didn't feel unhappy either at the realisation that I'd relinquished a position which had mattered a great deal to me for the past nine years. You might imagine that I was feeling relaxed at having removed from my shoulders the weighty burden of leadership, but that wouldn't be entirely true. On that journey home, my thoughts turned often to what the Federation might do next and what would happen to my extended family, the mining community. As I gave thought to such issues, even though I knew I would no longer be responsible for such matters, I still felt just as immersed in them and felt the same level of anxiety as if I was still directly involved. So, I hardly felt relaxed.

I suppose that if I was to apply just one word to what I was feeling, that word would be relief. A great burden of responsibility, one that had been weighing particularly heavily on me over the past three years, had been lifted. I knew that I would never distance myself from the great causes of the Labour Movement, but I realised with no little satisfaction that I would no longer be caught in the whirlwind that is industrial politics. I had been heavily involved in such matters for over forty years and, quite frankly, been drained by them. It would be a relief to stand back a little, draw breath, give myself time to rest and think, and perhaps lead a life with more ordinary challenges, the kind of life which most folk take for granted.

You will no doubt think that I was losing my mind at what I say now. You must judge that for yourself. Whatever, on that train journey I deliberately evoked a conversation with my late friend, Keir Hardie. How I had missed that wise and caring man over the past six years. There had been so many occasions when I had wished that I could have turned to him just once more to hear his wise counsel and relish the warmth of his companionship. If ever a cause really missed a man, the Labour Movement missed Keir Hardie. Perhaps I had missed him most of all. Not only had he been a great friend but, to a large extent, he had been my mentor and guide, my inspiration. Which may explain to you why at one stage of that train journey – I imagined that he was still with me and offering his advice.

'Well, Bob, you've travelled a right long road.'

'With perhaps a bit too much traffic on it recently,' I suggested, then I laughed. 'I think I got run over a few times.'

'Aye, but you got yourself up and carried on, didn't you?'

'I suppose I did,' I agreed. 'But did I carry on in the right direction?'

'History will judge that, though if I were you I'd wait till one of our fellows writes it before paying any attention to it.'

'But did I do enough, Keir?' I asked my ghost.

'No man could have done any more. Why, look at yourself, Bob. You're as tired of things as any man could be without being dead.'

'Aye, you're right,' I told him. 'As usual. But what now, Keir? In spite of appearances to the contrary, I'm not quite dead yet. Is there anything more I can do?'

'The first thing you have to do is get yourself home to that lovely wife of yours. Open your heart to Ann. Once you've done that, your future path will become clearer. Oh, and just one more thing.'

'What's that, old friend?'

'You've still never won a seat in Parliament, you useless bugger!'

I was still laughing at that when the Inspector came round and asked to see my ticket. Whatever you may think of my imaginary conversation with my late friend, that inspector gave me a look which clearly suggested that he believed himself to be in the presence of a madman!

Because I had caught the first train available, I reached my home in Larkhall before news of my resignation did. As soon as I was inside the door, I told Ann of my decision. She took the news in her usual calm manner. She just said, 'Oh, aye?,' then sat me down in my usual chair beside the pipe rack and bustled about in the scullery making a meal. It wasn't until we had finished eating – and my appetite had suddenly grown after weeks of picking at hotel food – that we discussed what I'd done. Even then, it wasn't a particularly long conversation.

'You're settled on it then, Robert?'

'I am, Ann.'

'Well, I'm glad to hear it.' She gave me one of her wonderful smiles. 'You've done everything a man could have done. More than anybody else, in my opinion. You have always put other people before yourself. You deserve a rest and the chance to think of yourself for a change. I'm proud of you. We all are.'

How I loved that woman! She could easily have said that I had put the cause before my own family, which to a great extent I had, but she never once accused me of that. It was wonderful to be home again, to be able to look forward to spending more time with her and our friends, and to be closer to our children. The only thing was that, with a wee smile, she positively forbade me from promising that I would never again spend time away from home, which I had been about to say. You see, like the imaginary voice of Keir Hardie, she knew me better than I knew myself and she realised that, one way or another, I would wish to continue serving the cause.

Over the next few weeks, I was frankly embarrassed by the number of people who sought me out to thank me for the work I had done on behalf of the miners over the years. Though I had never enjoyed criticism any more than anybody else, I had always felt uncomfortable in the face of great praise. But there was no escaping it. In the town, out on walks, watching the cricket, people would demand to shake my hand, thank me and wish me well. The knocker on our door never stopped chapping and, though I was human enough to feel a sense of pride at the tributes, I quickly began to wish that the fuss would die down. There were times when it felt like I was attending my own funeral and listening to the obituaries.

My good friend Herbert Smith wrote to me from Russell Square, the Federation headquarters. In addition to keeping me abreast of the news, which largely consisted of Frank Hodges picking up the gauntlet and trying with little success to press the miners' case on the Government, he was also kind enough to include extracts from the Federation meeting held shortly after the receipt of my letter of resignation. I was embarrassed to read some of the tributes paid to me. The one which struck me most forcibly, and almost moved me to tears, was the one given by George Barker MP. It was no secret that George and I, though we got on well enough, were quite often at loggerheads over union policy. He had been one of those who had believed that I was too obsessed with democracy and due process when I led the Federation into the Sankey Commission. He had been in favour of more direct action which had been a frequent theme of his during my presidency. That fact was why I was more moved than I might otherwise have been by his kind words:

We have come evidently to the end of the career of one of the greatest men that this Federation has ever produced. This letter of Mr. Smillie's will not only have significance for this Federation, but it will have significance for the whole of the Labour World. I have differed with Smillie many times, but there is no man living that has a greater admiration for his character and for his pugnacity than I have. I shall always remember him as one of the greatest workers who has ever fought the cause of the down-trodden and oppressed. I shall always remember Smillie fighting election after election in the greatest interest of the workers of this country. After being counted out one, two three, four, five, six and seven times, he still came up to fight for the workers.

I shall always remember him in the Sankey Commission when he was voicing the needs, and the distress, and the lack of houses for the workers of the country. It is in that light that I shall always remember Bob Smillie. I look upon him as a man who gave of his best to the movement, and now he recognises that the time has come when his physical powers are waning; he thinks he can render greater service by vacating the position and giving way for some younger man. I think that this Conference will be cruel to attempt to lash Smillie into any further effort after resigning, which we have had one, two, or three times from his hands. I shall always look upon him with the greatest reverence and regard, and I hope that this Federation will pay some tribute of a substantial character on his leaving the movement.

Herbert wrote that those words were greeted by a great ovation, followed by more words of a similar tenor from other Committee members. It was no great surprise to me that Frank Hodges did not speak. The meeting then passed the following resolution:

That we accept Mr. Smillie's resignation with regret, and thank him for his long and valuable services to the Miners' Federation of Great Britain, and trust that he will be spared for many years to serve as best he can and as his health will permit the great Labour Movement in general and the miners' cause in particular.

Herbert's letter concluded with him promising to keep me informed of events in the wrangle with the Government. He made the point that I would no doubt read about it in the newspapers but from that source was only likely to hear of things from one point of view and that would not be the miners. He was entirely right of course. I wrote back to Herbert to express my great gratitude to him. He knew me very well, of course, and realised that, though I was now 'out of the game', I would still be a more than interested spectator from the sidelines.

There was one more tribute to come and I suspect that Ann was heavily involved in it, though she never said and I never asked. On a Sunday a few weeks after I got home, we attended morning service, then took our usual walk. Ann suggested that we should visit the Miners' Hall because, so she claimed, a Mrs somebody-or-other would be there and she wanted to have a word with her. As some time had passed since my homecoming and I had fewer fears of being accosted by well-wishers, I agreed readily enough and we were soon inside, shutting the doors behind us. At which point, a huge cheer went up and I do believe that my jaw dropped in amazement. I had never seen our hall so full. It seemed as if the world and his wife were present. Well, all of Larkhall, at any rate. Particularly precious to me is the fact that most of my children, and many of my grandchildren, had journeyed to Larkhall to attend. As I suggested, I suspected Ann's role in all of this, but why would I complain about that?

The miners and their families, as well as many folk from other walks of life in Larkhall, had decided to honour me with a luncheon. As far as I know, that was the first occasion on which somebody had been honoured in this way. Thankfully, it was not a formal affair. There was a great deal of laughter as we ate, following which there was community singing as the smallest of the bairns played around the legs of the tables. Inevitably, there were some speeches. I grew red in the face such was my embarrassment at the laudatory nature of some of them.

Of course, I was expected to respond and was delighted to do so, even though I was totally unprepared. I do not recall exactly what I said though I spoke for several minutes about the problems facing the Federation, and exhorted the miners present to stick together in the face of whatever the future might hold. But I used more words in praise of my family, no doubt embarrassing them thoroughly in the process, offering to them my sincere thanks for their support and understanding. I reserved particular words of thanks for Ann who had tolerated my nomadic lifestyle without complaint and to whom I owed so much. The serious business over, we had another sing-song then concluded with a wee dancing session. I thoroughly enjoyed myself and felt a great debt of gratitude to everybody who organised the event and turned up to wish me well.

The news from London was bad, and would only get worse. Through letters, telegrams and the occasional pre-arranged telephone call, Herbert Smith kept to his word and let me know what was going on. On March 31st, 1921, the Government gave up control of the mines. The next day, a million miners were idle, locked out. The Emergency Powers Act was invoked by a proclamation issued in the name of the king. Troops were moved into the coalfields and on April 5th the War Office cancelled all leave and brought some troops back from Ireland where they had been engaged against De Valera's nationalists. I read all this with mounting concern. In Larkhall, as elsewhere, I saw the evidence of those things with my own eyes and loathed them. It was clear to me that Lloyd George was sending out a clear message, that the miners were dangerous agitators and could not be trusted. Otherwise, why send the troops in?

Meanwhile, while he demonstrated his iron fist, Lloyd George began a series of correspondence with the MFGB, urging them to come to the negotiating table, Frank Hodges replied several times on behalf of the Federation, and quite rightly took exception to Lloyd George's assertion that the miners were endangering the lives of pit ponies. However, he went on to say that the Federation would be willing to meet the prime minister 'with a view to arriving at an honourable settlement'.

When Lloyd George wrote back yet again on April 6th, he about-turned and said that, as the miners were not prepared to undertake pumping and other safety work while on strike, he was unwilling to talk to them. At 8pm that very day in the House of Commons, he announced that it was 'quite impossible to have negotiations whilst the mines are gradually crumbling owing to the difficulties of them being flooded'. He conveniently forgot that it was his decontrol of the mines which had allowed the owners to drastically reduce wages and provoke a strike, that it was he who had placed troops on the streets, and that it was he who had set conditions which had proved a barrier to continuing negotiations. He was, after all, a politician!

Amazingly enough, Lloyd George then entered into further correspondence with Frank Hodges as though his announcement in the House had never been made. The main reason for this was his fear that the Triple Alliance's constitution would come to the aid of the miners. He suspected that the transport workers under JH Thomas would prefer to negotiate rather than strike but he could not be certain of that. Hence the resumption of correspondence.

In all of this, I sensed the Lloyd George of old. As cunning as a fox, but just as unreliable; as wise as they came, but untrustworthy. And I strongly believed that any belief he had that the Triple Alliance would come to the rescue of the miners was sorely misplaced. When Herbert Smith phoned in great excitement to tell me that the railwaymen and transport workers were planning a great demonstration of solidarity with the miners on April 15th, I tried to conceal my doubts from my good friend. It was no great surprise to me to learn that the so-called solidarity was anything but solid. On the very day that the other unions were supposed to come out in support of the miners, the following decision, arrived at by the other two sections of the Triple Industrial Alliance, was delivered to the Miners' Federation by telegram:

Dear Mr Hodges,

The Sub-Committee which waited upon the Miners' Federation Executive this afternoon reported the result of their interview to the Executive of the National Union of Railwaymen, the Associated Society of Locomotive Engineers and Firemen, and the Transport Workers' Federation. After serious consideration of the whole position, they passed the following resolution:

'This joint meeting of the N.U.R., the A.S.L.E. & F. and T.W.F., having very carefully considered the latest situation in connection with the miners' dispute, decides to call off the strike.'

Yours faithfully,
C.T. Crump

Stabbed in the back by fellow workers! This was dire news indeed. Surely it was the darkest day in trade-union history. Small wonder that it became known as 'Black Friday'. I could only wonder how men like Frank Hodges and Herbert Smith must be feeling. Even at a distance, and no longer involved, I felt the pain of that day very sharply indeed. Either later that day or the next – I cannot quite remember which – I was at the Larkhall Branch for one of my pre-arranged telephone conversations with Herbert Smith. You will not be surprised to know that he was in a very sombre mood. Frank Hodges had offered his resignation, which had been turned down, and given a unanimous vote of confidence by the Executive. Herbert thought it likely that the miners would continue the struggle on their own and asked me to do what I could locally to bolster the spirits of the men.

When I walked around Larkhall talking to the miners, I found them in a resolute mood. Very few were for backing down; the vast majority felt that the Federation was in the right. There should be no temporary settlement of the wages question without the Government's acceptance of a National Wages Board and a National Pool of Profits. As far as the railwaymen and transport workers were concerned, I heard very little bitterness expressed against them, only a feeling of resigned disappointment. I reported as much back to Herbert Smith.

It was very obvious to me at that point that the whole situation had now become an endurance test. Left alone, our men were not prepared to back down and the Government, re-issuing the Royal Proclamation of Emergency, were clearly unprepared to do so either. Sir Robert Horne chaired several meetings with the Federation, but no progress was made. Then, as things dragged on through May, Lloyd George made it known through the press that the Government was prepared to make a new offer. Even four hundred miles away in Larkhall, I recognised his usual tactic of attracting public sympathy for his position by issuing a misleading statement through friendly newspaper editors. And the statement was misleading. There was nothing new in the allegedly new offer at all, except a proposal for arbitration in the event of a dispute.

The Federation did exactly the right thing. All districts were contacted and asked if, in light of this 'new' offer, they wished to suspend the strike and enter renewed negotiations. By June 3rd, every district had replied and not one of them accepted the offer. If Lanarkshire was any guide, feelings were still running high. I visited most of the collieries during that period and found little evidence of a desire to back down.

Then the coal owners became involved. They sent a letter to the Federation:

Pall Mall, S.W.1
June 5th, 1921

Dear Mr. Hodges,
The letter of the Prime Minister to you, which is published in this morning's papers, by putting a time limit upon the Government's proposal of a grant, introduces a factor into the situation which, in my opinion, the coal owners cannot ignore.
The offer of the Government to provide a sum of £10,000,000 as a subvention to wages, to tide over a difficult period, while it does not financially affect the coal owners in any way, is to the workers in the industry of immense value, which we are most desirous they should not lose; and I feel that if any elucidation of the position can be brought about by a conference between your Executive and our Central Committee,

we, on our side, should not allow any formal considerations to stand in the way of our taking a step which may perhaps be easier for us than for you.

I have therefore called a meeting of the Central Committee of the Mining Association for 10:30 tomorrow (Monday) morning, at which I shall propose that an invitation be sent to your Executive Committee to meet us to talk the matter over.

I remain, yours sincerely, EVAN WILLIAMS

The Executive accepted the owners' invitation and spent several days in negotiation with them. Then, following their own meeting on June 10th, they decided to ballot their members. The ballot paper was as follows:

MINERS' FEDERATION OF GREAT BRITAIN BALLOT PAPER

Are you in favour of fighting on for the principles of the National Wages Board and National Pool, with loss of Government subsidy of ten million pounds for wages if no settlement by June 18th, 1921?

Are you in favour of accepting the Government and owners' terms as set forth on the back of this ballot paper?

Please place your 'X' in the space provided for the purpose.

June 10th, 1921
Frank Hodges, General Secretary

[BACK OF BALLOT PAPER]
Note – The Government and owners, having definitely rejected the principles of the National Wages Board and the National Pool, now offer the terms fully set out below. You are now asked to say whether you will continue to fight for the National Wages Board and the National Pool, or accept the terms offered by the Government and owners. The Government offer of ten million pounds grant in aid of wages referred to below is to be withdrawn on June 18th unless an agreement is arrived at by that date.
TEMPORARY PERIOD
Government offers ten million pounds to prevent large reductions in wages where reductions are necessary.

First reductions not to exceed 2s. per shift for all workers of 16 years and upwards, and 1s. per shift for workers below 16 years.

No further reductions until August 1st.

Further reduction after August 1st to be agreed mutually until Government grant is exhausted.

The temporary agreement will come to an end as soon as the Government grant is used up.

PERMANENT SCHEME
Owners' Proposals

National Board to fix principles for guidance of districts. Board to be comprised of equal number of representative of both sides with independent chairman.

The parties have already agreed the principle that profits shall only be a fixed percentage of wages paid.

The Board to fix the amount of the percentage of profits to wages.

The Board to fix the amount of the new standard wage.

In this connection the owners have offered as a standard wage the total wages paid in July, 1914, plus district additions to standard, plus the percentage for piece-workers caused by the reduction of hours from 8 to 7, and a minimum percentage of 20 per cent added thereto. This minimum percentage to continue until June 30th, 1922.

The Board will also fix the items of cost, which must be taken into account by the district auditors when ascertaining the district revenue.

Wages during permanent scheme to be based upon the capacity of each district to pay.

In the event of a low paid day-worker receiving a wage which does not provide him with a subsistence wage, the District Board will fix a wage which will secure it for that workman.

The decision of the National Board as to the permanent scheme to be binding upon both parties for a period of twelve months and thereafter subject to three months' notice period on either side.

You should note that, as had happened several times in my day, the Executive did not recommend a particular course of action. They wanted the men to feel free to express their opinion. I entirely approved of that as the best way to ensure genuine democracy. In spite of which, the men decided by 435,000 votes to 181,000 to reject the terms of both the coal owners and the Government. This was after ten weeks of the lock-out when miners' families were running short of food and often had to rely on communal soup kitchens set up locally. I witnessed for myself the onset of hunger in and around Larkhall.

By then I believed that there could be only one outcome to this struggle. On one side were the miners, lacking money and food. On the other side was the might of the Government and the owners, backed up by the Emergency Powers Act, troops and the bulk of the press. Not only that but I suspect that, under the great pressures they were facing, divisions were beginning to appear inside the Executive Committee. Within that group there were men with very different experiences and political opinions. Alongside old warhorses like Tom Whitefield and Sam Finney, there were young bloods like Noah Ablett and Arthur Cook. In his communication with me, Herbert Smith hinted at the emergence of differing views about a way out of the situation.

In my opinion, Lloyd George sensed this and wrote again:

10 Downing Street
Whitehall, S.W.1
18th June, 1921.

Dear Mr. Hodges,

I very much regret to receive the information conveyed to me by your letter of last night.

It is a very grave step for the Miners' Federation to continue a stoppage which is bringing untold loss upon the country.

I previously indicated to you that the longer the stoppage continues the greater the loss to the resources of the Exchequer, and consequently the less able we are to give assistance to tide the mining industry over its present troubles. We were, therefore, compelled to announce a fortnight ago that our offer of ten millions would terminate this week-end.

The difficulties of the financial position can only be emphasised if the result of the ballot now communicated to me is to receive effect. Under these circumstances the Government have no option but to make final their decision that their offer of assistance cannot remain open after tomorrow night.

Yours faithfully
D. Lloyd George

The Executive contacted many other unions which had also threatened to take strike action but now no longer seemed willing to do so. Now the miners were truly between a rock and a hard place. I felt heartsore for them. So the Executive asked for a meeting with the Government and the owners 'with a view to negotiating a satisfactory wage agreement, which we can recommend our members to accept'. They knew that, even if they were to achieve some kind of concession on wages, that would fall way short of the demands for a National Wage Board and a National Pool of profits, the rejection of which had been the major cause of the dispute in the first place. But I, for one, could see no other direction they could take.

At the Board of Trade, the meeting duly took place. I was led to believe that it was a lengthy, often hostile meeting in which the owners were unprepared to make much in the way of concessions. In reality, all that was on the table for the miners was the Government's guarantee of £10,000,000 towards miners' wages to ease the industry back into private ownership. That sounds like a lot of money – it did then too. But when you bear in mind that there were around a million miners, that large total equalled £10 per man. Nevertheless, the Executive could not see any alternative but acceptance. I couldn't blame them for that; there really was no other alternative.

So, on June 28th, the following letter was sent out to all members. I got one myself and still have it somewhere:

TO THE MEMBERS OF THE MINERS' FEDERATION

Your Executive Committee have today provisionally agreed to terms of wages settlement with the Government and the owners. These terms are brought to your notice herewith with the object of getting them ratified, so that a general resumption of work may take place on Monday next. The important and responsible step of taking power as a Committee to negotiate a wages settlement, even after the last ballot vote, was the result of our certain knowledge that the National Wages Board, with the National Profits Pool, could not be secured by a continuation of this struggle. Every economic and political factor is dead against us. In order that no more suffering should be endured by a continuation of this struggle, we took upon ourselves the freedom to negotiate a wages settlement. This wages settlement which is now before you represents the maximum which can be secured in the present circumstances. It is an improvement upon the wage terms which were submitted by the owners and upon which you voted in the last ballot.

The Government grant has been restored; the maximum wage reductions in districts where reductions must take place are now known up to the 1st October. A minimum of 20 per cent will be added to the new standard wage, which will operate during the lifetime of this agreement, and not end on the 30th June, 1922, as originally proposed by the owners. This principle is of the greatest possible value in the mining industry. The remaining principles which are to govern wages and profits during the lifetime of the agreement have also been established. These mark an entirely new departure in the mining industry, and it is our sure belief that when anything like normal trade returns these principles will provide a more just method of fixing profits than we have ever had before in the industry.

Up to now the unity of the men has been magnificent, while districts which had nothing to gain in the form of wages have stood loyally by the other districts whose wage reductions would have been of the most drastic character. This loyalty and unity will have been maintained until the end of the dispute, despite the great odds against us, if a general resumption of work takes place on Monday next.

We, therefore, strongly urge you, with the knowledge of the seriousness of the situation, to accept this agreement, which we have provisionally agreed to today, and authorise your Committee to sign the terms by Friday next.

Yours, on behalf of the Executive Committee,
Herbert Smith, Acting President
James Robson, Treasurer
Frank Hodges, Secretary.

Four days later, the ballot results came back from the districts. The total vote was 938,760. Of those, 105,820 men voted to reject the proposed agreement, while 832,840 voted to accept it. Given that overwhelming majority, way beyond the two-thirds required, on July 1st, 1921, the Committee released the figures and authorised a return to work. The great lock-out was over. Without question, we had been beaten. The miners had come through great tribulation with very little to show for it. Perhaps the only positive thing was that the Federation emerged united.

I felt moved to write to Frank Hodges to thank him for his hard work and his achievement in keeping the Federation together. In spite of our personal differences, he wrote back civilly to me, thanking me for my letter and wishing me well.

As I said earlier, I have not tried to present the full details of what happened during that period. No doubt, I have missed out things and I accept any criticism for that. However, I believe I have dealt as fairly as possible with the major issues, issues which Ann and I talked about regularly.

'So, where does that leave us now, Robert?' I loved the way she always used the word 'us' when referring to the miners.

'Same place we've always been,' I replied. 'Fighting for fairness and Socialism.'

'Will we ever win?' she asked.

'We always win,' I told her. 'Even when we lose the battle we win, because the very fact that there is a battle shows how far we've come and how united we are.' Then I added, 'Wars are long affairs. Keir Hardie told me that. In the course of any war, you lose some battles. The important thing is to keep going and eventually you will win the war. That's exactly what the miners will do.' I'd always believed that, still did then and, for the record, I still do now.

XXIX
A Kind Of Retirement

HAVING BEEN SO very busy for such a long time, I suddenly found myself with more time on my hands than I had ever had. Even in my childhood days in Belfast, I had been working from the time I was old enough to be let out onto the streets. In Glasgow, I'd worked long hours from the age of fifteen, then even longer hours down the pit in Larkhall. Then as a branch secretary, I rarely had any time to myself and, after I became President of the Scottish Miners and was later appointed to the Executive Committee of the MFGB, I scarcely had time to draw breath. Nine years as president of that organisation with draining amounts of travelling and a hectic schedule, coupled with the need to meet emergency after emergency, had left me with no time to think of much else apart from getting home to Ann as often as possible. Now, by the end of March, 1921, everything had changed. I was at home, with very few demands on my time. What on earth was I going to do with myself?

Well, as I have already told you, throughout that summer I kept in touch with Federation business largely due to regular contact with Herbert Smith. That took up some of my time. I frequently addressed local miners' meetings, organised a few rallies, helped out with fund-raising events, and even took turns working in the soup kitchens beside Ann when families were crying out for food. But all these things put together occupied only a fraction of my time in comparison with what I was used to. At first, that did not bother me too much because I was not as fit as I should have been. Following my collapse in 1920, the protracted arguments with the Government and the owners in the early months of 1921 had really exhausted me again. So, for a time, I was reasonably content to be fairly inactive and regain my strength.

Not that I sat around the house all day. That wasn't my style at all, and Ann wouldn't have stood for it anyway. I helped Ann with her kitchen garden in the late spring and, even though I was a bit of a lummox when it came to gardening and got a few sharp words from Ann when I mistook young vegetables for weeds, I greatly enjoyed the fresh air. Not only that but the feeling of weariness after a heavy digging session was so much more natural than the kind of weariness, brought on by argument and frustration, that I was used to. In fact, I enjoyed working in the garden so much that, along with some of the retired miners in the town, I did some work in the gardens of some of the oldest bodies in Larkhall. I believe Ann was delighted. It meant that her precious vegetables were safer.

During the summer, I found myself spending a lot of time down at the cricket club, a pleasure which had been more or less denied to me over the previous forty years. I was part of a group of ex-players who gathered on the wooden benches by the boundary and relived past glories. Man, I'm telling you those ex-cricketers are worse than fishermen when it comes to exaggeration! After the match, we would wander along to one of the pubs, preferably one with a billiards table, and enjoy a glass of beer, a pipe, a game and a good blether. All of which was very pleasant, and I thoroughly enjoyed the companionship, but it wasn't keeping me busy and I was beginning to miss that.

My salvation at that time was finding out that some of the older miners' houses were in need of basic repairs and that the owners weren't prepared to carry them out, which came as no great surprise to me. So a group of us older men got together and formed what I suppose you might call a repair company. We visited the older houses, found out what needed to be done and, within the limitations of our abilities, carried out such repairs as we could. You might find it hard to credit this but, at first, the owner's factor tried to stop us, claiming that it was none of our business. Only when we threatened to make sure that the local newspapers would be made fully aware of his attitude did he relent. Working on those houses, doing what we could to help people who hadn't the means to help themselves, was my salvation that year. It made me feel useful.

I was also called on to do a little speaking. I was in Edinburgh twice and Glasgow once for Save the Children rallies and made speeches exhorting our members to do all they could to raise money for local and international projects. It was a privilege to be able to do so. On a subject perhaps more natural to me, I was asked by the Scottish Miners' Federation to talk to the men at meetings and rallies all over Scotland. In many ways, this was like a return to my roots for me. I had been president of the SMF until 1918 and only resigned that position because of the pressures caused by my presidency of the MFGB. It was a pleasure to be back among 'my ain folk' again. After one meeting in Motherwell, I was button-holed by one of the Executive. It may have been James Sinclair but my memory is not certain on that.

'Well, Bob,' he said, as we enjoyed a glass of beer, 'time moves on, eh?'

'Aye, there's none of us getting any younger,' I told him.

'Keeping yourself busy?'

'Aye, but not as busy as I'd maybe like,' I admitted.

'You're feeling better, then?'

'Much better, thank you. Not as fit as I once was, but none of us is getting any younger, are we?'

'True enough, Bob.' A few seconds of silence. 'And speaking for us, like today. You don't mind being involved again?'

'Not at all. You know me. A miner first and last.'

'Glad to hear it, Bob. Very glad to hear it,' he said. 'I'll bear that in mind.' Which, as it turned out later, he did.

But perhaps my biggest speaking engagement that year after leaving the MFGB was not in my home area at all. There was to be a by-election at Ashton-Under-Lyne on the east side of Manchester. William Robinson, a friend of mine, was standing as the Labour candidate against Sir Walter de Frece, who was the coalition candidate. William got in touch to ask if I was willing to speak on his behalf. To be honest with you, when I received his invitation I wasn't entirely sure what to do. I was much recovered from my unsettled and fatigued state of my London days, but I would have to be away from home for a few nights and I wasn't entirely convinced that I wanted to do that. You won't be surprised to know whose opinion I asked.

'Are you sure you're feeling up to it?' Ann demanded.

'I think so.'

'You think so? Don't you know?'

'Well, yes, I'm up to it,' I told her.

'In that case, get yourself down the road,' she said. She gave me a quick kiss. 'It'll get you out from under my feet for a few days,' she added.

Looking back, I know that she was concerned for me, unsure how I would react to being away from the security of Larkhall after my earlier collapse. But, wise woman that she was, she also knew that I was fretting to be involved again and was likely to become morose through lack of activity. Her approval was all I needed and I contacted William Robinson to say that I would be delighted to travel down and support him.

I was put up at the house of a member of the Independent Labour Party. Memory insists that he was called Arthur but I do not recollect his surname. He was excellent company, we shared many of the same opinions, and I was delighted to accept his invitation to attend a Sunday midday meeting at the local miners' union branch. It was a lively enough meeting at which I was made guest of honour and was called on to say a few words which were well received.

We went back to Arthur's house where I ate a splendid meal with his family. Then he invited me to go to church with him. At first, I was inclined to go with him but, when he informed me that the clergyman was on the side of Labour and there would be a large congregation keen to meet me, I baulked a little. I would not say that I flew into a state of panic exactly but it was close to that. You see, I had been fêted so much since leaving London that the thought of being the centre of people's attention was beginning to make me feel ... well, nervous is the best word I can use to describe it. Besides, I had to address a big meeting later that evening. You may wonder why the thought of that did not make me feel nervous. Well, it is simple really. I was well rehearsed, had my notes ready, and knew exactly what I was going to say. There was the security of certainty, if you like. Whereas mingling with strangers, being the focus of their attention, perhaps having to say a few unrehearsed words: well, that was a different matter. I was disposed to decline Arthur's invitation but, when he said how disappointed the congregation would be, I reluctantly relented and went along with him. In the event I was rather glad I did.

I remember that the church was named St John's and that the vicar was a man called Cummings. On the way there, perhaps sensing my nervousness, Arthur assured me that I would not be called on to make a speech, but insisted that Cummings was keen to meet me. When we got to the church, we were invited into the vestry where Cummings met us. We had the briefest of pleasant chats – there was no time for any more – then he told us that he had reserved two seats for me, in the choir pews among the singers. Obviously he had never heard me trying to sing. Ann always said I'd have put a bull to shame!

So we took our seats, Cummings entered the pulpit, and the service began. It quickly became clear to me that it was no ordinary service. It was far too informal for that. Then it dawned on me that it was more akin to a political rally. That was a new one on me. I'd never heard a minister in Larkhall going in for that kind of thing. I realised that Cummings was smiling at me and that everybody was looking in my direction. I felt an impulse to get up on my legs and run but I tensed myself and tried to sit it out. Then I picked up Cumming's words.

'We have a stranger in our midst today, in the person of Mr Robert Smillie, and on your behalf I welcome Mr Smillie, until recently President of the Miners' Federation, to our church.'

To my total astonishment, his announcement evoked as loud a round of applause as I'd ever heard. He waved me to my feet and, though my legs were weak, I stood up and the applause doubled. I even heard a good Scots' voice shout, 'Good man, Boab'. Thankfully, Cummings restored order and I was able to sit again. Just as well; I doubt it I could have stood for much longer.

Cummings then turned directly to political matters. For his sake, I hoped that the archbishop never found out about it. He reminded everybody that there was a by-election in which there was a Labour candidate standing. He praised William Robinson to the skies, never once mentioning his opponent Sir Walter de Frece. However, he was fair-minded enough to say that those of his congregation who were electors should judge for themselves the capabilities of the candidates by attending their meetings, listening carefully to what they had to say, and deciding which one to vote for according to which one they believed to be best fitted to represent them.

He could not in all honesty have prevented himself from remarking that William Robinson would be enjoying his support. He had made that abundantly clear from the beginning. I thought that perhaps he had finished with me but

I was wrong. 'Mr Smillie is with us today. Unfortunately it is against the rules of our Church that anybody should speak from this pulpit unless he wears a collar like this that I am wearing. Unfortunately, I have no other collar with me, and so I cannot ask Mr Smillie to preach to you today, though I am confident that you wish to hear what message he has to give you.'

Well, I thought I had been saved by the church rules. No collar, no preaching. I was pleased to hear that for I had been beginning to feel uneasy again at the thought of having to make an impromptu speech. But Cummings wasn't finished with me yet, not by a long shot.

'On the other hand,' he continued, 'while it is against the rules for Mr Smillie to preach to you here today because he does not wear a collar like mine, the rules of our church do permit me to catechise him, ask him questions as I can of any member of the congregation, and then he may answer. Mr Smillie, I am sure you won't mind if I ask you a few questions.'

As a matter of fact, I did mind. My unease was beginning to turn to panic. I could feel my chest tighten. I did not want to speak. I did not want to be there. I forced myself to listen to Cummings' words and the first one I made out was 'nationalisation'. He was asking me about the benefits of nationalising the mines. My mind immediately began to list the stock answers. He extended his question. Was nationalisation of the mines only in the interests of the miners or the community at large? I could envision answers to that alright. My head was beginning to clear. I was on familiar territory. Then he was asking questions about the social conditions for miners and their families and the standard of tied cottages. There was little I did not know about that. The tightness in my chest eased and my heartbeat slowed.

'Now, Mr Smillie,' he concluded, 'I have put these questions to you and, in so doing, have obeyed the rules of our Church. Would you be kind enough to come up to this pulpit and answer my questions? You may take five minutes or fifty minutes as you wish.' He bowed and left the pulpit.

Wonder of wonders, I entered the pulpit with no feelings of unease whatsoever. Almost certainly because I was dealing with familiar subject matters, I was able to relax. The fact that the congregation had reacted positively to Cummings' words and were clearly on my side helped as well. The result was that, even though I had no notes to rely on, I spoke for half-an-hour or so in answer to Cummings' questions. If there had ever been any doubt about the congregation's feelings, they were set aside when they applauded regularly my answers to the questions. As I left the pulpit, I felt refreshed rather than tired. Of course, I realised that the circumstances had been in my favour and that I was likely to come up against considerably less friendly audiences if I were to continue to accept public speaking engagements. However I felt that, in a small way at least, some kind of rehabilitation had begun.

For the record, William Robinson won the seat, much to my delight. However, there was a bitter outcome which I feel guilty about to this day even though I had done no more than I was asked and was not directly responsible for it. I much admired Mr Cummings, the vicar at St John's. I was told that the views which he expressed in his sermons had driven a number of wealthy people from his church but had attracted many poor people into it. Not only did they enjoy his radical sermons, they also enjoyed singing hymns which he had written himself.

But he was punished for his principles. More specifically, for inviting me into his pulpit. He had not only been vicar of St John's but also Chaplain to the Forces in the district. Yet, within a few weeks of welcoming me to his church, that position was torn away from him. He was told that inviting a Socialist into his pulpit was not acceptable. In the years that followed, I met him on a number of occasions and came to admire his collective Christianity. I honour and respect that man.

Of course, there have been times, and they are not over yet, when to proclaim oneself a Socialist has meant being regarded as unchristian, barbaric and despicable. Thinking about what happened to Cummings because of his views reminds me of an episode in which somebody found out that a Socialist is not always as black as he is painted. I smile when I think about it.

I do not remember the exact year, but it was certainly after the Great War. I was travelling by train from London to Leadhills, that small village with the remarkable library which I told you of earlier. At Preston Station, a gentleman boarded the train and came into the compartment where I was quartered, up until that point on my own. We nodded at one another but did not speak during the best part of the two hours it took to reach Carlisle. I had arranged to stay at Carlisle to avoid the need to go to Glasgow then return more than forty miles to Leadhills by a slow, local train. As I booked in at the Station Hotel, I found that my silent travelling companion was also booking in there. After finding my room and washing, I went to the dining-room which was busy and offered only one vacant table. Hardly had I sat down when I was joined by my ex-travelling companion.

'Mind if I sit down?' he asked, in a pleasant, educated voice.

'Of course not,' I replied, smiling. 'Fate seems determined to throw us together.'

'It would appear so,' he said, returning my smile.

Over dinner we chatted about ordinary enough things, the sorts of subjects British people tend to discuss when thrown together. The weather, train travel, sport, those sorts of things. Then, and I'm not sure how we got onto it, the conversation turned to coal and a fairly technical aspect of it, the by-products of carbonisation at high or low temperatures. He seemed to be quite knowledgeable on the subject which we continued to discuss after dinner once we had gone through to the smoking-room.

'I can tell you are interested in the subject,' my new friend said, 'so I will tell you what I will do. I will post on to you a periodical which contains a number of interesting articles on the subject.'

I told him I would be very grateful for his kindness. He gave me his card but, as I never carried cards, I had to write my name and address on a piece of hotel stationery and hand it to him. As he read it, I could see a puzzled look come over him. Perhaps, I thought, it was due to my handwriting which had never been of copperplate standard. But it wasn't that at all.

'My word, you had me worried there for a moment,' he said.

'Really? Why is that?'

'Well, when I saw your name.' He gave me a sharp look. 'You are not a friend of that other fellow, I hope?'

'Which other fellow?' I asked in some confusion.

'That other Smillie. You know, the miners' man,' he explained. 'My word, but he's a dreadful chap.'

'Is he really?' Half-smiling, I pointed at the piece of paper. 'I regret to have to tell you that that is the man.'

'Oh, my word!' His face turned red with embarrassment. 'Eh ... Mr Smillie ... I ... eh ... I don't know what to say.'

'Don't worry,' I told him. 'It's of little matter and I'm well used to it.'

'But, look, I must apologise for the way I spoke to you just now.' He looked extremely contrite. 'I took my opinion of you from the newspapers.'

'So do a lot of people,' I told him. 'And the papers are no friends of mine.'

'I rather gathered that,' he said, finding a smile at last. 'Please believe me that I had no idea that the man I believed I knew from the newspapers could possibly have been the same as the pleasant companion I have so much enjoyed talking to tonight.'

'Say no more about it,' I insisted. 'It is an unfortunately common mistake to judge people's characters by hearsay or newspaper gossip. Why, I have done it myself.' Which I hope wasn't true but I wanted to make him feel less embarrassed.

After that, we enjoyed a long and amiable conversation in the course of which I discovered that my new friend, in addition to being a fellow Scot, was a manufacturer in a large way on the outskirts of Manchester. His knowledge of carbonisation and other processes had been learned from his father who was apparently something of an authority on all things geological and had passed his keen interest on to his son. We parted on the best of terms. Before we parted, he insisted that I must call and see him when I was next in the Manchester area. It was a very kind offer but I was rarely in that part of the world and was never able to take him up on it.

A few days after I got back to Larkhall, the postman delivered a large package which turned out to be not only the promised periodical but a number of others as well. Enclosed there was also a most pleasant letter saying that the package had been sent in memory of the most delightful evening spent in my company in Carlisle. I think this all goes to show that ignorant prejudice can be overcome when people come face-to-face and enjoy a wee blether.

As the cold winter of 1921 moved into an even colder start to 1922, I was feeling greatly restored. Not quite my old self, you understand, but a lot healthier and feeling a lot more confident than I had been for much of 1921. It was then that I received a signal honour which proved yet another restorative to my confidence. I was invited to a Scottish Miners' Federation meeting at the grand Usher Hall in Edinburgh. It was always such a pleasure to be around the men on whose behalf I had worked for so long that I readily accepted. I remember that it was a bitingly cold January day when I caught the Edinburgh train but that the 'Auld Country' looked as beautiful as ever in the bright winter sunshine.

To begin with, the meeting ran its usual course. There was debate, of course, and I was flattered to have my opinion sought on a number of matters. Several resolutions were passed, though I could not vote on them as I was not an officer. Then, just as the meeting seemed to be drawing to a close and I was wondering if I could catch the early train back to Larkhall rather than the later one, I was taken by surprise. In a brief but flattering statement, the secretary praised my earlier work on behalf of the Scottish miners and my later efforts as President of the MFGB. He then astonished me by saying that, during a morning session at which I had not been present, the committee had voted unanimously to invite me to take up the role as their president. Would I be kind enough to accept?

Well, I was absolutely floored by this. Committee members were clapping and cheering and punctuating their cheers with exhortations like 'Come on, Bob!' I tell you, it was wonderful to feel so wanted, particularly by my own people. I fear that my voice must have been a little shaky with emotion, but I managed to tell them that I was honoured by their invitation and would be delighted to accept. Then it was handshakes all round, somebody produced a few bottles, and we spent quite a time swopping stories, mainly about the old days. Even as we talked and laughed, a wee voice in my head was telling me, 'You're back, Bob.' Of course, I knew that the presidency was really a figurehead position and that the secretary was the really influential man. But I didn't care. Even if it was just as a representative, I would be back working on behalf of the people who meant most to me. By the way, it was the last train I caught home that night! When she found out the reason why, Ann didn't mind at all. A very sensible woman, my Ann.

In the wider world, our prime minister was coming under great pressure. Lloyd George had lost a lot of working-class support following the collapse of the miners' strike and workers in many other trades such as engineering, shipbuilding, dockwork, building and textiles being forced to accept wage reductions.

Which just about proved to me how tenuous a thing a grip on power can be. There was much that I would happily have blamed him for, but a slump in world trade was not one of them. Moreover, it was clear to anybody with an interest in politics, and I was certainly one of those, that his Conservative friends in the Coalition Government were beginning to see him as a liability rather than an asset. At the beginning of 1922, I was fairly sure that his days as prime minister were numbered. Ann put it quite succinctly.

'He'll no' see the year out as Prime Minister,' she told me. I was beginning to think that I had married a prophet!

XXX
Rehabilitation

AS THE YEAR crawled its way towards the spring, I was certainly feeling more relaxed than I had been at the same period in 1921. I had had a much-needed rest, had spent much more time than I had been used to with my beloved Ann in Larkhall, and enjoyed an unusual amount of fresh air and exercise. Also, I had begun to drag myself back into the world of public debate through my work for Save the Children and the Scottish Miners' Federation, as well as attending and speaking at a number of political rallies. Indeed, I was beginning to feel so much better that I began to long to be more actively involved again. All of which might explain to you why I was delighted to receive a particular invitation towards the end of March 1922.

The General Council of the British Trades Union Congress asked me if I would care to attend the International Trades Union Congress in the ancient city of Rome. Not only because I was keen to be active again, but also because I had never previously had the opportunity to visit the Italian capital, I was only too delighted to accept. I was to be one of ten delegates. Among others, men like JH Thomas, Henry Gosling and Ben Tillett would be in our party. I was delighted to note that, for the first time in my experience, a woman would be one of our delegates. About time too! She was Miss Julia Warley of the London Women Workers. I noted that wives and husbands could accompany their spouses if they wished. I asked Ann if she wanted to go.

'Rome!' She exclaimed. 'Rome? I've far too much to do here, Robert Smillie. You can tell me all about it when you get back.' My Ann was a real 'home body' as we say in Scotland.

By sheer coincidence, just at the time when that invitation came through, I had been catching up on my reading, which had suffered over recent years, and had just come across a specific reference to Rome. You know that I was always a great lover of the poetry of Robert Burns, and I believe to this day that no man wrote more movingly on behalf of the common man. Yet there is one stanza written by another man which I believe to be above anything Burns wrote as far as a description of Socialism is concerned. That man is Thomas Babington Macauley, another Scot, who was not only a poet but also an orator and historian of some repute. That stanza of his to which I have just referred is as follows:

Then none was for a party,
Then all were for the state;
Then the great man helped the poor,
And the poor man loved the great;
Then lands were fairly positioned,
Then soils were fairly sold,
The Romans were like brothers
In the brave days of old.

I found that an inspiring piece of writing, even though I always believed that the last line was a syllable short, and I read over it again on the train down to London. It was rather odd heading down that same line again, that line which I'd travelled on literally hundreds of times before. This time, of course, I was heading for the docks rather than MFGB Headquarters in Russell Square.

Well, we ended up in 'The Eternal City' in early April, rather like tourists searching out a classic shrine, the city of the Caesars. Let me tell you from the start that we were vastly disappointed in what we found. Far from finding beauty and, in Macaulay's words, an ideal State, we found a city of faded glory and great inequality. There was no great sweetness in the lives of the working people in a city which housed one of the two great bodies of organised Christianity.

We were comfortable enough in our hotel, but we found that the hotel keeper 'rooked' us on the price of everything, introducing charges which we had never heard of at home. But what could we do? We were strangers in a foreign land, guests of the Italian Trades Union Congress, and certainly didn't want to be the cause of some diplomatic incident. So, with as good grace as we could muster, we paid up, trying to remind ourselves of the old saying, 'When in Rome, do as the Romans do'. Though in our case we had it done to us. Mind you, there was a potentially serious side to this. We were all on expenses which would be checked thoroughly on our return to Britain. We could easily imagine being asked why we didn't find a cheaper hotel. Well, there could only be one answer to that, the plain truth – there wasn't one!

The main business of that International Conference was an attempt to secure international solidarity of the trade unions of the world. American unions did not take part as they had not at that stage even seen fit to join the International Trades Union Congress. Unfortunately, Russia was also absent due to friction between the new Red International and their older trade unions. I truly regretted that. I would have dearly loved to have had the chance to talk to their men to discover what was really happening in Russia. There were plenty of stories coming out of that country, some of them telling of a horrific number of deaths, but it was hard to get at the real truth.

In spite of two major countries being missing, some headway was made. But it was slow work and in a most unpleasant environment too. We were based in the Theatre Argentina and JH Thomas was the chairman. Fairly soon, I was sure that he wished that he wasn't because the venue was packed to the point of suffocation and there was no ventilation. I had travelled steerage on a liner to the United States but that was a haven of fresh air compared to the Theatre Argentina. In no time, delegates were staggering outside for fresh air. I was in as bad a state as anybody and left the auditorium on several occasions. I did not envy JH Thomas his role as chairman one little bit. Only the Italians themselves seemed not to be affected. Of course, it was their city and they were used to its stifling atmosphere.

Another major problem we encountered was that of language. With so many nations involved, there was a need for interpreters all the time. This had the effect of diminishing the effect of many speeches. I found that out for myself. One of my contributions was a statement about the brotherhood of man. I suspect that I quoted from Robert Burns. Whatever, when I sat down, I received a round of applause from English-speaking delegates. But my speech was still being translated into a number of other languages. This took varying amounts of time and it felt very odd sitting there and receiving sporadic bursts of applause from around the auditorium. It was high time for a common language I told myself. Speeches would then have more immediate impact and a lot of time would be saved.

By a quirk of coincidence, the International Miners' Committee was meeting in Rome at the same time. One day, on a conducted tour of the Forum, who did I bump into other than Thomas Ashton, Herbert Smith and Frank Hodges? We had not been together since I resigned from the MFGB and I was a little apprehensive about their likely attitude towards me. However, I need not have worried. It was all very pleasant and all three men, Frank included, shook my hand and enquired after my health. They congratulated me for taking on again the role of the Scottish Federation, but we did not discuss the present work of the MFGB. I was reluctant to do so as it might seem as if I was interfering.

Of the four of us, Frank was undoubtedly the best speaker and, as we were in the Forum, he decided to treat us to a little piece of drama, re-enacting the scenes which would have taken place there in Cicero's day. Man, but he made a wonderful thespian. A number of English speakers stopped to listen and, when he had finished, gave him a warm round of applause. For a moment, I was reminded of the Romans' view of Cicero: 'The Gods have come down among men'. We parted on the best of terms, with promises to keep in touch.

On the Sunday of that Congress, we had a day away from the stifling Theatre Argentina. I was not sorry about that. In the mid-afternoon and early evening, we visited St Peter's, the Vatican and the Colosseum and were as impressed by these magnificent buildings as any other tourist would be. But it was the morning excursion which proved to be the most memorable.

We met at the Central Tramway Station at eight o'clock in the morning. I don't know if I was alone in grumbling at such an early start. After all, for a miner a Sunday is the one day of the week when a lie-in is normally assured. Anyway, we were all there on time, only to be told that there was a slight problem. This was the first occasion on which I realised that the Italians were masters of understatement. Our destination was intended to be Tivoli but, in that area, we learned that the Communists on Tivoli Town Council had posted signs all over the place proclaiming that our Congress wasn't properly Socialist and that we should not be allowed to visit. Perhaps some people of Liberal or Conservative persuasion in Britain might find that hard to believe! Whatever, a more sympathetic group, the White Guards of Tivoli had retaliated by tearing down the Communists' signs and replacing them with their own.

By the time we were gathering at the station, the whole area of Tivoli was reported to be in an uproar, verging on civil war. In the unrest, the Mayor of Tivoli was shot dead by a White Guard. We were advised that it would not be safe to continue with our planned visit. You may not be surprised to know that not one of us disagreed with that opinion. Instead, we were offered an excursion to Frascati, and we were very pleased that we accepted.

Our party, with two guides, was taken into a hilly district in four open, horse-drawn vehicles. We climbed and climbed, then reached a point where the horses could go no further. We continued the ascent by foot, climbing higher and higher. On both sides we saw flocks of sheep tended by shepherds and dogs. I was struck by how old and shabbily dressed the shepherds were. There was almost a grey pallor about them. And the dogs were more like small hounds than the collies I was used to seeing on the farms in Scotland.

Then we descended the other side of the hills and came to the small town of Frascati itself. It was probably the most delightful little place I had ever seen. Nestling in the lee of the hills, there were beautiful houses in many different colours, some of them ordinary enough in size while others were mansions. At the time of our visit, spring was enriching the landscape and the foliage of the trees and bushes was beginning to show the promise of beauty to come.

Needless to say, our guides were keen to point out the site for which Frascati is renowned. A little way from the centre of town lie the ruins of what had obviously once been a great villa. It had been the great Cicero's home. In spite of the degradation, there was still a large fish pond and we could make out his private theatre and the dressing-room used so long ago by actors. I found it a quite wonderful experience.

We ate a picnic lunch in the ruins of Cicero's villa and I found myself reflecting on the idea of fame. This man was dead for the greater part of two thousand years. How long, I wondered, would the fame of men like Lloyd George and

Bonar Law last? Not for two thousand years, I was quite certain of that. Though, I thought to myself, the notoriety of a fellow called Robert Smillie just might!

I also found myself, not for the first time in my life, bemoaning my lack of formal education. How I wished that I had learned Latin as a boy. If I had done so, I could have read Cicero in the original, instead of having to rely on translations. I knew from experience how much was often lost when translating broad Scots into standard English, and wondered how much more was lost in translating from Latin. I had no chance to develop that line of thinking because our guides wanted us to move on as our transport would shortly be waiting for us.

We returned by a different route, just a mountain path with no more room than would allow two people to walk side-by-side. Half-way down, we came across a laddie of maybe twelve years of age. I do not tell a lie when I say that he might have stepped out into the twentieth century straight from the middle ages. His trousers and jacket were made of sheepskin, the wool still attached to them. His boots were large, clumsy affairs made either of raw hide or perhaps half-tanned leather. On his head he wore a time-worn, battered felt hat. For all the world, he looked like a walking jumble sale.

Yet he had a sweet, innocent face and smiled shyly at us as we approached. I noticed that in his hand he held a whistle, obviously home-made from the branch of a tree. I was immediately reminded of Charles Murray's charming poem 'The Whistle,' and the lines:

> He cut a sappy sucker, from the muckle-rodden tree,
> He trimmed it, and he wet it, an' he thumped it on his knee.

By the time we were close to him, the Italian laddie was playing on his whistle, no doubt a lullaby to calm his sheep who were somewhat disconcerted by our approach. I noticed that the instrument was considerably longer than the ones we used in Scotland and, as far as I could tell, there were no punched holes in it to allow for a continuous scale of notes.

I put my hands out and performed a probably none-too-clever mime of me playing the whistle. To my great satisfaction, he passed it over to me and I attempted to get some notes from it. I enjoyed a little success, at which he was all smiles. Then I passed it back, nodding rapidly at him. Amazingly, he understood what I wanted and began to play. Our whole party stood and listened as he played a sweet little tune. I saw that he made up for the lack of holes in the whistle by placing the little fingers of his right hand over the mouth and moving it a small amount at a time to produce different notes. When he had finished, we gave him a good round of applause and he flushed red with astonishment.

I had a quick word with Julia Warley, who I knew spoke a little Italian and, on my behalf, she persuaded the boy to cut down a branch from the tree from which he had made the whistle. I wanted to take it home to Scotland to see if I could make one. In return for his entertainment, we each gave him a small amount of money which he shyly accepted. Julia asked if there was anything else he wanted. He was such a bonny-looking wee soul that we all felt rather sorry for him. He said he wanted cigarettes, which rather surprised us until our guides told us that cigarettes could be bartered for almost anything. None of us had any so we gave him a little more money then left, him waving goodbye until we were out of sight. In my mind's eye, I see him still.

When I got back to Scotland, and Ann asked me about Rome, I had to tell her that I had been disappointed by it. It certainly hadn't been as I'd expected from my reading of history books and Macaulay's poetry. To be sure, the ancient sites had been impressive enough but Rome in general I found rather tawdry, like it needed a good clean. I hadn't much enjoyed our hotel, the Congress venue had been downright unhealthy, and we had been over-charged for just about everything. Worst of all, many of the working people I had met had seemed without any real spirit, as if they'd somehow been squashed by their history. And, as I have mentioned, agricultural labourers, and their method of working, were positively primitive compared to our farming folk. The only thing I was able to report positively was our visit to Frascati and Cicero's villa. My mistake: there was one other thing.

'Mind, there's a lot of bonny lassies in Rome,' I told Ann.

'Aye, maybe,' she replied. 'Just a shame that you're such an ugly old man isn't it, Robert Smillie?' As usual, Ann had the last word.

So, I was picking up the threads of life again. The presidency of the SMF and occasional work for Save the Children kept me reasonably occupied, and the trip to Rome, though it had added little to my general education, had whetted my appetite for doing more. There was one other interesting episode in 1922 which I am about to tell you of but, before that, there was a development in the MFGB. As was only right, given the fact that he had been Vice-President, Herbert Smith was confirmed as President of the Federation. I was confident that he would serve in that role with some distinction. I had known him long enough to be sure of that. However, there were rumours – I cannot call them more than that because I was no longer a member of what you might call the inner circle – that Frank Hodges had been promoting himself for the position. To be honest, I thought that that was unlikely because, as secretary, Frank was already in a position of great influence. From what I have already told you, you will know that he was the contact with Lloyd George during that awful period leading to Black Friday. I wrote to both men, offering my congratulations to Herbert, and offering to them my best wishes for the future. Both of them wrote back to me and I was pleased to note that there seemed to be no suggestion of any tension between the two of them. That was a great relief to me.

That year, Sidney Welsh asked me to go to Durham to support his candidature in an election there. I was delighted to accept his invitation and spoke on his behalf at several meetings. I spent several days there and was based in a hotel which had other 'political' guests. There were Sidney Webb and his wife and the former Government minister, Richard Haldane who, by that time, had been ennobled. For reasons which were not always positive, I had known Lord Haldane for some years. You will no doubt know that he was at the War Office in the years leading up to the Great War and had played a major part in modernising the British Army. Later, he became Lord Chancellor and served his country with distinction.

However, when I first knew him, we were hardly fellow travellers. Indeed, we clashed on many occasions. The reason for that was my outspoken anti-war stance. Even at the time, though I did not agree with him, I could see things from his position. There he was, between 1907 and 1912, doing his best to prepare Britain's military machine for an increasingly likely war. Meanwhile, there was I at the same time, the 'Socialist agitator' as I was commonly portrayed, preaching against all things military. Little wonder that we did not see eye-to-eye. We disagreed in public on a number of occasions, rather harshly as I recall, but the truth was that in private he behaved very cordially towards me.

In fact, I believe that Haldane was the subject of a great deal of unfair criticism during that period and, indeed, during the war which followed. Although, as you will understand, I was hardly an ally of his at the time, I felt that by the time the war began he was becoming very sympathetic to the view that a great national effort was needed to improve the social conditions of working people. He was also beginning to crusade for a better system of education to improve the opportunities of working-class children. I felt that he rarely got the credit for the development of those views.

I first became aware of Haldane in 1883 when I was beginning to become active in union politics during my early years in Larkhall. This was a few years after Gladstone's famous Midlothian campaign, the aura from which helped Haldane capture the Haddingtonshire constituency for the Liberals. One of his strongest supporters during that campaign was a dear friend and colleague of mine, Robert Brown, who was secretary of the Scottish Miners' Union. The only thing Robert and I ever fell out about was party politics. Unlike most of us who were striking out for Independent Labour Politics, Robert still retained his strong leanings towards radical Liberalism. For all that, he was a grand fellow, Robert Brown.

He was very influential in Haldane's winning of the seat and, I am led to believe, Haldane was well aware of that. However, once elected, he faced a dilemma. The Eight Hours Day Bill was in front of the House of Commons, and he was not disposed to support it. Robert Brown, on behalf of the miners, was livid about this and invited me to accompany him to London to see Haldane and 'set the man straight' as he put it. Reaching London, we made for the House of Commons at a time when the Bill had reached a critical stage. Robert absolutely demanded to see Haldane and we waited for him in the Outer Lobby.

When Haldane arrived, the three of us sat in seats reserved for visitors, Robert on one side of him and me on the other. Robert took first strike, I took the second, but we weren't getting anywhere. Haldane was sticking to his guns. As he saw it, there was no good reason to legislate for the fixing of hours that grown men should work. Eventually, Robert grew angry and jumped to his feet.

'Look here, Mr Haldane,' he said, waving a calloused forefinger at his MP, 'I helped to put you in this House and I can assure you in the name of the Good God that I can help to put you out of it as well. I'm telling you this clearly, man to man. If you do not promise to vote for this Bill, I am going home now to begin work to keep you out next time. I think you know as well as I do that you won't stand a chance of re-election in Haddingtonshire if the miners turn against you.' He was breathing heavily by this time.

'Well, Mr Brown,' Haldane said with a calmness I rather admired given the verbal beating he'd just taken, 'I hear your advice and I suppose I must agree to your ... your request.' Later, he did vote in our favour.

As we were leaving the Commons, Robert Brown stomping his way in front of me, he turned round and, in such a loud voice that they probably heard him back in Larkhall, he told me, 'There's only one way to deal with these damned politicians, Smillie.' And for all I know he may have been right!

These early memories flashed through my mind that night in Durham when Sidney Webb, Haldane and I enjoyed a long conversation about Sidney Welsh's chances of success in the election and the subject of politics in general. Of course, Sidney and I were much cheered by the fact that this famous man had now declared himself on the Labour side. He had endured a long, painful divorce form the Liberals, first taking Asquith's side against Lloyd George, then becoming disenchanted by Lloyd George's reliance on the Conservatives to preserve the Coalition Government. It had taken some courage on his part to throw in with us and we were delighted that he had. That night it was he who began a conversation which ended up in great amusement for me.

'Tell me something, Mr Smillie,' he began. 'You have known many politicians in your time. Indeed, you have got to know some of them very well indeed. Don't you think that modern politicians are more difficult to deal with on social questions than their predecessors were?' He didn't actually name Lloyd George or Bonar Law, but it was clear who he was thinking about. 'It appears to me almost impossible to persuade today's leading politicians that much needs to be done to improve the living conditions of working-class people, and I'm sure it was not so difficult some years ago. What do you think?

'Well,' I replied, 'I'm not so sure that previous politicians were any easier to deal with.'

'Oh, come now, Mr Smillie,' he protested. 'Surely that's not the case.'

'Well now, I remember a politician who had to be terrorised into doing something for working men.' Trying to keep a straight face.

'Really?' Sidney put in. 'That sounds interesting. Tell us more.'

'I'm sure Lord Haldane could tell the story as well as I,' I laughed. Seeing the puzzled look on Haldane's face, I added, 'Robert Brown and the Eight Hours vote. Do you remember that, my Lord?'

'Oh heavens, not that,' Haldane chuckled. 'Yes I do remember it, only too well.'

'What on earth are you talking about, Bob?' Sidney asked.

'Well, as I am sure Lord Haldane remembers, Robert Brown and I had occasion to badger him on the subject of the Eight Hours Bill. Robert and I were for it, but this gentleman was against it. Am I right, Lord Richard?'

'As usual, Mr Smillie.' Grinning in spite of himself.

'Well, Robert Brown said that he'd make sure you would lose your seat if you didn't vote for the Bill,' I paused briefly. 'And how did you vote?'

'I admit it; guilty as charged,' Haldane said, bursting out laughing.

'So you see,' I concluded, 'politicians were just as difficult to deal with in the old days.' Following which, the three of us had a right good laugh and a long blether.

Then in October 1922, Ann's political prophecy came true. At a meeting of the Conservative Carlton Club on the 29th of that month, 185 Conservative MPs voted in favour of ending their support for Lloyd George, only 85 voting to support him. It was Stanley Baldwin's speech which was mainly responsible for swaying the vote against the prime minister. Lloyd George immediately resigned – what choice did he have? – and Andrew Bonar Low became prime minister of a Conservative Government. In essence, the Conservatives had decided to abandon Lloyd George because he had outlived his usefulness.

I experienced very mixed feelings when the news came through. Certainly, I had no reason to welcome a Conservative Government, given the attitudes of many Conservatives during the Sankey Commission and the events leading up to my resigning the presidency of the MFGB. I was confident that they would prove to be no friends of ordinary working people. To that extent at least, the fall of Lloyd George was hardly welcome news.

On the other hand, what was I to make of Lloyd George himself? Heaven knows, I had met and crossed swords with him often enough. In some ways, he had proved to be the natural successor to Gladstone and had accomplished a good deal for working people. Even in the difficult days of the postwar coalition, where he was more surrounded by Conservatives than Liberals, he had still secured some important reforms including the Sex Disqualification Removals

Act, the Addison Housing Act, the Rent Act and the extension of unemployment insurance. I would never have levelled the charge at him that he did not care about people. Simply that he did not care enough.

At first hand, I had witnessed the vileness of his temper when he felt that he might not get his own way. I found it revealing that he was particularly annoyed when those arguing with him were ordinary working folk like me. And therein lay the greatest paradox of Lloyd George and Liberals in general as I knew them. Their impulses were sound enough, and they certainly wished to improve living conditions, but always from above us. They were not of us and tended to treat us like wilful, errant children, which was the main reason, of course, why we had founded a party from among ourselves in the first place.

So Lloyd George passed. Largely due to him, so did the Liberal Party, fractured by his argument with Asquith and his alliance with the Conservatives. In spite of everything, I believed that I would remember him with some admiration and not a little personal affection as, in private, he and I had got on surprisingly well. But of one thing I was quite certain. He would never be as famous for as long as Cicero. No politician ever will.

XXXI
A Parliamentarian At Last

YOU WILL NO doubt remember that, on far too many occasions, I made unsuccessful attempts to gain a seat in the House of Commons. Perhaps you found my innocent and rather fumbling attempts quite amusing. Frankly, looking back over the years, I certainly do. By the time that 1923 came along, I had not given a single thought to entering Parliament except as a visitor – sometimes welcome, sometimes not – for a very long time. In fact, the only time when the matter crossed my mind was at the end of that rather odd conversation I had with the voice of Keir Hardie when I was travelling back to Scotland having resigned the presidency of the MFGB. But there was no seed planted that day, no flowering of ambition. I was perfectly happy to ignore the calls of a parliamentary career. As far as I was concerned, it was just another of the items on the list of things I hadn't done in my life.

But we are not always masters of our own destiny, are we? In fact, at times in my life I have felt that I had never been the master of mine. In the late spring of 1923, I fell mercy to the fates. It all began with a letter.

May 23rd, 1923.

Dear Bob,

In consequence of the death of Mr. Cairns, we will have a by-election in the Morpeth Division. I have been asked by a number of our leading men whether or not you would run as Labour candidate, if chosen by the L.R.C. of the constituency. I said that I would write you privately on the matter.

There will be a contest, but for a real Labour man, and especially a miner, it is a foregone conclusion.

Yours Sincerely,

William Straker,
Secretary,
Northumberland Miners' Association

Of course, I had known of the death of John Cairns and had been much saddened by it. He and I had been friends for years and I had spoken on his behalf in the Morpeth Constituency on a number of occasions. I had also talked to him often in the House of Commons when I was on Miners' Federation Business. Now John was gone, and William wanted me to take his place. What on earth was I going to do? I had so long ago given up the idea of becoming an MP that I had no ready answer to offer. Naturally, I asked Ann for her opinion. She seemed very much in two minds about it. On the one hand, she could see that, almost in spite of myself, I was interested in the offer. And Ann had never stood in my way before, and was never likely to. But on the other hand she was worried how it would affect me. There would be a campaign to be undertaken then, if successful, I would be back in London again. Not only that, but I would have a constituency to look after which might well mean that I got home less often than I had when I was with the MFGB. And she no doubt remembered only too well the effect that that had on me. I certainly did. Without doubt, if William Straker's offer had arrived only six months earlier, I would have turned it down flat. I simply would not have felt well enough. But now? Well, I was tempted, I have to admit. I had got back into the swing of things over the past few months and, while I was still not as well as I had once been, I was fairly sure that I was well enough. Besides, the cause of Socialism was beckoning.

'So, what should I do then, Ann?'

'I think you should follow your heart, Robert,' she told me.

The very next day, I wrote back to William Straker in the following words:

May 26th, 1923.

Dear Mr Straker,

I thank you very much for your kind letter of yesterday, and I am writing you in reply, as I will not be at the conference at Blackpool, and so will not be able to talk matters over with you.

Like you, I got a great shock when I heard of the death or Mr. Cairns. I was in London last week and on Tuesday and on Wednesday nights had the room known as Mr. Cairns' room, at No. 28 Cartwright Gardens. When I came in for breakfast on Thursday morning, Miss Bowman gave me the morning papers and told me what had taken place.

Needless to say we were all very much upset at the suddenness of the call. I have sent a message to Mrs. Cairns, through your office.

About the point raised in your letter, you know fairly well, I think, that I have no personal desire to go to Parliament; that I am growing old and not able to put up the fight of former days.

My Glasgow friends have offered me a seat again and again; but I have declined. The point which you put to me is a difficult one, and I am slow to give a reply. You know the high regard I have for you Northumberland people, and I recognise that love and respect for me has prompted the question put to me, through you, by some of your leading mining folk.

It is the highest compliment that I have ever had paid to me, and I am at a loss to know what to do. You, my best friend, must feel that I should allow my name to go forward, or you would not ask me. Mrs. Smillie will not say yea or nay. What am I to do?

Well, if your executive and council were anything like unanimous, and I were put forward as a Miners' Federation candidate, and chosen by the L.R.C., I would agree to stand. Details could be settled afterwards. Your president is already mentioned by the Daily Herald and, of course, I would not, on any account, stand in competition with one of your people.

Am I quite clear? I am not anxious for a seat. I am not the young, strong fighter I was. I have lost none of my rebel spirit, nor my faith. If the miners want me to fight the seat, I will do so; but not in competition with any of your people. I take it that whoever fights for you will be a Miners' Federation candidate.

I would not be disappointed if, under all the circumstances, your people do not ask me to fight the seat, but I will do so, if they desire it. You will think this is a mixed-up letter, I am sure, but the circumstances are new. I hope that you may get this before you leave for Blackpool.

Yours sincerely
Bob Smillie

William wrote back once more to confirm that my name had been put forward and that he expected no dispute about my nomination. Sure enough, he contacted me again to invite me south and, after a stop-start rail journey and a warm welcome from William and a number of other Northumberland miners, I was adopted at a meeting held at Bedlington Station. It was all done at great speed with the approval of the Labour Representative Committee because my main opponent had already taken to the field.

With the Conservatives now in Government, you might have thought that they and the Liberals would be snapping at one another's heels. Well, I have to tell you that they weren't doing that during that by-election in Morpeth. Between them, they decided that they would only put up one candidate who happened to be the Liberal who had previously contested a three-cornered fight against a Conservative and John Cairns. Their strategy was quite obvious. They had no desire to split the anti-Labour vote. In particular, they were concerned that because I was so well known among the Northumberland miners, in a three-cornered fight I might win easily. In short, their aim was to prevent 'Big Bad Agitator Bob' from winning the Morpeth seat.

With William Straker's help and organisation, I began campaigning immediately. In my opinion, my Liberal opponent made the great mistake of concentrating his campaign in Morpeth itself. I campaigned there too, of course, but also took good care to make myself known in Ashington and smaller places like Hepscott, Mitford, Pegswood and other wee villages which, to my Liberal opponent, may have just been specks on the map but which I knew to be the beating heart of the area. I visited all the pit villages and, by the reception I got there, I knew that I was building up a head of steam as the saying goes.

The local newspapers did a pretty fair job of reporting the events of the campaign. However, in one respect they were all guilty of an error of judgement. Not that I blamed them, mind you. I might have made the same mistake myself. You see, in John Cairn's last election, he had secured a victory but his votes had not matched the total of the other two candidates put together. So the newspapers believed that in a two-cornered fight the votes of the Liberals and the Conservatives together would defeat me. Well, I am glad to say that it didn't work out that way at all. After a splendid campaign, in which I got whole-hearted support from local members of the Labour Movement, I won the seat with an increased majority. In celebration, we had a great party in Morpeth and then an even greater one in Larkhall when I got home. Man, I had laid the curse. I was an MP at last. Keir Hardie would have been delighted!

Even as my success sank in, I knew that it might only be short-lived. The Conservative Government was not at ease with itself. Just before my election, Bonar Law fell ill and resigned and Stanley Baldwin became prime minister. He was soon faced with that he considered to be a crisis of conscience even if Lord Curzon, one of his leading men, saw it as no such thing and went so far as to describe his own leader's attitudes as idiotic. The issue was tariff reform. Baldwin decided that trade tariffs had to be reintroduced. However, Bonar Law had earlier promised that the Conservatives would not do this. It was not long after Baldwin became PM that the rumours began to circulate that he was considering calling a general election to gain wider approval for the reintroduction of tariffs. I believed that it was likely that he would do just that, which is why I was expecting another campaign fairly soon. And we all know that campaigns can be won or lost!

I won't deny that I felt a surge of pride the day that I took my seat in the House. I suppose that if I had any regrets they were because I wasn't representing my own folk back in Larkhall, though I was pleased enough to represent the Morpeth folk, and that I wasn't younger and fitter. But I was happy enough with how it had worked out. What made the day truly special for me was that, not only were William Straker and a number of other supporters there to see my induction, but so too was my beloved Ann, on her first-ever visit to London. That meant a lot to me, I can tell you. Even if I had a wee tear in my eye at the thought that my dear friend Kier Hardie would not be present on my first day as I had been on his. By the way, I courted no controversy with my headwear. I wore neither a cap nor a lum hat. I did not wear any kind of headgear at all.

No sooner had I arrived in the Commons than it was time for the summer recess. Man, but they do themselves well, these parliamentarians – compared with miners at any rate. But it meant that I had a proper holiday for once. The previous year didn't count as far as I was concerned as I had been recuperating. I made it my business to get to know my constituency better and visited it several times that summer. Ann came with me on one occasion and we made a proper wee holiday of it. The good folk of Morpeth took as well to Ann as she did to them. The highlight of that visit for me was being asked along to present the trophies at a local village cricket tournament. I thoroughly enjoyed myself. What Ann thought about it may well have been another matter.

When the House re-opened for the new session, it was done with great pomp which I found interesting but hardly necessary. But I suppose that's just me moaning, as usual. I have to be honest with you and say that I found that first session rather disappointing. One reason for that was it became clear to me early on that as an MP you belonged to the party. I had always thought that you were there to represent your constituents and advance their interests. In my case, that meant the miners and, as you can imagine, their cause was dear to my heart. However, it wasn't as simple as that. Ramsay MacDonald, who had regained the leadership of our party only months earlier, was determined that there had to be unity. It was his opinion that, above everything else, we had to show ourselves to be a responsible, unified group who could be trusted. Otherwise, he argued, how could we ever aspire to Government? He was right about that, of course, but it meant that we were rarely free to vote with our consciences. By and large, that didn't matter to me because I normally agreed with our policies. But I did not greatly enjoy the feeling of being filtered.

Another thing which had no great appeal for me was the attitude displayed by some parliamentarians. There were those who seemed to feel that they were there as a right and treated the House as if it was a kind of private members' club. There were some who rarely attended debates and seemed to turn up only for votes and even then with some reluctance. I found that true mainly of some Conservative members but there were some Liberals and one or two of our men who were not immune to it either. I was not particularly impressed by the overall atmosphere in the House. It was wonderful theatre at times but nothing like the kind of debate I was used to and had expected. I was used to arguments being laid out in a measured way followed by debate about points made in an argument. In the House there was often what I believed to be an unfortunate tendency to go in for points-scoring, sometimes at a quite personal level, rather than dissecting an argument. It reminded me very much of my experience in the Cambridge Union, a background from which many members came – perhaps too many in my opinion!

Above all, the business of the House during the autumn of 1923 was not as varied as I had hoped. I found few opportunities to present the views of my constituents. It seemed that almost whatever was on the agenda of the House, it ended up in the same place, the argument about tariff reforms. Baldwin was all for it. Reunited under Asquith's leadership, the Liberals were against it. As were we, because we believed that continued free trade and foreign imports would help to keep down prices for working families. I made my maiden speech on the benefits of free trade for the people of Northumberland. I was raucously heckled by the Conservatives and roused a few cheers from the Liberals and my own men. It all seemed rather childish behaviour to me.

Eventually Baldwin lost patience and, believing that his tariff reform policy would command wide support across the country, he called a general election. So it was a return to the stump in Morpeth for me. It was a cold December in the North of England that year, but I was greatly warmed by the reception I got from the good people of Morpeth. Following a strong campaign, I was re-elected with an increased majority. Back home in Larkhall, I was naturally anxious to know the overall results. In the event, the seats won were as follows: Conservatives 258, Labour 191, Liberals 159. From these figures, you might believe that the Conservatives had won but, in fact, they had lost. Let me explain.

Yes, the Conservatives had the greatest number of seats but, if you look carefully, you will see that the Liberals and ourselves together outnumbered them. In some circumstances, the Conservatives might have tried to push on with a minority Government, but not this time. You see, the election had been fought on one major issue: tariff reform. Only the Conservatives were supporting that so, when it came to the vote which it surely had to, they knew that they would be defeated. As tariff reform had been their main election issue, they could not simply push it to one side. It would have to be dealt with and the Conservatives would lose. We all waited with baited breath to see what would happen.

In fact, Baldwin hung on for six weeks while discussions within and among the parties took place. Some Conservatives tried to persuade Baldwin to patch up his differences with the Liberals and form a Government of National Unity with them, but he was too strongly in favour of tariff reform for that. Then Asquith promised Liberal Support for Labour if, as the larger of the opposition parties, we formed the next Government. Baldwin, a very astute man, actually encouraged this because he knew that, in that event, more right-wing Liberals like Churchill would defect to the Conservatives. Oh, it was a real Machiavellian state of affairs, I can tell you.

In the seventh week following the general election, Ramsay MacDonald went to the Palace, accepted an invitation to form the next Government, then kissed his monarch's hand. Within the Labour Movement, there was considerable jubilation. At last we had a Labour Government! I have to tell you that I did not share in that jubilation. In fact, had I had a voice in the matter which, as a mere backbencher I did not, I would have strongly advised MacDonald not to touch the seals of office with the proverbial bargepole. Indeed, I was very doubtful indeed about the wisdom of forming a Government. Given the arithmetic of the situation, we could not possibly embark on a proper Socialist programme. Any attempts to do so and the Liberals, who promised to support us on trade and some other matters, would take the side of the Conservatives and vote us down. And what use is a Labour Government if it cannot follow a Socialist agenda? It would be a case of office without power. Before returning to London, I said as much to Ann and she agreed with me. Like me, she believed that it would be better to wait until we were in a position to follow our own agenda with assured power to carry it out.

However, by the time I got back to London, other counsels had prevailed and Ramsay MacDonald was prime minister. Of course, to an extent I could understand it. The desire to form the first-ever Labour Government must have been powerful, as was our determination to keep the Conservatives out of office. But I still though it unwise. Even so, I was delighted to accept an invitation from MacDonald to visit him at 10 Downing Street in January, 1924. Amusingly enough, from previous experience I knew the place better than he did, and took some delight in pointing to him the various rooms I had been in during negotiations with Lloyd George among others.

Perhaps I should offer an opinion about Ramsay MacDonald. After all, I had known him for a long time before that interview with him. I had come across him at the formation of the Independent Labour Party in 1893 and came to have a great respect for him. You will know that I did not have the easiest of upbringings. MacDonald's was even more difficult. He was the illegitimate son of impoverished parents in Lossiemouth in north-east Scotland. He had a limited education at the local board school where he later became a pupil-teacher. He travelled to London where he worked as a clerk before becoming a political journalist and joined the ILP in 1893. That was when I first made his acquaintance. In 1900 he became Secretary of the Labour Representatives' Committee, then in 1906 became the Labour MP for Leicester. He lost his seat in 1918 after briefly being the Labour leader, then regained it in 1922 and, soon after, became leader again.

On a personal level, I liked the man very much. We were not exactly political bedfellows. I always felt that he was a wee bit close to the centre ground whereas I was always Socialist in my views. Nevertheless, we hit it off well together. Perhaps the fact that we were both Scots helped. Besides, he had a natural dignity and courtesy about him which appealed to me. I think that maybe I sympathised with him a wee bit as well because, like me, he was no great orator, preferring to make his statements in a relatively quiet, fact-laden manner. It made me wonder how he would stand up to the other parties' experienced political heavyweights at the dispatch box. I feared for him a little, I have to confess. In some ways, he was rather like me and I certainly could not imagine myself taking on either Bonar Law or Asquith in a fierce, unrehearsed debate of the kind which typified much of what went on the the Commons. But he had an inner strength, James Ramsay MacDonald. If he had not possessed that, he would not have got as far as he had. I just prayed that it would be enough to see him through the difficult days which undoubtedly lay ahead.

'Come away through to my private office, Bob,' he told me on that cold evening. He showed me through, sat me down, and told me to have a pipe if I wanted one. 'Congratulations on your re-election, by the way.'

'And you on yours,' I replied. 'But you're flying a wee bit higher than me now, Ramsay,' as I puffed gently on my pipe.

'Aye, and there's those say that, like Icarus, I'm flying too high and I'll get my wings clipped,' he laughed. Then he looked at me carefully. 'You are feeling better these days?'

'Grand, thank you.' I was wondering where this conversation was going.

'I'm glad to hear it,' he said. 'Now, I'm in the process of putting together a cabinet and I wondered if you had any views on the matter.'

'Me?' I gasped.

'Yes you, Bob Smillie. Man, you've been round longer than I have. There's hardly a politician in the land you haven't met and dealt with. Besides, you have the pulse of the miners and I want to do right by those men. So, come on. Tell me your opinion.'

Well, I suppose I was flattered and I was certainly pleased to do what I could to help. If I was initially surprised at his request, I could see that it made some kind of sense. Most of the advice he would be getting was from fellow politicians, some of whom were perhaps too close to the centre of things to see the wider picture. The kind of men who'd advised him to form a Government in the first place, but I kept that thought to myself. And it was certainly true that I knew the likely candidates for cabinet pretty well and perhaps with the advantage that I did not see them with political eyes. So we talked for a while and I mentioned a few names. Men like Henderson, Thomas, Webb and even Snowden. I didn't believe that Snowden would be Socialist enough for my liking but, as I have already explained, with Labour as only a minority Government there would be little room for Socialism anyway. At that point, I thought that the conversation was over, but it wasn't.

'There's one name you've left out, Bob.'

'And who might that be?' I racked my brains.

'Bob Smillie, of course,' he said quietly.

'What?' I gasped, almost dropping my pipe in surprise.

'I want you in the cabinet, Bob.'

'Me? Doing what?'

'I haven't made my mind up about that,' he replied. 'I'm perfectly happy to negotiate that with you. There are cabinet roles dealing with trade and industry and, to persuade you to join us, I would even create a new cabinet post.' He slapped his knee. 'What do you say, Bob?'

'I hardly know what to say.' I was virtually stammering, I was so shocked. But deep down I knew what my answer had to be, 'Prime Minister,' I said, believing that the conversation had taken such a turn as to demand formality, 'you do me a great honour,' I sighed deeply. 'A few years ago, I would have jumped at the chance. But now? Not now, I fear.'

'But why not, Bob?'

'I am too old. Not only that but I have suffered health problems in the past.' I told him a little of my months of despair and uncertainty following my resignation from the MFGB. 'If I were put in a public position again, with the great demands of Cabinet Office, I believe it would not be long before my health suffered again.'

'I see, Bob. I am very sorry.' He sounded genuinely disappointed.

'Besides, Ann would never let me,' I added, trying to make light of the matter.

'Aye, there's always the wives,' he agreed, smiling. 'But I'm sure there's something you can do to help us, Bob.'

An hour later, I left Downing Street, having agreed to take the post of Chairman of the Parliamentary Committee. In that role, which was mainly organisational, I could be of help to the Labour Party without having to become a very public figure which, to be frank, would have filled me with foreboding. I was greatly heartened by the time I spent with Ramsay MacDonald. He seemed in good spirits and determined to make the best of this rare opportunity. He confided in me that he did not believe it would last very long and that he was determined to impress on the country that Labour could govern responsibly. I entirely saw his point. Competence would have to be established first. Real Socialism would have to wait a little longer.

In the event, that first Labour Government lasted for only nine months. It came to an end in a bizarre fashion when the Liberals combined with the Conservatives in protest against our having published an article urging soldiers not to fire on striking workers. Strictly speaking, it was not a vote of confidence but Ramsay MacDonald treated it as such. An election was called and parliament was dissolved. You might imagine that, having a life of only nine months, that first Labour Government could not have done very much. Surprisingly enough, you would be wrong.

In spite of the fact that the Government had neither the time nor the parliamentary support to pursue a Socialist programme, it did manage to enact some measures for the benefit of ordinary people. There was a Housing Act to provide £9 million a year to build council houses, old age pensions and unemployment benefits were increased, and free places in grammar schools were increased while spare scholarships to universities were brought back, having been got rid of some years earlier. I managed to overcome my reluctance to participate in public debate by speaking in those debates dealing with housing and unemployment benefits.

I felt proud of MacDonald's efforts on foreign affairs. He took the role of foreign secretary as well as prime minister and saw his mission as helping to unify the recently warring states of Europe. Given his short tenure, he was remarkably successful in this. He was largely responsible for the Dawes Plan which eased the very tense Franco-German relations, for a time at least. He became heavily involved in the League of Nations, in which he believed passionately. I, too, was a strong advocate of the League, believing that anything which offered hope of a future without war was worth pursuing, and spoke twice in the House on its behalf. More controversially, but entirely rightly in my opinion, MacDonald gave full diplomatic recognition to the new regime in Russia, signed a peace treaty, and even opened negotiations about a British loan to that scarred country. I fully approved of those measures, even if the Conservatives and many Liberals disapproved.

I would say that there were some real achievements during those nine months. There was a rather strange consequence. Within the wider public, there was recognition of Labour's competence but, among our natural supporters, there was disappointment that the Government had not been Socialist enough. It was in that public mood that we all entered the general election. Only four days before polling, the Conservatives indulged in political misbehaviour which I would have thought beyond any party. The *Daily Mail* – whose friend is that? – published the Zinoviev Letter, alleging that it proved collusion between the Russian Communists and the British Labour Movement. This caused a sensation at the time. It would be much later before it was proved to be a hoax involving Conservative Central Office, British Intelligence and White Russian émigrés. It did little to help us in the general election. Allied to some workers' discontent at Labour's failure to develop Socialism, it caused a loss of support. The Conservatives swept the boards with 419 seats, we took 159 and the Liberals suffered a disaster, winning only 40 seats. It was clear that we were in for a long period of Conservative Government.

Had the Labour Government lasted longer, I would not have sought re-election. I said as much to William Straker shortly before the 1924 Election was called. I explained to him the absolute truth. That I was getting old – I was now sixty-seven years of age – and that I was none too certain of my health. Perhaps I should have been more explicit with him. Although they were relatively mild, I was beginning to re-experience those symptoms which had plagued me during late 1920 and for much of 1921. I was having great difficulty in getting a good night's sleep, so was often fatigued. My eyesight was sometimes good, at other times not so good. My confidence was not particularly high. Perhaps most worryingly, when on my own I sometimes found myself having conversations with people who were not there: Ann, our children, Keir Hardie. None of these symptoms was regular, and they were relatively mild. Yet I knew that there was something amiss with me. I feared it was only likely to get worse.

Had I had the chance to talk to William again, I am sure I would have explained it to him more fully. But soon after I told him that I wasn't quite a hundred per cent (and had said no more than that), the general election was called. Labour had nobody else ready to contest the Morpeth seat so my name went forward again. I was re-elected once more with a large but slightly reduced minority. Before returning to London, I spent some time in Larkhall with Ann. I said nothing to her about my doubts, even less than I had said to William Straker. I should have told them both everything. That I didn't was one of the biggest mistakes of my life.

XXXII
By The Wayside

SO WE WERE landed with a Conservative Government backed up by a huge majority. Oh, if only Ramsay MacDonald had had that, we could have achieved so much more. But if I was hardly delighted to see Baldwin and his men in power, as a democrat I could hardly complain about it. Quite a few people on our side were of the view that the Conservatives won because of the effect on the public of the Zinoviev Letter. To be honest, I had a wee laugh with Ann about that. It may well have been true that the publication of the letter gave us a deal of bad publicity, but it was clear that it only affected the margin of the Conservatives' victory and not the result itself. During the election, our opponents made much more of the facts that we had done little for ordinary people and that we were negotiating with the Bolshevik Government than they made of the letter. As politicians always do, they played around with our record in Government. Which is not quite the same as saying that they told a pack of lies, though at times they came close to it. Ann agreed with my views on the matter, so I must have been right!

I drew solace from the fact that we had at least established ourselves as the main opposition to the Conservatives, with the Liberals nowhere. Though that was little comfort as the Conservatives swung into action and began their programme of legislation. You will find full details of this if you wish to consult a history book but, to refresh your memory, let me remind you of the main details. Domestically, they passed the Widows, Orphans and Old Age Contributory Pensions Act. They also extended the vote to women over the age of 21. In foreign affairs, they signed the Locarno Treaties which guaranteed national borders but omitted to deal with Germany's eastern frontiers. They also signed the Kellogg-Brand Pact, along with sixty-five other countries, renouncing war as an instrument of national policy. This sounded an excellent idea but the pact had more holes in it than a lump of Gorgonzola cheese. Finally, they were totally against developing any relationship with Russia and renounced the treaties we had signed with that country.

There were other matters, to be sure, but the above were the most significant. I actually supported two of their measures, on pensions and unemployment insurance. Not because I believed that they were perfect, far from it, but because I believed that they both moved in the right direction. I did not speak on those issues in the House. I simply listened. Neither did I vote in favour of them: I simply abstained. There are, after all, certain niceties to be observed when you are a member of the opposition. The only major issue on which I did speak was on the Government's irrational behaviour towards Russia. We were dealing with countries with which we had recently been at odds in a most bloodthirsty war and yet we would not deal with another country because our Government disliked its politics. How foolish, partial and naïve mankind can be at times! Which view I expressed briefly in the House before making a hasty exit before some Conservative started railing against 'that old Socialist agitator'.

The awful truth, which I quite candidly confess, is that I played little part in the debating chamber during those five years. When able to, I attended, listened, and voted. But, beyond helping our Parliamentary Committee, I did little else. I just did not feel able to. The fires which had burned so brightly within me were dying down. The optimism and determination I had once possessed were waning. Frankly, I grew to hate the House. Or, should I say, I began to detest the ineffective role I was playing within it. Not only was I getting old, I was also regularly unwell.

It is impossible to convey to you exactly how I was feeling for the simple reason I could never find the words to describe it to myself. That I was tired, I could put down to poor sleeping habits and growing older. The occasional blurring of my eyes and failure to remember things clearly were perhaps also due to age. But the increasing sense of panic when meeting new people, even people I knew; what was causing that? And the feeling that I was moving in slow motion while the world around me was moving at a normal speed: how could I explain that to myself? And why was I happier on my own than in company? Why did my whole body sometimes tense to the extent that it felt that I was about to burst? I could answer none of those questions and tried to brush them aside. Not that that made things any better. It came to a head late in 1925 when I spent five minutes talking to a man I was convinced I did not know. When my head cleared, I discovered to my total embarrassment that it was Ramsay MacDonald. He insisted on accompanying me back to my lodgings and sending for his own doctor.

I do not remember the doctor's name, only that he was kind and patient. After giving me a thorough examination, he told me that he could find no signs of organic problems but that he was concerned about my reflexes. Trying to make light of it, I told him that I had dropped many catches at cricket in my time, but he would have none of it. He was insistent that I needed bed-rest, at the very least, and that I should consult my doctor who knew me best as soon as possible. I insisted on paying his fee out of my own pocket. I did not want it going through Party funds and people knowing that I was unwell. Ramsay could not have been kinder. He helped me pack and accompanied me in a cab to the station so that I could catch the next train home. He told me to make sure that I was feeling better before I gave thought to returning to London, and then the train was pulling out. I cannot vouch for the mood of the other passengers on what was a fairly quiet train, but I know that I was in despair.

It didn't take Ann long to work out how tired I was and, the day after I got home, Andrew MacQuillan was taking a good long look at me. By then, I was rested enough to think that it should have many been the other way round. Andrew MacQuillan had been a local doctor for so long that he was almost part of the furniture, as the saying goes. You know what it's like. You get to know somebody well and, in the back of your mind, you imagine he'll be around forever. That day though, and two years older than me, Andrew was wheezing like an old accordion. He said he'd had a bit of a chest infection but I reckoned it was more likely the result of years of smoking those cheroots he was so fond of. Not that he paid any attention to my opinion of his health, mind you. What doctor ever does?

'Your blood pressure's a wee bit low,' he told me.

'Better than being high, isn't it?' I replied.

'Aye, but in the middle's better,' he said, wheezing huskily. 'Now then, Bob, you just do what I tell you.'

He had me following his finger as he moved it one way and another in front of my eyes. Then he had me counting fingers as he stuck them up and withdrew them in all sorts of variations as quickly as he could. Then he barked out commands, telling me how many of my fingers he wanted to see held out, demanding that I did it quickly. Oddly enough, I was almost enjoying it. It reminded me of some of the parlour games Ann and I used to play with the bairns when they were small. Then it was time to move my arms, first one way then the other, have my knees tapped with a small hammer and all the rest of it.

'Well, Robert,' he said, putting away the various tools of his profession, 'you're quite fit for a man of your age.' Conveniently forgetting that I was actually younger than he was. 'But ... '

'But I'm not right. That is what you were going to say, isn't it, Andrew?'

'Aye, that's about it.' Then echoing the words of Ramsay MacDonald's doctor, he added, 'I'm not happy with your reflexes.'

I couldn't draw him out on what exactly he meant by that though, in all likelihood, he wasn't clear about it himself. Andrew was as good a local doctor as I ever came across, but he was no specialist. On the other hand, he knew a man who was, a good friend of his at that. Which was why a week later I found myself in the offices of a specialist in Sauchiehall Street in Glasgow. I should tell you that by that stage I had an inkling of what Andrew and the London doctor had been driving at. My knowledge of the workings of the human body were as limited as the next man's but, given the symptoms I had been experiencing and the fact that both doctors had expressed concern over my reflexes, I had formed the opinion that their view was that my problem lay with my brain. Which was not exactly a comforting thought, I can tell you. Ann had seen where opinion was heading too and wanted to accompany me on my visit to the specialist. But I was having none of that. In the event of bad news, which was what I was expecting, she would become upset. I wasn't sure that I could cope with that in front of a stranger so I went on my own.

I was not long in the waiting-room before I was shown in to see the specialist. As he is probably still practising to this day, he being a lot younger than me, I will not reveal his real name. Let me call him Mr Auchterlonie. When he stood to meet me and shake my hand, I felt a distinct urge to leave. He was tall, thin and as pale a man as I had ever seen. Dressed in a black suit, his hair slicked back, he had slightly protruding teeth and a freezingly cold handshake. I can remember telling myself, 'If he asks to take some blood, Bob, run for the door!'

I should have stuck to my old belief never to judge a man by his appearance. Mr Auchterlonie turned out to be as warm and humane a man as I had ever met. He told me that he specialised in neurones then, seeing that I had no idea what he was talking about, explained a little about brain dysfunction, how they could take many different forms and why, on the basis of Andrew MacQuillan's notes, he felt that I was likely to be suffering from one kind or another. He was good enough to avoid medical jargon, which would have been way beyond me, and he offered his explanations in layman's terms.

In the forty minutes or so I was with him, he put me through a series of tests. And no, he didn't draw blood! In fact, he did nothing invasive at all. He repeated a number of things that Andrew had done, checking the reactions of my eyes, fingers, arms and knees. But he spent longer asking me questions, taking notes all the while. The questions were not particularly searching, mainly about the events in my life, the people in my family, that sort of thing. I was aware of the fact that I paused now and again, but I did answer all of his questions. Finally, he put me through a series of what he called verbal reasoning tests designed, I suppose, to assess how well my mental faculties were working. When he had finished, he told me that he could not make a full diagnosis based on one visit. In simple terms, he suspected that my brain was not functioning quite as it should but that he needed to see me again some time later to confirm that view. We made an appointment for three months from that date, I thanked him for his time, then went home.

I told Ann what had happened and what Auchterlonie had said and she immediately took the view that I should resign my seat in parliament. That thought had occurred to me too but I was loath to do it straight away. The local party in Morpeth would need time to select a new man and, given that the tide of public opinion was in favour of the Conservatives, there was no guarantee of success in any subsequent by-election. So I decided to write to William Straker to let him know everything. I offered to resign if that was what he felt was best but said that

I was prepared to carry on until such a time that he felt I should be replaced.

Almost by return of post, I received William's reply. He expressed great sympathy for my condition but asked that, as long as I felt fit to do so, I would continue to represent Morpeth. In the meantime, and as unobtrusively as possible, he would take steps to identify a political candidate in case my health should suffer further. He also told me that I should reduce my number of visits to the constituency, instead returning to Larkhall more often to be with Ann. And that was how matters hung a month or so later when, much against Ann's judgement, I returned to London.

I immediately sought out Ramsay MacDonald and explained to him in full how things were with me. I offered to continue chairing the Parliamentary Committee until I next saw Mr Auchterlonie but advised him that he should begin looking for somebody to replace me as I felt it likely that, at the very least, the specialist would tell me to reduce my workload. Ramsay was both sympathetic and understanding, and agreed to my suggestion. That seen to, I tried to return to my work as a Constituency MP.

This was at a time when there was a great deal of industrial unrest and the seeds of something greater brewing. As ever, the miners were in the thick of it. How I yearned to be fit enough to become more actively involved. Of course, the mines had not been nationalised, which left some festering resentment among my people. Private owners were refusing to invest in the mines which meant that, as late as 1925, four out of five tons of coal were still being hewn by picks rather than coal-cutting machinery. Our exports were damaged by a return to the gold standard and, in the autumn of 1925, the owners announced lower wages and longer hours. Baldwin intervened with a temporary subsidy and yet another Royal Commission but the miners' mood was dark indeed.

Not just the miners either. The Trades Union Congress made it clear that they supported the miners because, if the miners' wages were reduced, it was likely that the wages of other workers would soon follow. The message was clear. In the event of a reduction in wages, there would be a general strike. Everything now hinged on the report of the Royal Commission chaired by Sir Herbert Samuel.

That was the general situation when I returned to Glasgow for my second appointment with Mr Auchterlonie. He was as kind and welcoming as he had been on the first occasion. I was put through the same series of physical and verbal tests again, then sat for a while in the waiting room while he went over his notes. Then he called me back through to deliver his opinion. Again, he was wise enough not to use technical terms. The substance of his diagnosis was that I was suffering from a degenerative disease of the brain. It was his opinion that it could not be treated, that there were some medicines newly arrived in the market which claimed to be able to delay the degeneration, but he had no confidence in them as there was little evidence to back up the claims made for them. As a good physician should, he gave me his opinion slowly and clearly, without causing me undue fear or making any attempt to raise false hopes.

'So, it's here to stay and can't be stopped,' I suggested.

'That's entirely right, Mr Smillie.'

'And from your use of the word degenerative, I assume that it can only get worse.'

'I'm afraid so.'

'Do you know how quickly and what the effects will be?' I asked him.

'The speed of degeneration is impossible to calculate,' he told me, then looked in his notes. 'In the three months between your visits, there has been a slight deterioration in the nature and speed of your reflexes. If we assume that that rate of deterioration is maintained, then you have quite a few years of relatively normal life left in you yet. It is the same with your verbal reasoning responses. A little change, but not much.' He paused briefly to consider his next words. 'As time goes by, you will probably experience your symptoms such as unease and panic rather more frequently. But there will probably be times when you are relatively free of them. I'm sorry that I cannot be more specific, Mr Smillie, but this kind of illness does not lend itself to precise diagnosis.' He shot me a quick glance. 'How have the past few months been?

'Pretty fair,' I told him, which was more or less true. 'I have kept my workload reasonably light, so don't feel too bad at all.'

'You'll have been responding to the Pensions Bill, I suppose,' he said, showing that he knew more about my work than I did of his. 'A lot of reading, I dare say.'

'A fair bit,' I admitted, 'but I do less than I used to. I talk a lot to other men and fill the gaps in my knowledge that way.'

'Very wise, Mr Smillie. I would recommend that you do as little close reading as possible.' Then he smiled. 'Hard for an MP, I imagine. Do you intend to see out this parliament?'

'I agreed with my wife that I would make a decision on that after hearing your opinion.'

'Goodness me, I see. Well, I can only give you a medical opinion, not a political one.'

'I understand that,' I told him. 'But from what you have said, I understand that my condition will get worse, though perhaps only slowly. But will I be aware of that?'

'Oh yes, Mr Smillie,' he replied. 'I do not anticipate dramatic changes. You will become aware of your reactions slowing down. Perhaps your levels of fatigue will increase and you are likely to experience depressive moods. But these things will not jump out on you. You will be aware of them.'

'That's fine,' I said. 'That means I will know when I have to throw the towel in. For now, I would like to continue.' I shrugged. 'After all, what else would I do with myself?'

'You could try taking a rest,' he laughed. 'But I fear that I am about twenty years too late with that advice.'

When I got home, I told Ann about my decision to stay on and, although I could see the concern in her eyes, she supported that decision in the same understanding way that she had always done. I wrote to William Straker giving him the news and he sent back by telegram the best wishes not only of himself but of all the members of the local party in Morpeth. When I got back to London, I confirmed with Ramsay MacDonald my desire to withdraw from the chair of the Parliamentary Committee. He thanked me for my support and candour, then set the wheels in motion to find a replacement.

Strangely enough, having had my illness diagnosed, I felt rather calmer about things. Perhaps it was just the typical human reaction which says it's better to know, however grim that knowledge might be, than to let your mind wander into foul imaginings. At any rate, I was calm enough to set down a working schedule for myself, a strategy suggested by Mr Auchterlonie and strongly supported by Ann, who insisted that I had to cut back on my work. That schedule involved fewer hours in the House, only making occasional supporting speeches in debates, reducing the number of visits to Morpeth, and spending more time at home with Ann in Larkhall, simply resting. I more or less stuck to that schedule during the last three years of my working life. I was in a state of semi-retirement, if you like.

Of course, the major event of those years was the General Strike of 1926. The Samuel Commission delivered its verdict in March 1926. It recommended that mine owners should press ahead with long overdue modernisation and should, in no circumstances, demand longer hours from the men as that would only lead to over-production. Neither should they reduce wages but the Government should withdraw its subsidy which would mean some reduction in wages, but in the short-term only. Or so they hoped. Given the history and record of owners, I believed that that was a forlorn hope indeed. For once, the miners and the owners were united. For very different reasons, they both rejected Samuel's proposals. The Government tried to promote negotiations but they did not get far. The situation prompted Lord Birkenhead to observe, 'I thought that the miners' leaders were the stupidest men in the country until I had the misfortune to meet the mine owners.' Hardly flattering to our men but an even worse slap in the face for the employers.

On April 30th, the owners planned to reduce wages and the MFGB responded by saying that, in that event, they would strike on May 1st. The Government reacted on April 30th when, under the provisions of the Emergency Powers Act, they declared a state of national emergency and had the king sign the following proclamation:

BY THE KING

A proclamation

George R.I.

Whereas by the Emergency Powers Act, 1920, it is enacted that if it appears to Us that any action has been taken or is immediately threatened by any persons or body of persons of such a nature and on so extensive a scale as to be calculated, by interfering with the supply and distribution of food, water, fuel , or light, or with the means of loco-motion, to deprive the community, or any substantial portion of the community, of the essentials of life, We may, by Proclamation, declare that a state of emergency exists:

And whereas the present immediate threat of cessation of work in Coal Mines does, in Our opinion, constitute a state of emergency within the meaning of the said Act:

Now, therefore, in pursuance of the said Act, We do, by and with the advice of Our Privy Council, hereby declare that a state of emergency exists.

Given at our Court at Buckingham Palace, this Thirtieth day of April, in the year of our Lord One thousand nine hundred and twenty-six, and in the sixteenth year of Our Reign.

GOD SAVE THE KING

To this proclamation were added any number of regulations, very draconian in nature, some of which were:

'If any person attempts or does any act calculated or likely to cause mutiny, sedition, or disaffection among any of His Majesty's forces, or among the members of any police force, or any fire brigade, or among the civilian population, or to impede, delay, or restrict any measures taken for securing and regulating the supply or distribution of food, water, fuel, light or other necessities, or for maintaining the means of transit or of locomotion, or for any other purposes essential to the public safety or the life of the community, he shall be guilty of an offence against these regulations ...

' ... provided that a person shall not be guilty of an offence under this regulation by reason only of his taking part in a strike or peacefully persuading any other person to take part in a strike ...

'If any person, without lawful authority or excuse, has in his possession or on premises in his occupation or under his control, any document containing any report or statement, the publication of which would be a contravention to the foregoing provisions of this regulation, he shall be guilty of an offence against these regulations unless he proves that he did not know and had no reason to suspect that the document contained any such report or statement, or that he had no intention of transmitting or circulating the document, or distributing copies thereof to or amongst other persons.'

As it turned out, the owners brought the industry to a halt. On the same day as the wage reduction was to take effect, they effected a lock-out. Immediately, the

MFGB reacted and the coal strike began. Ernest Bevin, one of the great men of the Labour Movement, then announced that if the owners would not come to terms then a General Strike would begin on May 3rd. Given my history, you might wonder if I played any part in all of this. Well, I did, but it was only a minor role. In my office in the House, I had a succession of visitors seeking my advice. I talked to Ernest Bevin, Herbert Smith, Walter Citrine, Arthur Pugh, AJ Cook and even had a visit from Ramsay MacDonald to discuss the Labour Party's stance.

With no negotiations in sight, the General Strike began on May 4th rather than May 3rd due to a frustrated belief that the owners were about to announce that they would enter negotiations, which they did not. History has it that the Government was well prepared which the strikers were not. To a large extent that was true, though as soon as the strike began great efforts were made to organise things, as is proved in the words of the pamphlet *The Nine Days* by AJ Cook:

Tuesday, May 4th, started with the workers answering the call. What a wonderful response! What Loyalty! What solidarity! From John o'Groats to Land's End the workers answered the call to arms to defend us, to defend the brave miner in his fight for a living wage.

Hurriedly the General Council formed their Committees, made preparations to face this colossal task – the first in the history of this country. No one could over-estimate the greatness of the task that faced the General Council, and to the credit of many of the members – especially Ernest Bevin – they made every effort possible to bring into being machinery to cope with the requirements.

The difficulties of transport, of communication, of giving information, were enormous; but the foresight and energy of the officials in the country and of the rank and file rose to the occasion. Links were formed, bulletins were issued; officials, staff and voluntary workers of the T.U.C. and the Labour Party worked all night and day to create the machinery necessary to link up the whole movement – machinery that would have been prepared by common sense leadership months and months before.

It was a wonderful achievement, a wonderful accomplishment that proved conclusively that the Labour Movement has the men and women that are capable in an emergency of providing the means of carrying on the country. Who can forget the effect of motor conveyances with posters saying "By permission of the T.U.C."? The Government with its O.M.S. were absolutely demoralised. Confidence, calm, and order prevailed everywhere, despite the irritation caused by the volunteers, blacklegs, and special constables. The workers acted as one. Splendid discipline! Splendid loyalty!'

Of course, many people other than the miners were involved. Even looking back at it from some distance, I still marvel at the level of solidarity shown as the strike began. In the industries called out; including road, rail, gas, docks, printing, electricity, building, iron, steel, chemicals, textiles, as well as coal-mining; the response was almost one hundred percent. Over three million men came out, on the surface in support of the miners but, in reality, to protect working people in all industries where wage reductions were planned.

It was hoped that once industry was at a standstill, the Government would be forced to intervene and make the mine owners see reason. The TUC was very moderate in its language, making it clear that this was an industrial strike, not a political one. They were not trying to bring down the Government. All they wanted to do was force the Government to defend miners' wages and jobs and, by implication, wages and jobs in other industries.

I was appalled to hear of violence in some areas. This was largely caused by volunteers, by the middle-class men, who responded to the Government's call to man essential services. In Glasgow, a crowd attacked a tram depot where volunteers were about to take the trams out. The same happened in Leeds, where a crowd of about 5,000 people threw coal and stones at trams driven by volunteers. In Middlesborough, a crowd stopped the movement of trains by blocking the track with stolen cars while in Aberdeen strikers attacked buses being driven by student volunteers. Miners from Crawlington derailed The Flying Scotsman and in Preston a large crowd stormed a police station to secure the release of a man arrested for throwing a stone at a bus being driven by a volunteer driver.

I was in despair at all of this, for two reasons. First, as you know, I had always abhorred violence as a means of securing aims. It achieves nothing proper for the perpetrator or the victim. Second, violence simply lent legitimacy to the strikers' opponents and the press made much of that. In the main reports of the time, there was little mention made of the Emergency Powers or the roles of the police and the army. It was all about the terror of violence. In turn, that prompted even more volunteers to turn up and do the work of the strikers. I can see them to this day, those fresh-faced boys and well scrubbed men delighting in their temporary roles as industrial workers. How exuberant they would have felt if faced by a lifetime of poorly paid, industrial labour is, of course, another matter.

I believe I was as surprised as anybody when the TUC called off the General Strike after only nine days. I believe it was because they were totally unprepared for the effort, were alarmed by Sir John Simon's view that the strike was illegal and that the leaders could be sued for damages, had seen £4 million spent already and no softening of the owners' attitudes and did not believe that they were getting enough support from us in the House of Commons because Ramsay MacDonald had declared himself against sympathetic strikes. It was at that stage, May 12th, that as a result of all the tension in the air, I began to feel unwell and returned to Larkhall, from where I could more sedately follow events.

The miners decided to continue their strike in spite of the collapse of the General Strike. In honesty, I never felt that that would have any positive outcome for them. The position of the owners and their friends in Government had been strengthened by the TUC's failure. In spite of donations from overseas trade unions, the largest of which was from Russia, I knew that the finances of the MFGB were not sufficient to withstand the demands imposed by a long strike. And, man, but it was a long strike. How they fought for their livelihood, those brave boys! The strike did not end until November 30th, 1926. It had lasted for over seven months. Nothing had been gained except, perhaps, a little self-respect. There is so much more I could say about that awful episode, but I will refrain from doing so. As a last word on the subject, I will simply offer some extracts from an MFGB statement on the matter. I believe that the following words speak for themselves:

FELLOW TRADE UNIONISTS!

After seven months of grim struggle, on a scale the like of which has not been known in Trade Union history in this or in any country of the world, the M.F.G.B., in common with the other Trade Unions, is called to give its judgement on the events of the first fortnight of that struggle.

The population of these islands had never previously experienced anything resembling the situation created by the general Strike of May 4th to May 12th. Limited though it was both in number of workers affected, in the objective aimed at and in the time it lasted, the General Strike showed the working class to be possessed of qualities of courage, comradeship, and disciplined resource that had not hitherto been called forth and that gave good omen for future solidarity.

If we were deserted and forced to fight a lone fight, it was not by the workers that we were abandoned. Their hearts beat true to the end. From the workers of our country, and of the world, and especially from the Trade Unionists of Russia, we obtained unstinted aid. For the help given, whether from Union funds or from individual workers, we convey the gratitude of the miners' wives and children.

The fight is not over. The conditions of the employers are imposed conditions and bring with them no goodwill or spirit of conciliation. Longer hours and lower wages cannot bring peace in the coalfields; nor will we allow district agreements to shatter our strength and unity. Our organisation is still intact, and we are determined to recover the ground that has been lost. In this endeavour we look with confidence for the full support of the whole Trade Union Movement.

Yours, etc.,
On behalf of the Miners' Federation of Great Britain.

HERBERT SMITH, President.
T. RICHARDS, Vice-President.

W.P. RICHARDSON, Treasurer.

J. BAKER	H. HUGHES
J. BERRY	J. JONES
S.BLACKLEDGE	W. LATHAM
P. CHAMBERS	P. LEE
T. CAPE	W. MANSFIELD
S.O. DAVIES	P. MCKENNA
J. DOONAN	J.A. PARKINSON
EBBY EDWARDS	G. PEART
S. EDWARDS	A. SMITH
J. ELKS	J. SMITH
T. FLATLEY	J.W. SMITH
C. GILL	W.K. SMITH
J.M. GILLIANS	W. STRAKER
J. GILLILAND	J.E.SWAN
FRANK HALL	C. THOMPSON
W.S. HALL	T. TROTTER
F.J. HANCOCK	F.B. VARLEY

A.J. COOK, Secretary.
January 12th, 1927

As for myself, I spent the next two years almost as much at home as I did at Westminster. Several times, I asked the committee in Morpeth if it might not be wise to let somebody else challenge for the seat, Each time they said the same thing: that they would consider it an honour if I would see out the parliamentary term. So, for their sakes, I did. I did visit the constituency on a number of occasions, though not as often as I would have liked, and felt humbled by the warmth of the reception that I always got there. They were good folk, the people of Morpeth, and I liked them a great deal. I would place only my own folk in Larkhall above them.

I visited Mr Auchterlonie every six months and, each time, he detected a slight worsening of my condition. But he was happy enough with me and pleased that I had stuck to his suggestion of a lighter schedule. Then in 1929, we were due for another election. I spent that summer saying my goodbyes to the men I had worked with. That was not as emotional as it might have been, because they had been aware of my deteriorating health for some time. I wrote to the committee in Morpeth, formally tendering my resignation. I did the same with the Scottish Miners' Federation whose president I had been on two occasions. In both letters, I cited ill health as my reason for resigning. Then I tidied my office, packed my bags, and left London for the last time. I would miss my friends but I was not sorry to go. At home, I took interest in the results of the general election. Labour won 288 seats, the Conservatives 260 and the Liberals 59. So, Ramsay MacDonald would be prime minister for a second time though, if they voted together, his opponents could defeat him. I expected him to have a difficult time and I prayed for him.

At home, I settled easily enough into retirement. Not simply because I was only a few months short of my seventieth birthday, but also because, as I remarked before, I had been semi-retired for a couple of years. So many men find it very difficult to adjust to retirement because they have done nothing but work throughout their lives and they don't know what to do with themselves when that important part of life comes to an end. In my case, I was prepared for it. Not only had I been winding down, but I had also been giving some thought to what I would so with the extra time I had at my disposal.

Spend more time with Ann, of course, without the cloud hanging over us of my next departure. Visit our children and grandchildren, and have them visit us. That would be a great pleasure for both Ann and myself. I had also determined that I would take our vegetable garden more seriously. Without ever getting in Ann's way, I wanted to learn more about growing produce. I would re-join the cricket club, as a non-playing member of course, and do what I could to help foster it. And, as long as our health permitted, Ann and I would take up walking again in the pleasant countryside around Larkhall. There was one more thing that I promised myself and I promised Ann to secrecy on it. No, don't imagine for a minute that I was going to indulge in gambling or any other vice. Instead, I was going to catch up on my reading. No sin there, of course, but you may remember that Mr Auchterlonie had warned against close reading in case it aggravated my condition. Which is why Ann was sworn to secrecy. Actually, I found that Larkhall Library stocked a fair range of large print books, so I never did contravene doctor's orders. Well, not too much anyway.

One thing I promised myself I would not do was to live in the past. Memories are all very well but I had seen too many people become bitter at their inability to accept the present far less contemplate the future. I did not wish that to happen to me so, in my idle moments, I began to give thought to what might happen next. Not to me, because my life had already run most of its course, but to that cause which had meant so much to me: the Labour Movement.

We were in power again, but hindered by arithmetic. I saw little prospect of real Socialism arising out of that. But we had risen, as the Liberals had fallen, and I was confident that one day we would be returned to power with enough of a majority to follow a truly Socialist programme. I was not at all convinced that I would ever see it at my advanced age, but I was sure it would come. After all, Labour was a young party and had suffered growing pains as all fledglings do. It was hardly more than fifty years since Alexander MacDonald became the first Labour MP to be elected. Now, for the second time, we were in power.

It was my earnest hope that, when the arithmetic allowed, we would remember the ideals on which our Party was founded back in the days when Keir Hardie, myself and others worked so hard to secure its foundation. If the Labour Party were not to fight to deal fundamentally with social evils, it would not be worthy of its name. I felt confident that the men in charge would be mindful of that. Did I say men? We must not forget women either. I was delighted when Ramsay MacDonald appointed Margaret Bondfield as Minister of Labour. I was confident that the status of women would grow and even amazed Ann by telling her that, at some time in the future, I was certain that a woman would be in residence at 10 Downing Street. She was not inclined to agree with me so I had to point out to her that, as women ran most households and families – Ann certainly ran ours – it was inevitable that one day a woman would run the country.

Looking to the future, I hoped that this country would one day see an education system which would aid the development of all children and eliminate the waste of whole classes being ill-educated. I would wish to see better industrial relations based on mutual respect and less of the 'devil take the hindmost' spirit which had bedevilled the nation. And other things too, of course: equal access to good housing, health services and care for the infirm and the elderly, nationalisation of the key industries and redistribution of wealth. Man, my list was a long and challenging one.

I believed that all of this would take vision and boldness. But I believed that our people at that time, and no doubt those to come in future, were capable of showing those qualities. You might not believe this but, in our early days when we were struggling to find our political feet, we received advice from a rather surprising source: none other than Lloyd George. He told us that, if we ever were to achieve fundamental change, we would have to be audacious. He was quite right too, not that we needed telling. But if audacity or boldness, or whatever other words you would care to use, was the order of the day, it would have to be displayed without the services of Robert Smillie. My innings, a long one be it said, was over and it was time for me to retire to the pavilion, leaving others to play the great game.

XXXIII
The End Of The Road

I WILL BE frank with you. The past decade had not been easy. Not easy at all. Not for me; not for Ann and our children. As far as I can tell, it had not been a good period for much of the world, though I do not feel responsible for that. But it is my fault that Ann and our family have been put through so much misery. It is the last thing she has deserved after so many years of devotion, the last thing I would have wished on her. But it turned out that Mr. Auchterlonie's prognosis was accurate. All too accurate, I am afraid.

There have been times during that period when I have felt – how can I put it? – well, normal I suppose. When, apart from the creaking of old bones and not being able to walk as far as I once did, I felt more or less at ease with myself and the world. But there have been other times, the dark times, when I have felt ill-at-ease, short of temper, impatient with my own shortcomings, unable to cope with anything, in the depths of despair. At such times, Ann has been driven to tears, and she has never in her life been a woman prone to that. And I have been the cause of it.

I have lost count now of the number of times I have been in this hospital. At my lowest ebb, I was hardly aware of it, and had no idea how long I spent here. Mr Auchterlonie has been kindness itself. It would have been at his suggestion that I was hospitalised each time though I had no clear knowledge of that. What I do know is that he came to visit me on a number of occasions, driving all the way from Glasgow in his fine new motor car. On one occasion – a bright summer day it was – he took me for a spin in his car and treated me to lunch in a small hotel in Maxwelltown, close to the River Nith. I am embarrassed to relate that I became quite tearful at his generosity. He didn't seem to mind at all. He simply lent me his good silk handkerchief to wipe my tears away.

He became as much a friend as a doctor. Like any true friend, he always told me the truth. My condition was deteriorating – I hardly needed to be told that! – and he was sorry but, apart from draughts to help me sleep, there was little he could do to help me. He explained the reasons for my increasing moroseness and occasional physical aggression, which mean that I was usually tended by male nurses, and insisted that I should feel no shame about it. It was, he said, just nature's way. I felt greatly comforted by his presence and his words.

He was also honest and decent enough to suggest to me that I should consider making my will. I was in Larkhall at the time, during one of my better periods, and I completely saw the sense in his suggestion. He even went so far as to procure the necessary papers and act as my witness. I must have been feeling reasonably in command of myself at the time because we had a wee joke about it all.

'That's all taken care of then, Bob,' he told me.

'And everything goes to Ann,' I said.

'Aye, that's right.'

'You'll do me a favour then?' I asked.

'What's that, Bob?'

'Don't let the money go to her head!'

At the time, there was the huge amount of £9 in my only account. We had a right good laugh over that. I'm telling you that seeing Mr Auchterlonie was a tonic in itself. I owe him a great debt of gratitude.

Every time I came to this hospital, I had a stream of visitors. Of course, Ann was the most regular of those. Occasionally, she came on her own but she preferred to travel in company as it was a long way from Larkhall to Dumfries. My old friends in Larkhall could not have been more helpful, finding ways to help Ann with the journey. Whenever she came, she had a small present for me – some tobacco for my pipe or home-made scones, simple things like that. Not that I always repaid her devotion and kindness too well. There were times when I would deliberately pick an argument with her, just for the sake of it. I have no excuse for that, none at all. I knew what I was doing, well most of the time anyway. I simply had no idea why I was doing it and, once any outburst was over and I had regained my composure, I bitterly regretted it. Too late then – it always was. How Ann put up with it, I will never know.

The only good thing about being here in a hospital like this this is that you know you are safe. Safe from the world and ... well, I don't know really. I can't say that being here ever pleased me. Who is ever happy laid up in hospital? On the other hand, I felt protected somehow. Protected from myself as much as anything else. The other small bonus has been that newspapers have always been available. And unlike my old days in Larkhall when we had to club together to buy quality newspapers, here they are free. So, in my livelier moments, I have been able to keep abreast of events. Not that I always felt pleased by what I read.

Ramsay MacDonald's Labour Government lasted only two years. Perhaps they got one or two things right. They renewed the subsidy for the building of council houses and passed a Coal Mines Act reducing the miners' working day to seven-and-a-half hours. But that was about all there was to show for two years of Labour Government. They were limited by their lack of a working majority and a world economic crisis, of course, but where was the zeal, the radicalism that we had fought for over the years?

Then I was appalled to find out that my old friend Ramsay decided that, because he could not secure unanimous agreement within his own cabinet for economic measures, he had to cut and run. He handed in the Government's resignation to George V but stayed on himself as the leader of what was called a National Government which included Conservatives and Liberals. I hate to say this of an old friend, but I considered this as a betrayal, a lack of backbone. In the 1931 general election, Labour lost many seats. MacDonald didn't last much longer and Baldwin took over. I could hardly tell the difference.

I was at home in Larkhall during one of my healthier periods. It was some time in late 1936 or early 1937, I can't be sure of which. I was delighted when my son Daniel and his son Robert, named after me, came visiting from their home in Ayr. Daniel had done well for himself. After leaving the army, he attended Glasgow University and later became a professor at the Agricultural College near Ayr. His wee boy, Robert, was a pleasant-looking lad of about nine years. I had the impression of somebody who was normally lively but, in my company at least, he was well behaved and sat quietly while Daniel and I discussed the affairs of the day.

I seem to remember we talked for ages about two matters. The first was unemployment. In the staple industries at the time, unemployment was a real curse. Many men were idle in the Larkhall area alone. It was distressing to see them. With a National Government predominantly made up of Conservatives, there was little chance of relief either. At that time, 25% of miners were unemployed. And there were dreadful regional variations too. At the same time as there was 68% unemployment in Jarrow and 62% in Merthyr Tydfil, in St Albans it was only 3.9%. But would a Government run by Conservatives lose any sleep over the North-East and South Wales as long as their heartlands were managing? I think you know the answer to that as well as I do.

The other subject Daniel and I blethered about for ages was the war in Spain, the Spanish Civil War as it was called. The fascists under General Franco revolted against Spain's legitimate left-wing Republican Government. Most European countries signed an agreement not to interfere but the Italians and Germans, under Mussolini and Hitler, broke the agreement and sent extensive help to Franco. In Britain, many people of a left-wing persuasion like myself wanted our Government to support the Spanish Government against France. I was disappointed that the Labour Party, now led by Clement Attlee, shrank back from that position because they did not want to co-operate with British and International communists. As a country we did nothing. Was Baldwin ever likely to support a foreign, left-wing Government? But volunteers from this country, mainly unemployed miners, and volunteers from around the world, flocked to Spain to fight against Franco. Daniel and I were deploring what was going on there. Then he dropped his bombshell.

'Young Bob's gone there,' he told me.

'What? Young Bob? Alex's boy?'

'Aye,' he said grimly. 'Like yourself, father, he has no time for the fascists.'

'Oh, dear brave boy' I almost cried in anguish. Then I noticed my grandson Robert staring at me. He must have been wondering what an old man like me was getting worked up about. I moved towards him and bent over his seated figure. 'You've been a good boy, young Robert,' I told him, 'giving your father and me time to blether. Now you go through to the scullery and I'm sure your Gran will have something for you.'

He scampered back through a few minutes later, Ann smiling by his side. He was clutching a poke of sweets, probably treacle toffees which Ann was a dab hand at making. Before leaving with his father, he shook my hand, me telling him to be a good boy, which I am sure he would be. Since then, I have seen Daniel and my other children both in Larkhall and here in the hospital, but I haven't seen young Robert again. I think of him often.

I must have been keeping in reasonable health at that time because I was still at home in June when dreadful news arrived. Over in Spain young Bob had died from natural causes, something which caused him terrible stomach pains. In that case under my bed, I still have a copy of a letter from Fenner Brockway, Secretary of the Independent Labour Party, who had just returned from Spain and offered these words of comfort:

My first overwhelming impression is of the affection with which he [Bob] was held everywhere. I found this among the comrades in Barcelona and still more among the boys who had been at the Front. They literally loved him, and they told me that among the Spanish comrades and in the villages behind the Front he was almost a legendary figure. When the news came of his death even soldiers cried ... he will be an inspiration to very many Socialist comrades.

That letter was some consolation but scant enough. Heaven only knows how Alex and the rest of his family felt at such awful news. I did not see them at the time. No doubt they were consumed by grief and needed privacy to mourn. I do know that news of our grandson's death hit Ann hard and it had a most depressing effect on me. It was not long after that that I returned to hospital here and have hardly been out of the place since. During this last period, I have known periods of calm but have also been severely affected by low moods.

I could offer you my opinion about so much more that happened during the 1930's because, when I was able to, I took my usual interest in what was going on. There was a period of growth for Communism and Fascism in this country. How I loathe that man, Oswald Mosley! The death of a king, the accession of another, then abdication, which had the country agog as if reading some penny romance. Most of all, of course, yet another build-up of arms across Europe and Hitler making demand after demand and politicians everywhere, including our own man Chamberlain, being fooled by the German dictator. Then, last year, only two decades since the end of the Great War, yet another European War broke out.

When will mankind learn? Is it capable of learning? As if there has not been enough evidence of the folly and waste of war. Yet still we allow ourselves to become enmeshed in it and more young men die. Who knows when this conflict will end and how many, perhaps millions, will lose their lives because of man's inability to find peaceful solutions? And at the end of it, who will be better off? The winners, people say, and that is why we must win. Well, we were on the winning side in the Great War and what did that bring us? A huge national debt, recession, unemployment, depression, greater unemployment, misery. So what did that war solve for the mass of mankind? Nothing, absolutely nothing! It never does.

But I have not the energy to consider these issues at greater length and you would no doubt be bored by an old man's opinion anyway. These days, when I'm able, I find myself more thinking about the past than the present. I suppose most old men do. And is it just me, or do most people nearing the end of their days focus on their regrets? I know that I have been doing a lot of that just recently. Which is a wasteful way of passing the time, I know, but I seem unable to help myself. In fact, there are many minor things in my life which I regret, but they are too trivial to deal with here. But two things keep coming back to me.

Why did my brother James disappear from my life? Twice I lost him, when he moved from Belfast to Glasgow, then from Glasgow to Larkhall, but found him again. But it is now some sixty years since we parted in tears and, occasional letters aside, I have had no contact from him. The parting of our ways is still incomprehensible to me. I did not understand it then and still do not now. Over the years I heard that he was living for a while in the Highlands, then in Glasgow. I should have made a greater effort to find him but it seemed that he did not wish to be found and I was always so busy. Of all my regrets, losing my brother is the greatest.

Then finally there are regrets over my family, for the fact that I was away so often and, to an extent which horrifies me now as I look back, missed so much of our bairns' growing years. The burden it placed on Ann was far too great and the fact that she never complained just showed what a strong and loyal wife she has always been. If only I could have that family time back again. If only I had spent more time with Ann, my companion these past sixty years and more. If only ... two very small words with awfully big meanings.

Now and again, particularly as I spend more and more time lying in bed, I think of what you might call the high points of my working life. There were so many but some particularly gladden my heart. My friendship with men like Keir Hardie and William Small, playing my part in the strengthening of the Labour

Movement and the formation of the Labour Party, crossing swords with some of the so-called great men of my time: sometimes gaining the upper hand on them, sometimes not. But the continuous thread throughout all that was the mining community, my own folk, whether at home in Larkhall or in mining towns and villages throughout Britain. I never felt let down by them, even when we disagreed, and I always did my best not to let them down. They can judge better than I can whether I succeed or not.

Man but I'm tired! I seem to spend more time asleep than awake. There again, I am a very old man. Over the past few months, in addition to being visited by family and old friends, I have made a new friend, a young reporter by the name of Robert James MacGregor. What he can possibly find of interest in an old fogey like me is a matter of conjecture but he has been at my bedside, pen and notebook in hand, frequently of late and I have greatly enjoyed his company and our long blethers. Just today he asked me a very interesting question.

'Tell me, Bob,' he said, 'many years from now when you pass away, what would you like your epitaph to be?'

'I doubt if it will be that long,' I told him, 'and I've never given the matter much thought.'

'Please try, Bob,' he urged me.

'Aye well, laddie. Let me see.' I thought about it for a moment or two then the answer came clearly enough. 'I suppose you might say that I always saw my working life as something of a crusade in which I was struggling as best I could and felt that the struggle was always as much reward as the occasional success. But maybe that's a bit long for an epitaph.'

'Probably,' he said. He thought for a moment. 'The struggles are greater than the successes?'

'That sounds fine,' I told him. 'Now if you'll excuse me, laddie, I'm very tired. I'm ready for my sleep ... a good long one.'

POSTSCRIPT

I NEVER KNEW the author of *Labour of Love*, my maternal grandfather. He was killed at the battle of El Alamein in October, 1942. I only ever saw two photographs of him, a wedding photograph taken in 1939, and one of himself among a group of other smiling soldiers, desert stretching away in the background. That must have been taken shortly before he was killed. Anything else I ever found out about him, which wasn't much, came from his wife Jean, my grandmother, who came to live with my parents and myself in 1972, when I was five years old, and stayed with my mother and father until she passed away in 1999. By then I'd left our home in Invergordon, moved to North Wales, married and become a father.

I visited my parents when they got in touch to say that Gran was ailing. She was laid up in bed, hardly breathing, far gone. She just had enough strength to open a bedside drawer, draw out a package and give it to me, her hand shaking with the effort. She whispered to me, 'Robbie always wanted that published. See what you can do, son.' I promised that I would, though I had no notion what she was talking about and, shortly afterwards, set off on the return journey to North Wales. I had hardly got in the door when the phone rang. It was Dad. Gran had passed away.

Later that same night, I inspected the package. Whatever was inside it was covered in a cloth of some kind. I opened it up, horribly aware of the smell of oilskin, and drew out the contents. Pages, hundreds of pages, each one clearly-typed in the kind of print made by elderly typewriters. The first page bore a title: *Labour of Love*. The second page, and a few more, were a prologue written by my grandfather only a few months before he was killed. There was no contents page. It began with an introduction, then moved into chapters, thirty-three of them altogether. Like my grandfather before me, as mentioned in his prologue, I read everything at a single sitting. By the time I was finished, it was the early hours of the morning and the rest of the house was silent. I sat back for a while, wondering at what I had just read.

The style wasn't exactly an attraction: John Grisham is more to my taste. But what a story! At this point, I should explain that I'm a bit of a writer myself, even having experienced the pleasure of seeing my name in print a few times. I suppose that's why Gran passed the manuscript on to me. But I'd never read, far less written, anything like what my grandfather had produced. The scope was immense and it was all written in such a way as to suggest the deep respect he had felt for his subject, Robert Smillie. I was in no doubt. This was a story which deserved to be read.

I gave some thought to whether or not I should do any work on the manuscript. Written between 1939 and 1940, it was not in a style which normally attracted a large readership. I wondered whether I should perform surgery on it then, almost as quickly as that thought had occurred to me, I rejected it as unworthy, even arrogant. After all, my grandfather had known Robert Smillie and I had no doubt that he had written the manuscript in as near to his friend's words as possible. What right did I, or anybody else, have to make amendments which would probably only have distorted what Robert Smillie had wanted to say? I decided to leave the main text as it was.

However, I did take some trouble with it. I re-read it and corrected any mistakes I came across. In honesty, I have to admit that there were fewer than in most of my drafts. Then, as far as I could, I checked the accuracy of dates and other factual information. Not being half-way towards computer literacy, I tended to rely on textbooks for that and made use of:

Arnot, RP: *The Miners*
Arnot, RP: *The Miners in Crisis and in War*
Bailey, C: *Black Diamonds*
Coates, K (Ed.): *Democracy in the Mines*
Lowe, N: *Mastering Modern British History*
Smillie, R: *My Life for Labour*
Smith, HBL (Ed.): *The Encyclopaedia of the Labour Movement*

I acknowledge here my debt to those publications, even though I found remarkably few factual errors in my grandfather's text. At his advanced age, Robert Smillie's memory was obviously in better order than mine is now!

There was only one more service I could provide for my grandfather's manuscript. Following Robert Smillie's death in 1940, when my grandfather was no doubt busy with the text, his family, and his job, the passing of the grand old man was widely reported in the press. I will only cite three of many such reports. You should note that only one of them stems from his heartland, the West of Scotland. Newspapers the length and breadth of Britain commented on his passing, which should indicate just how significant a figure he was. Locally, one newspaper even reported on the great effort made by one man to attend the funeral:

Labour Leader Buried
SAILOR FRIEND PAYS TRIBUTE

So deeply do miners throughout Great Britain feel the loss of their veteran leader, 'Bob' Smillie, that a Yorkshire pit worker – now a sailor in the Royal Navy – got special leave yesterday to attend the funeral of the old friend he had met so often at miners' meetings. The dark blue sailor's dress of Councillor Arthur Pickersgill, of Castleford, Yorkshire, stood out among the sombre garb of mourners – many of them Lanarkshire miners who had been in the pits a few hours before – as they joined the procession to Glasgow Crematorium.

Coalmasters and great bankers joined with M.P.'s, trade union officials, and the Lanarkshire folk, among whom 'Bob' Smillie spent his life, to mourn him. They had all known him as a friend and a great fighter to improve the working and living conditions of the Scottish Miners – and latterly all the pit workers of this country.

Notables attended

Among those who attended the service were: - Mr James Maxton, Mr David Kirkwood, Mr Duncan Graham, and Mr George Buchanan, from the House of Commons; Lord Provost P.J. Dollan and many members of Glasgow Corporation; Sir George Mitchell, the prominent Scottish Industrialist, and Mr P.M. Richie, chairman of the Lanarkshire Coalowners' Association; Mr Ebby Edwards of the Miners' Federation, and numerous Scottish miners' officials; Mr Neil Beaton, chairman of the S.C.W.S., and Mr Arthur Stoker, senior Inspector of Mines, who represented the Secretary for Mines, Mr Geoffrey Lloyd.

Mr James Maxton, political 'pupil' and a great personal friend of 'Bob' Smillie, spoke of his life work for the miners, and as he did so Mrs Smillie, surrounded by her seven sons and two daughters, sobbed quietly in her seat near the coffin.

'We regarded him,' said Mr Maxton, 'as our man, and we in the West of Scotland took pride in his integrity, his courage, and his human affection for all suffering humanity.'

The *Daily Herald* presented the news in the form of a brief biography:

Bob Smillie Dies in 83rd Year.
Bob Smillie, pioneer of the Mineworkers' Federation, died in Dumfries yesterday within a month of his 83rd birthday.

He had been ailing for the last two years, and had lived in retirement for over eight years.

Bob Smillie was born in Belfast of Scottish parents, and was left an orphan when three years old.

Here are the highlights of his life of devoted service to the cause of the workers:-

Aged 11 – Was taken on as a half-timer in a mill. It was his fifth job. A year later he went on full-time.

Aged 17 – Attracted by the higher wages, reaching 18s. 6d. weekly, on which there were seven people to be kept, he took a job as a pit pump-man. He settled in the Lanarkshire village of Larkhall, which remained his home for the rest of his life.

'There was no official recognition,' he once said, writing about those early days, 'of the fact that walking to and fro in the position of a half-shut clasp-knife was really harder than our actual work.'

Aged 21 – He married Annie Hamilton, to whose 'self-sacrifice and comradeship' he constantly referred throughout his long life of struggle for his fellow workers.

Aged 28 – During an agitation for the restoration of the five-day week, Mr Smillie made his first speech in public and was elected secretary of the local Miners' Association.

It was the beginning of many years of untiring work for Trade Unionism and Socialism.

Aged 51 – 'The scheme for pithead baths was born in Bob's cottage – 29 Miller Street, Larkhall, 32 years ago,' said Mr John McGurk, President, Lancs and Cheshire Miners, yesterday. 'The improved conditions which miners enjoy today are a monument to the memory of a great man.'

Aged 52 – Became a member of the Sankey Commission on the coal industry and leapt into fame by his examination of the witnesses.

Smillie's cross-examination started a great wave of public sympathy with the miners as he brought to the light of day the facts about the dangers of coal-getting, the shocking pit housing, the low standard of living.

Aged 55 – The first national coal strike took place in 1912, and yielded a partial victory to the miners.

Smillie then became President of the Miners' Federation, a post he held until compelled by bad health and failing eye-sight to resign in 1921.

Aged 59 – Was asked to become Food Controller in the Great War. He refused, partly because he foresaw that all his watchfulness would be needed to defend the miners' rights during the war, and partly because he was not promised the power to 'hang profiteers'.

Two of his sons were officers in the Army, and another went to prison as a conscientious objector.

Aged 66 – Elected M.P. for Morpeth. He had previously fought seven Parliamentary contests.

Aged 71 – The Scottish I.L.P., of which he was a foundation member, honoured his golden wedding with a social gathering at which Mr and Mrs Smillie were described as the 'Father and Mother of Scottish Socialism'.

Miners' leaders paid tribute last night to the life and work of a loved pioneer.

Mr Will Lawther, President of the Mineworkers' Federation of Great Britain: 'Bob Smillie will be principally remembered by his tremendous effort as a member of the

Sankey Commission. The firm stand he took up then, and the ideals he put forward, were indeed an achievement that will endear him for all time to the miners and their wives.'

Mr Oliver Harris, secretary of the South Wales Miners' Federation: 'He was one of the great forces that built up the Mineworkers' Federation.'

Even in London *The Times*, no friend of Robert Smillie or the opinions he held, paid tribute.

DEATH OF MR ROBERT SMILLIE
MINERS' LEADER

Mr Robert Smillie, former leader of the Scottish miners and founder of the miners' trade union movement in Scotland, died yesterday at the age of 82. For the past 10 years his health has been bad and he had been living in retirement in Dumfriesshire, where he died.

For a generation he was one of the most prominent figures in the coal mining industry. He was president of the Scottish Miners' Federation from 1894 to 1918, and from 1923 to 1929 he was Labour M.P. for Morpeth.

Throughout the Labour movement there was no Mr Smillie nor even Robert. Always and everywhere he was plain Bob Smillie. He was a man of strong character and rigid views, a trade union leader of inflexible purpose – one who possessed the physical and moral qualities for leadership of men who, like the miners of his day, were disposed to brood over their grievances, and to endure desperately in strike or lock-out. No trade unionists have a greater sense of loyalty to each other than the miners, no trade union leader had a more intense sense of loyalty to those who followed him than Bob Smillie. Tenacious and even menacing in his assertion of the miners' claims, he seemed to be inspired, not only by a sense of the wrongs he shared with them, but also by an active resentment of wealth everywhere but most of all when it had been acquired in the mining industry. He had the constitution of a social rebel.

He was president of the Miners' Federation of Great Britain from 1912 to 1921 which from beginning to end was a troublesome period. A wave of unrest was spreading in the years before the Great War; the time of the war brought its own problems and then, after a spell of feverish activity came a reaction and the need for sharper readjustments. The miners were demanding nationalisation of the mines, Smillie was in the forefront of the agitation. The Government of the day appointed a Coal Commission, under the chairmanship of Mr Justice (now Lord) Sankey, and as a member of the Commission Smillie examined witnesses with relentless persistence. He was taken ill not long after and would have retired in 1920 from the presidency of the federation, but his colleagues, hoping for his recovery, gave him leave of absence instead. So his resignation was postponed for a year, but it took effect before the strike of 1921 for national unification of the industry and a national pool to equalise wages.

But his leadership and his spirit had done not a little to nerve the miners for a hard struggle.

But there was another side to his character. No faithful picture of Smillie could conceal his innate combativeness, but his strong personality had other and more genial qualities when his public attitude relaxed in private. In his personal relations he was a man of quick sympathy, kindly emotion and humour. One of the experiences of his early life which may have had immeasurable influence of his character was his 'fortnightly entombment in the pit' when as a youth of 17 he spent 24 solitary hours underground minding a pump – 'and rats' eyes in the dark', he wrote in a brief memoir of his life, 'are by no means reassuring'.

In 1917 Smillie was offered the post of Food Controller in succession to Lord Devonport. He did not entertain the proposal. His one purpose in life was the betterment of the miners' lot.

In 1878 he married Anne Hamilton, who survives him with seven sons and two daughters.

I find it impossible to read tributes such as these in conjunction with my grandfather's manuscript and not wonder about how we humans view greatness. If any one of us was asked to name the thousand greatest people of the past 150 years, I can only be sure of one outcome: Robert Smillie's name would not be on the list. Our lists would be comprised of famous men and women from across the world. Most of them would be monarchs, statesmen, soldiers, adventurers and, in this day and age, no doubt a number of entertainers. Yet how many of them would have devoted themselves as selflessly to others as Robert Smillie did? Precious few, in my estimation. But then, as my grandfather remarked, men like Robert Smillie – and, heaven knows, there are very few of them – do not write history books, have no desire for a personal legacy, and do not court publicity. I would contend that such selfish modesty, allied to achievements on behalf of others, is the mark of true greatness.

My grandfather's manuscript is completed and ready for the world to do with it what it will. I hope that his efforts and Robert Smillie's life receive the acclaim which they both deserve. I will conclude this postscript by dedicating the whole manuscript to the memory of my grandfather and his friend, Robert Smillie, humanitarian, inspiration and Socialist.

Torquil Cowan
North Wales
May 2011

APPOINTMENTS

Secretary of the Larkhall Branch of the Lanarkshire Miners
President of the Lanarkshire Miners' Federation
Member of the Larkhall School Board
Co-Founder of the Independent Labour Party
President of the Scottish Miners Federation (on two occasions)
Co-Founder of the Scottish Trades Union Congress
Chairman of the Scottish Trades Union Congress
Vice-President of the Miners' Federation of Great Britain
President of the Miners' Federation of Great Britain
Co-Founder of the Industrial Triple Alliance
President of the National Council Against Conscription
    (from 1917 known as the National Council for Civil Liberties)
Member of the Comité D'Honneur de Secours aux Enfants
    (Save the Children)
MP for Morpeth
Chairman, Labour Parliamentary Committee

Robert Smillie twice turned down Government posts offered by Lloyd George and Ramsay MacDonald.

A scholarship to Ruskin College, Oxford, was also created in his honour.

APPENDIX I
Mining Commission and Royalties

SMILLIE'S RESEARCH INCLUDED corresponding with persons with specialist knowledge of the history of land ownership. The following letter was received from John K. Murray, a Motherwell solicitor.

Robert Smillie, Esq., J.P.,
Miners Federation
55 Russell Square
London, W.C. 1.

6th May, 1919

Dear Mr Smillie,

MINING COMMISSION & ROYALTIES

I have been requested to communicate an open letter to you, on account of the uncertainty in many minds as to the difference between the statute law of England and the Statute law of Scotland, dealing with mines and minerals.

In 1372 there was passed the Act 5, Henry IV., Chapter 4 constituting the Crown of England the owner of the mines and minerals of England.

In 1688 there was passed the Act 1, William and Mary., Chapter 30, which narrated the Act of 1372 and declared that in future no mines in England containing copper, tin, iron or lead should be considered royal mines, even although gold and silver might be extracted from any of the metals raised.

The Act of 1688 still left doubts as to the extent and effect of the repeal of the 1372 Act, and in 1694 the Act 5 and 6, William and Mary., Chapter 6 was passed 'to prevent disputes and controverses concerning the royal mines'. After making it perfectly clear that the owner of the surface should enjoy the mines and minerals within his lands, it was enacted that the Crown could purchase the following ores at the following prices:- 'for all ore selected made clean and merchantable wherein is copper' £16 per ton, lead £9 per ton, tin £2 per ton, and iron £2 per ton. The only exceptions from the Act were the Charters, liberties, or privileges to the tinners of Devon and Cornwall.

The Acts of 1372, 1688 and 1694 refer to England alone, so that our Scottish Act of 1592, with which I dealt fully in a former letter to you, is in no way affected by the Acts passed in the reign of William and Mary.

Closely allied to the question of mines and minerals, are the questions of the titles to land in Scotland and the Act of 1617 dealing with prescription.

Nine tenths of all lands in Scotland fell under the term 'Ward Holding' otherwise known as 'Military Holding'. That is to say, the grant of nine tenths of the land in Scotland carried with it an obligation to provide so many men for military service within the Kingdom.

In the 1745 Rebellion, the Government troops under the Duke of Cumberland were almost defeated at Culloden by the Barons and their retainers, who held their land in exchange for military service.

The Scottish Parliament of that period [Murray presumably means the British Parliament] was elected by, and consisted of, landowners drawing at least £400 per annum from heritable subjects, – excepting a small minority representing the Royal Burghs, and elected by the Burgesses and Guild Brethern [sic] of these Burghs.

After the din of battle had subsided, the Scottish Parliament [sic] met in 1746 and passed an Act dealing with the Crown purchase of entailed estates 'for the preservation of the public peace, and the further civilizing of the inhabitants of the Highlands of Scotland'.

As a further step towards civilization the same Parliament passed the Act 20, George I., Chapter 50 which freed the lands of the Barons from all military service in future. The Act did not declare that the value of these military services should be converted into a money payment and made an annual charge on the lands. The Barons then became the holders of their lands free from any payment to the Crown. But hark what follows!

The Barons had already subfeued part of their lands to yeomen on condition that the yeomen should render military service to the Barons, and so enable the latter to perform their military duties to the Crown. Did the Barons sitting as a Parliament in 1746, declare that the yeomen should retain their lands as free from burden as the Barons themselves? Certainly not! On the contrary, it was enacted that the value of a yeoman's military service should be converted into cash, and paid as an annual feuduty to the Baron. In the event of a yeoman failing to satisfy the cupidity of the Baron, the Act set up machinery whereby the Court of Session might compel the yeoman to pay.

It will occur to the very dullest of readers that if Parliament were justified in 1746 in freeing the lands of the Barons from the burden of military service, the lands of the yeomen ought to have been similarly dealt with. Conversely, if it were right to convert the value of the yeomen's military service into an annual money payment, it was 'just, meet and proper' that the Barons' services should have been converted into an annual sum payable to the Exchequer.

The point I wish to emphasise is, that we have a parliamentary precedent for fixing feuduties, and that we can take up the matter where it was left off in 1746, and now assess the annual feuduties to be paid by the Barons in lieu of the abandoned military services.

Long prior to the abolition of 'Ward Holding', part of these military lands, as they are popularly called, were gifted by their owners to the then Catholic Church of Scotland. The Reformation, beginning in the reign of James V, passing through the reign of Mary Queen of Scots, and terminating in the reign of James VI., saw a plundering of the Church lands by the Barons for which history can find no parallel. Neither the Catholic Church, nor the Reformed Church, nor the Crown, but the Barons only profited from the distribution of the Church lands. As Dr. Rankin, the historian of the Church of Scotland, wrote in 1888, 'In this way a large proportion of Scotland rests on a basis utterly rotten and fraudulent; not on natural succession, honest purchase, military service, conquest in war, or reclamation of waste, but on violence, knavery, fanaticism and servility'.

During the reign of James VI, disputes regarding the Church lands began to be rather frequent, and a parliament of landowners in 1617 passed an Act 'Anent prescription of heritable rights'. That Act was meant to fortify, and did fortify those landowners who had held possession of the Church lands for forty years, and has proved a sure defence to many a landowner since then, whose title to land could be better traced to possession than to righteous ownership.

I trust that the above explanations may tend to clarify public opinion regarding the question of land, mines, minerals and mining royalties, and demonstrate to the public that restitution may be demanded from the great landowners of Scotland, without infringing any principle either of justice or equity.

I am,

Yours faithfully,

John K. Murray

APPENDIX II

Extract from The Times, *21st July 1848*

SMILLIE ALSO CONSULTED R.P. Arnot, a renowned industrial historian who forwarded him an extract from *The Times* of some matters tabled in the House of Lords between the Earl of Lincoln and Lord Morpeth regarding the ownership of mines.

<u>1592</u> <u>ACT</u> <u>(Scottish)</u>
The Times – July 21, 1848

Q. Lincoln
A. Morpeth

The Earl of Lincoln wished to ask the Noble Lord at the head of the Woods and Forests a question of which he had given notice a few days ago. His question referred to an action which had been brought very recently under the direction of the Commissioners of Woods and Forests against the proprietor, or rather reputed proprietor, of certain mines in Scotland; by which action it was intended to raise, under what had hitherto been considered an obsolete Act of Parliament, a claim on the part of the Crown to the whole of the minerals in Scotland, nor merely of the precious metals, but of coal and iron also. The action was commenced by issuing a summons declaratory against Richard Anderson Alexander, and the Act under which it was brought was of so old a date as that of 1592, being in the reign of James I of England. *[He was not James I of England until 1603. The Act was passed while he was James VI of Scotland].*The noble lord was, of course, aware that the law of Scotland and of England, as regarded the claim of the Sovereign to all minerals, was precisely similar until it was altered by two Acts of Parliament, the 1st of William and Mary, cap. 30, and 5 William and Mary, cap. 6. But these Acts related only to England, and, since that time, the claim of the Crown in England applied to mines of gold and silver. But the action brought against Mr. Alexander was founded upon the Act of James I, under which the Crown claimed the whole of the minerals throughout Scotland, without any other advantage to the proprietors of the soil than a preference of purchase.

The Lord-Advocate said this claim did not apply to coal.

The Earl of Lincoln was aware that, practically, it did not, as the mineral in question was called 'black-band', and this was a mine which had recently been discovered. He apprehended that the only advantage which was given under the Act of James I to the land proprietor was that of having the option of taking the mine, on condition of paying one-tenth of the produce to the Crown. Could this claim be established, the practical result would be the closing up of almost all the mines in Scotland.

The question, therefore, which he wished to ask the Noble Lord was whether he would undertake to introduce any Bill in the present session for the purpose of assimilating the law of Scotland with the law of England on this subject, and of quieting the titles of all parties to the minerals in that country – a measure which practically would not only be abandoning the claim raised against Mr. Alexander but preventing any similar claim being raised in future.

Lord Morpeth observed that in answer to the question of the Noble Lord he had to state that the declaratory summons issued by the Woods and Forests was under the advice of his honorable friend the Lord Advocate of Scotland, as the law adviser of the Crown, who advised that department to try and establish the right of the Crown to these mines. But it was never the intention of the board to resort to any oppressive or injurious proceedings towards the proprietors of the mines.

Under that advice the Woods and Forests had proceeded, and they were now in communication with the Lord Advocate to consider whether they should not bring in a Bill to settle upon that subject, and by which they hoped to put it upon a footing satisfactory to the proprietors in Scotland. He could not, however, undertake to introduce such a measure during the present session, but he could, at least, give the assurance that no further proceedings would be taken under the ancient Statute of James I until full consideration had been given and the intention of the Government amended on the subject.

LABOUR OF LOVE